(continued on back)

S0-ASP-012

WASTES IN THE OCEAN

ENVIRONMENTAL SCIENCE AND TECHNOLOGY
A Wiley-Interscience Series of Texts and Monographs

WASTES IN THE OCEAN

Editors: Iver W. Duedall
Dana R. Kester
Bostwick H. Ketchum
P. Kilho Park

WASTES IN THE OCEAN
Volume 2

DREDGED-MATERIAL DISPOSAL IN THE OCEAN

Edited by

DANA R. KESTER
University of Rhode Island
Kingston, Rhode Island

BOSTWICK H. KETCHUM
Senior Scientist, Emeritus
Woods Hole Oceanographic Institution
Woods Hole, Massachusetts

IVER W. DUEDALL
Department of Oceanography and Ocean Engineering
Florida Institute of Technology
Melbourne, Florida

P. KILHO PARK
National Oceanic and Atmospheric Administration
Rockville, Maryland

A WILEY-INTERSCIENCE PUBLICATION

JOHN WILEY & SONS

New York   Chichester   Brisbane   Toronto   Singapore

Library of Congress Cataloging in Publication Data

Main entry under title:

Dredged-material disposal in the ocean.

(Wastes in the ocean; v. 2) (Environmental science
and technology, ISSN 0194–0287)
    Includes index.
    1. Dredging spoil—Congresses. 2. Waste disposal
in the ocean—Congresses. I. Kester, Dana R.
II. Series. III. Series: Environmental science and
technology.

TC187.D7 1983   363.7'28   82-17370
ISBN 0-471-09771-3

Printed in the United States of America

10 9 8 7 6 5 4 3 2 1

We, the remaining editors, honor

DR. BOSTWICK H. KETCHUM
January 21, 1912–July 15, 1972

who, until his death, had worked for and
believed in the immortality of
humanity and science

Iver W. Duedall
P. Kilho Park
Dana R. Kester

CONTRIBUTORS

ARIMOTO, RICHARD, Graduate School of Oceanography, University of Rhode Island, Kingston, Rhode Island 02881

BOEHM, P. D., Environmental Sciences Division, Energy Resources Company, Inc., Cambridge, Massachusetts 02138

BOKUNIEWICZ, HENRY J., Marine Sciences Research Center, State University of New York, Stony Brook, New York 11794

CHAVE, KEITH E., Department of Oceanography, University of Hawaii, Honolulu, Hawaii 96822

COLLINS, ANTHONY G., Department of Civil and Environmental Engineering, Clarkson College of Technology, Potsdam, New York 13676

DAVIS, WAYNE R., U.S. Environmental Protection Agency, Environmental Research Laboratory, Narragansett, Rhode Island 02882

DAYAL, RAMESH, Department of Nuclear Energy, Brookhaven National Laboratory, Upton, New York 11973

DUEDALL, IVER W., Department of Oceanography and Ocean Engineering, Florida Institute of Technology, Melbourne, Florida 32901

FENG, S. Y., Marine Sciences Institute, University of Connecticut, Groton, Connecticut 06340

FIEST, D. L., Environmental Sciences Division, Energy Resources Company, Inc., Cambridge, Massachusetts 02138

FUHRMANN, MARK, Department of Nuclear Energy, Brookhaven National Laboratory, Upton, New York 11973

HANSEN, JOHN C., Marine Bioassay Laboratories, Watsonville, California 95076

HEATON, MONTEITH G., Interstate Electronics Corporation, Anaheim, California 92803

KAMLET, KENNETH S., National Wildlife Federation, Washington, D.C. 20036

KESTER, DANA R., Graduate School of Oceanography, University of Rhode Island, Kingston, Rhode Island 02881

KETCHUM, BOSTWICK H., Senior Scientist, Emeritus, Woods Hole Oceanographic Institute, Woods Hole, Massachusetts 02543

McLEESE, D. W., Fisheries and Environmental Sciences, Fisheries and Oceans Canada, Biological Station, St. Andrews, New Brunswick E0G 2X0, Canada

MILLER, JACQUELIN N., Department of Oceanogrpahy, University of Hawaii, Honolulu, Hawaii 96822

MORTON, ROBERT W., Science Applications, Inc., Ocean Science and Technology Division, Newport, Rhode Island 02840

PARK, P. KILHO, Ocean Dumping Program, National Oceanic and Atmospheric Administration, Rockville, Maryland 20852

PARKS, JAMES M., Center for Marine and Environmental Studies, Lehigh University, Bethlehem, Pennsylvania 18105

PEDDICORD, RICHARD K., U.S. Army Engineer Waterways Experiment Station, Vicksburg, Mississippi 31180

PEQUEGNAT, WILLIS E., TerEco Corporation, P.O. Box 2848, College Station, Texas 77840

RAY, S., Fisheries and Environmental Sciences, Fisheries and Oceans Canada, Biological Station, St. Andrews, New Brunswick E0G 2X0, Canada

WEISMAN, RICHARD N., Department of Civil Engineering, Lehigh University Bethlehem, Pennsylvania 18105

SERIES PREFACE
Environmental Science and Technology

The Environmental Science and Technology Series of Monographs, Textbooks, and Advances is devoted to the study of the quality of the environment and to the technology of its conservation. Environmental science therefore relates to the chemical, physical, and biological changes in the environment through contamination or modification, to the physical nature and biological behavior of air, water, soil, food, and waste as they are affected by man's agricultural, industrial, and social activities, and to the application of science and technology to the control and improvement of environmental quality.

The deterioration of environmental quality, which began when man first collected into villages and utilized fire, has existed as a serious problem under the ever-increasing impacts of exponentially increasing population and of industrializing society. Environmental contamination of air, water, soil, and food has become a threat to the continued existence of many plant and animal communities of the ecosystem and may ultimately threaten the very survival of the human race.

It seems clear that if we are to preserve for future generations some semblance of the biological order of the world of the past and hope to improve on the deteriorating standards of urban public health, environmental science and technology must quickly come to play a dominant role in designing our social and industrial structure for tomorrow. Scientifically rigorous criteria of environmental quality must be developed. Based in part on these criteria, realistic standards must be established and our technological progress must be tailored to meet them. It is obvious that civilization will continue to require increasing amounts of fuel, transportation, industrial chemicals, fertilizers, pesticides, and countless other products; and that it will continue to produce waste products of all descriptions. What is urgently needed is a total systems approach to modern civilization through which the pooled talents of scientists and engineers, in cooperation with social scientists and the medical profession, can be focused on the development of order and equilibrium in the presently disparate segments of the human environment. Most of the skills and tools that are needed are already in existence. We surely have a right to hope a technology that has created such manifold environmental problems is also capable of solving them. It is our hope that this Series in Environmental Sciences and

Technology will not only serve to make this challenge more explicit to the established professionals, but that it also will help to stimulate the student toward the career opportunities in this vital area.

Robert L. Metcalf
Werner Stumm

PREFACE TO
WASTES IN THE OCEAN

This is the second of several volumes considering the problems of *Wastes in the Ocean* in which we consider the following subjects:

Volume 1, "Industrial and Sewage Wastes in the Ocean,"
Volume 2, "Dredged-Material Disposal in the Ocean,"
Volume 3, "Radioactive Wastes and the Ocean,"
Volume 4, "Energy Wastes in the Ocean,"
Volume 5, "Deep-Sea Waste Disposal," and
Volume 6, "Near-Shore Waste Disposal."

The objectives are to present a comprehensive overview of the state of our knowledge concerning the disposal of waste in the ocean and to present new and original contributions to the evaluation of the impact of the disposal of waste materials on human life and well-being, on the marine biota, on amenities, and on legitimate uses of the ocean. The chapters included in this and succeeding volumes of this series have been subjected to both external and editorial reviews. We are especially grateful to the reviewers of these chapters for the time and effort they devoted to the development of the final manuscrpts.

The burgeoning human population on earth and the continuing development of complex industrial technology have inevitably led to enormous increases in both the quantity and the kind of waste material that must be disposed of in ways that do not cause an intolerable degradation of our environment. The optimum solution to the problem is to recycle the waste material in ways that produce a beneficial effect. This is not always possible and various types of treatment can be employed to minimize the quantity of waste and to make the product of the treatment less damaging to our environment. Even after treatment, there will be some residue that must be contained or discharged to the environment.

The options for environmental discharge are limited: on land, into the atmosphere, or into the hydrosphere. Before any one of these particular environments is selected for any specific waste material there should be a careful scientific analysis of the possible impacts of such a disposal operation. It is hoped that this series will provide the framework for the evaluation of the impact of specific types of waste in the ocean.

From time immemorial people have been disposing of waste materials into the marine environment or into the rivers and streams that ultimately lead to the sea. For millienia it was assumed that the oceans are so vast that our puny efforts would have no measureable or damaging impact. Within the last century it has become clear that some semiconfined bodies of water were being degraded seriously and that the disposal of waste into the hydrosphere must be managed and controlled in order to preserve the integrity of the oceans. We now know that some pollutants are distributed worldwide and can be identified and measured in the waters of the open sea far from the source. The problems associated with ocean disposal of waste material require careful and critical evaluation so that we may assure that the valuable resources of the sea are preserved and protected for future generations. This will require the most careful evaluation of the impact of waste disposal at sea so that we may use the oceans wisely.

We are very thankful to Mr. Treville Leger, Editor, John Wiley & Sons, for his constant encouragement and for being very helpful in the preparation of these volumes.

THE EDITORS

Long Island
June 1981

PREFACE

This book contains a series of chapters related to the disposal of dredged material in the marine environment. The manuscripts were reviewed by at least two referees and in most cases were revised by the authors based on the recommendations of the reviewers and the editors.

The disposal of dredged material from marine waterways is a long-term problem which must be addressed to maintain marine transportation. The problem exists primarily to the extent that coastal and harbor sediments have been contaminated by pollutants from municipal, shipping, and industrial sources. The problems of contaminated sediment disposal are evident to countries which now must dredge harbors that have accumulated sediments and pollutants during decades of poorly controlled waste disposal in coastal waters. It is important that maritime countries that are presently expanding their industrial activities also consider the risks and costs of contaminated sediment disposal. While it should be possible to minimize the chronic pollution of coastal sediments through adequate waste management practices, there remains a significant probability that inadvertent chemical spills will contaminate nearshore sediments. The contributions in this volume report the results of recent research on dredged material disposal.

This volume is arranged in five parts. The first part consists of an introductory chapter and two chapters related to the regulatory aspects of contaminated dredged-material disposal as practiced in the United States. A series of case studies provides information on specific aspects of physical and chemical characteristics of dredged material dumpsites in U.S. waters. The third part includes three chapters on biological investigations related to contaminated sediments. Three chapters consider procedures for sediment disposal that are alternatives to dumping material in a mound in open waters. The last chapter examines the present state of knowledge and the areas where further scientific information is needed.

Many people have contributed to the preparation of this volume. We would like to express our appreciation to the members of the Second International Symposium Executive Committee which, in addition to the editors, included Professor Michael A. Champ, Dr. Thomas P. O'Connor, and Dr. Marshall H. Orr. Marilyn A. Maley, Jo-Anne Degidio, Jacquelin Restivo, Mary Ann Lau, and Laura Antonacci assisted in preparing the manuscripts. Marie Gladwish and Vivian Abolins provided valuable assistance in preparing many of the illustrations. For the photographs and illustrations on the part title pages we thank G. M. Capriulo, G. E. Mayer, J. H. Parker, Bergin Publishers, and the U.S. Army Corps of Engineers. This work was supported in part by U.S. National Oceanic and Atmospheric Administration Grants No. 04-8-M01-192 and NA-81-RA-C-00064.

DANA R. KESTER
BOSTWICK H. KETCHUM
IVER W. DUEDALL
P. KILHO PARK

West Greenwich, Rhode Island
December 1982

CONTENTS

GLOSSARY OF ACRONYMS

AAS	Atomic absorption spectrophotometry
ACOE	U.S. Army Corps of Engineers
CEC	Cation exchange capacity
CEQ	U.S. Council on Environmental Quality
DAMOS	Disposal Area Monitoring System
DMRP	Dredged Material Research Program of the ACOE
EPA	U.S. Environmental Protection Agency
FDA	U.S. Food and Drug Administration
GC	Gas chromatography
GCMS	Gas chromatography–mass spectrometry
IAPH	International Association of Ports and Harbors
IMCO	Inter-Governmental Maritime Consultative Organization
LC_{50}	Lethal concentration needed to kill 50% of the test organisms
LDC	London Dumping Convention
LORAN	Long Range Navigation
LPC	Limiting permissible concentration
MERL	Marine Ecosystems Research Laboratory
MESA	Marine EcoSystems Analysis
MPRSA	U.S. Marine Protection, Research, and Sanctuaries Act
NOAA	U.S. National Oceanic and Atmospheric Administration
NWF	National Wildlife Federation
PAH	Polynuclear aromatic hydrocarbons
PCB	Polychlorinated biphenyl compounds
PCM	Percent moisture content
TOC	Total organic carbon

WASTES IN THE OCEAN

PART I: INTRODUCTION

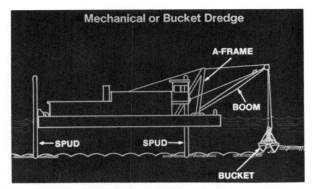

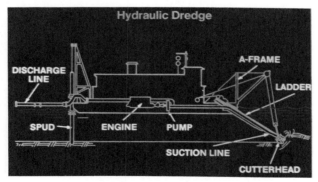

1

THE PROBLEM OF DREDGED-MATERIAL DISPOSAL

Dana R. Kester

Graduate School of Oceanography
University of Rhode Island
Kingston, Rhode Island

Bostwick H. Ketchum

Senior Scientist, Emeritus
Woods Hole Oceanographic Institution
Woods Hole, Massachusetts

Iver W. Duedall

Department of Oceanography and Ocean Engineering
Florida Institute of Technology
Melbourne, Florida

P. Kilho Park

Ocean Dumping Program
National Oceanic and Atmospheric Administration
Rockville, Maryland

3

ABSTRACT

The disposal of dredged material in the ocean is the largest input of waste substances on a mass basis. Existing data are too incomplete to provide a reasonable estimate of dredged-material disposal on a global basis, but it is evident that it is a worldwide practice, and developing countries may be substantial contributors of dredged material to the marine environment. Four approaches have been used to characterize dredged material chemically: bulk analysis, the elutriate test, selective chemical leaching, and bioassay tests. The selective chemical leaching provides the most informative assessment of the chemical state of pollutants associated with sediments. The bioassays provide an operational measure of biological effects. A wide range of alternatives may be considered for the disposal of contaminated sediment. In addition to open-water dumping, various types of containment may be feasible either on land or in the marine environment. Economic considerations of dredged-material disposal most often include capital, operating, and transportation costs. There is a need to obtain sufficient information on the environmental effects of contaminated dredged-material disposal so that the impact on other uses of the marine environment can be assessed.

1.1. DREDGING OPERATIONS IN THE MARINE ENVIRONMENT

The removal and relocation of coastal and harbor sediments is often essential to establish and maintain navigational waterways and port facilities. On a mass basis dredged-material disposal represents the greatest amount of wastes deposited into the ocean. But it does not follow that dredged material is the most environmentally important waste placed in the ocean. Dredging of sediment can be distinguished as being for new construction or for maintenance of existing channels. Although disposal of both types of dredged material requires similar scientific and technical considerations, there are also different issues that arise when considering new construction and maintenance dredging. As a first approximation we could regard new construction dredged material to be the relocation of natural sediment which might produce detrimental environmental changes due to physical and sedimentological alterations, but not due to chemical pollution. Maintenance dredging, on the other

Table 1.1. Summary of Incidents of Human Poisoning by Toxic Metals in the Aquatic Environment of Japan (Förstner and Wittmann, 1981)

Location	Year	Metal
Minamata Bay	1953–1960	Mercury
Niigata	1964–1965	Mercury
Goshonoura	1973	Mercury
Fuchu	1947–1965	Cadmium
Tokyo	1975	Chromium

hand, implies the removal of relatively recently deposited sediment from previously excavated channels. In many cases this sediment has been contaminated with a wide variety of wastes that have spilled or been discharged into the harbor, estuary, rivers, and coastal region.

A number of chemical problems arise when dealing with contaminated sediments. Four general categories of chemical contamination can be identified: high concentrations of organic matter leading to anoxia and the presence of hydrogen sulfide, transition- and heavy-metal contamination, petroleum hydrocarbons, and synthetic organic chemicals. The most striking impact of metal contamination associated with sediments and waste disposal is human poisoning. Five tragedies of human poisoning due to toxic metals have been documented in Japan over three decades (Table 1.1). In each case the concentration of the metals in a sediment phase and subsequent transfer to the food chain was a factor. Consequently there is good cause to understand the chemical behavior of metals in the disposal of contaminated dredged material.

This chapter will provide a general overview of several aspects of the problem of dredged-material disposal. These aspects will include an attempt to estimate the magnitude of dredged-material disposal on a worldwide basis, the characterization of dredged material relative to potential environmental impacts, the potentially important impacts of contaminated dredged material, and a brief summary of alternate methods for dredged-material disposal.

1.1.1. Dredging Techniques

Some general relationships exist between the technique used to dredge sediment and the type of sediment to be removed and the disposal method of the dredged material. Dredging devices are usually classified as either mechanical or hydraulic (Table 1.2). Mechanical dredges bodily lift the sediment from the bottom and transport it to the disposal site. Hydraulic dredges generally suspend the sediment in a slurry with water and pump it to the discharge site. An agitation dredge is the oldest means of dredging, dating back more than 2000 years, and it involves aspects of both mechanical and hydraulic dredging (Mohr, 1976). This type of dredging consists of dragging an object along the bottom in the presence of a flowing current of water which carries away the resuspended sediment. The fluidization

Table 1.2. Types of Dredging Devices and Their Relationship to Sediment Type and Disposal Method

Dredge Type	Sediment Type	Disposal Conveyance
Mechanical devices		
Dipper dredge	Blasted rock	Vessel
Bucket dredge	Coarse grain size	Vessel
Ladder dredge	Fine grain size	Vessel
Agitation dredge	Mud, clay	Prevailing current
Hydraulic devices		
Agitation dredge	Mud, clay	Prevailing current
Hopper dredge	Fine grain size	Vessel
Suction dredge	Soft mud, clay	Pipeline
Cutterhead dredge	Consolidated, coarse grain size	Pipeline
Dustpan dredge	Sand	Pipeline
Sidecasting dredge	Fine grain size	Short pipe

process described in Chapter 13 could be regarded as a modern variant of hydraulic dredging. While some types of dredges are most efficient for certain types of sediment, the relationship between sediment type and the selection of a dredging device is not an exclusive one as might be inferred from Table 1.2. Other factors often enter into the choice of a specific type of dredge such as availability of equipment, maneuverability, conflicts with prevailing maritime traffic, and historical precedent for a specific region (Mohr, 1976). Those dredging techniques which discharge through a pipeline are not likely to be suitable when the disposal site is in the ocean, because of the large transport distances.

1.1.2. Global Assessment of Dredged-Material Disposal

The need to dredge is most often related to marine transportation in commerce, though in some cases marine recreation is also an impetus to dredge. Even though dredged material is the number one waste discharged in the ocean on the basis of mass, it is difficult to obtain a global assessment of its magnitude. In recent years the Inter-Governmental Maritime Consultative Organization (IMCO) has received reports from some of the participating nations to the London Dumping Convention (Inter-Governmental Maritime Consultative Organization, 1976) of the permits issued for waste disposal in the ocean. These reports provide one basis for estimating the magnitude of dredged material disposal in the ocean (Fig. 1.1). However, a number of limitations exist in such an estimate. These quantities represent the amounts that have been authorized by the governments of the participating nations, not the amounts actually dumped in the ocean. Secondly, only a small number of countries (six to nine) have reported their dredged material permits to IMCO for the years 1976 through 1979 (Table 1.3a).

The International Association of Ports and Harbors (IAPH) provides a second

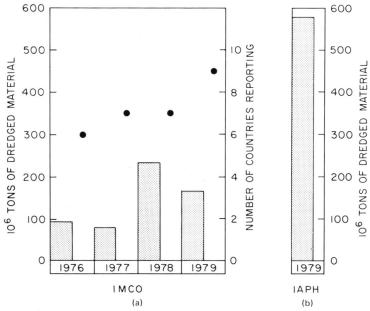

Figure 1.1. Annual quantities of dredged material on a worldwide basis. (a) Amount of dredged material permitted for ocean dumping by countries reporting to IMCO in 1976 through 1979 (the bars); and the number of reporting countries (Inter-Governmental Maritime Consultative Organization, 1979a, b; 1980; 1981). (b) Amount of material dredged during 1979 based on an IAPH questionnaire by 108 ports in 37 countries.

Table 1.3a. Countries That Reported to IMCO Their Ocean Dumping Permits for Dredged-Material Disposal During the Period 1976 to 1979 (Inter-Governmental Maritime Consultative Organization, 1979a, 1979b, 1980, 1981)

Country	1976	1977	1978	1979
Belgium				X
Canada	X	X	X	X
Denmark	X	X	X	X
France			X	X
Hong Kong		X	X	X
Netherlands	X	X	X	X
New Zealand	X	X	X	X
Sweden	X	X		
United Kingdom				X
United States	X	X	X	X

Table 1.3b.   Additional Countries in Which One or More Ports Reported to the IAPH their Dredging Activity During 1979 (International Association of Ports and Harbors, 1981)

Australia	India	Norway
Bahamas	Ireland	Pakistan
Bangladesh	Israel	Panama
Burma	Japan	Phillipines
Cyprus	Kenya	Poland
Federal Republic of Germany	Malaysia	Singapore
Finland	Netherlands Antilles	Taiwan
Haiti	New Guinea	Thailand
Honduras	Nigeria	United Arab Emirates

source for estimating the magnitude of dredging worldwide (International Association of Ports and Harbors, 1981). This organization distributed a questionnaire pertaining to dredging activity to port and harbor authorities in 70 countries. They received 108 responses from 37 countries. This questionnaire sought information on the quantity of maintenance dredging for 1979 and the amount of new construction dredging for the 5-y period 1975 through 1979. We have combined the 350×10^6 tons of maintenance dredging for 1979 with an average annual new construction dredging of 230×10^6 tons to estimate a total for 1979 (Fig. 1.1). All of the countries that reported to IMCO were represented in the IAPH survey as well as 27 additional countries (Table 1.3b). The IAPH survey found that about one-fourth of all dredged material is ocean-dumped and another two-thirds is deposited in wetlands and nearshore. Dredged-material disposal in the marine environment is clearly a worldwide phenomenon. A preliminary global perspective on dredged-material disposal is depicted in Fig. 1.2 based on the permits reported to IMCO. The lack of data on a worldwide basis is evident. The IAPH results indicated that three countries (India, Kenya, and Nigeria) accounted for about one-half of the reported dredging and these three countries are not yet included in the IMCO data. One may note that the preceding assessment of global dredging does not include important maritime nations in South America, Asia, and eastern Europe.

1.2. DREDGED MATERIAL AND MARINE POLLUTION

In considering the problems associated with dredged-material disposal a basic distinction should be made between natural sediments and sediments that are contaminated by anthropogenic substances. There can be environmental impacts resulting from the improper disposal of natural sediments, because large masses of material typically are involved. These impacts, however, can be fairly well predicted with existing knowledge, and they should not present a substantial obstacle to disposal of dredged material. In many instances natural dredged material is a

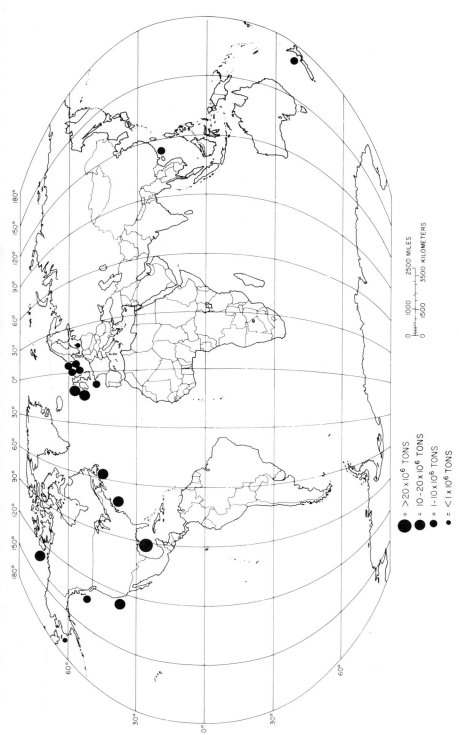

Figure 1.2. Global distribution of ocean-disposed dredged material in 1979 based on the IMCO permit records (Inter-Governmental Maritime Consultative Organization, 1981). The locations of the circles indicate general regions of disposal (e.g., U.S. east coast) and do not imply specific dumpsites.

resource that is used to modify the shoreline to make it suitable for commercial and industrial use by filling marshes and wetlands. In some instances these modifications have been so large that they may alter the nearshore ecosystem of a region.

Boston, Massachusetts is an example of extensive shoreline modification. When the American continent was first colonized by Europeans, Boston consisted of Beacon Hill connected to the mainland by a narrow spit with extensive wetlands and shallows on both sides of the narrow strip of land as shown by the 1711 chart reproduced here (Fig. 1.3a). Soon after independence the shallows to the north of this land strip were filled in, creating land which today is the most valuable real estate in the city (No. 1 in Fig. 1.3b). Additional land fills by Boston and the adjacent cities of Cambridge and Chelsea completely changed the waterfront and within the current century, Logan Airport was developed mostly on extensively filled mud flats and shallows in Boston Harbor (Fig. 1.3b, No. 2). There are many other examples. The Bermuda airport was constructed on land filled with dredged material of coral rock from the bottom of Castle Harbor (B. H. Ketchum, personal observation). Squires (1981, p. 68) states that in the vicinity of New York Harbor:

> The great building complex in the Hackensack meadows of New Jersey, the New Jersey Turnpike's northern extent, Port Elizabeth, Newark Airport and Battery Park City, are all built on sand from beneath the harbor.

and that the shoreline of New York was expanded by 61 km^2 of new land using steel bulkheads and land fill.

1.2.1. Composition and Properties of Dredged Material

Sediments that are contaminated by chemicals from industrial and domestic wastes present a difficult problem when assessing potential impacts resulting from disposal. The first requirement is to obtain a characterization of the dredged material. Sediments are classified physically on the basis of grain size (Table 1.4). Grain size is important because it determines the conditions under which sediment will be resuspended or deposited, it determines the basic habitat available for benthic organisms, and it also determines the surface area to volume ratio of the solid phase which is important in chemical exchange processes with the aqueous phase.

The chemical composition and physical properties of dredged material are highly variable. The mechanical properties of the sediment will depend on the grain size and on the water content. Mineralogy also plays an important role in the properties of sediment. The water content is increased greatly during hydraulic dredging. Engler (1981) discussed a number of the properties of dredged material that are important when considering their disposal. These properties include their cation exchange capacity, their organic matter content, and their concentrations of phosphorus, nitrogen, sulfide phases, toxic metals, and salt. Table 1.5 lists the range of constituents that are expected for dredged material. The variability of dredged material must be recognized in considering its disposal in the environment.

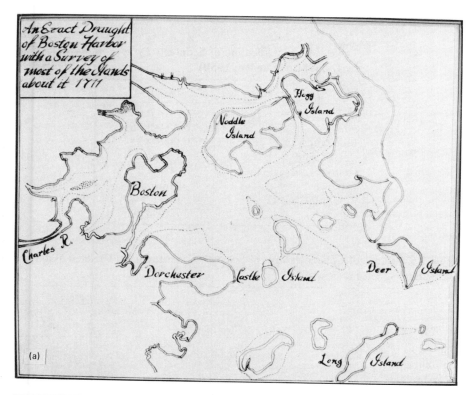

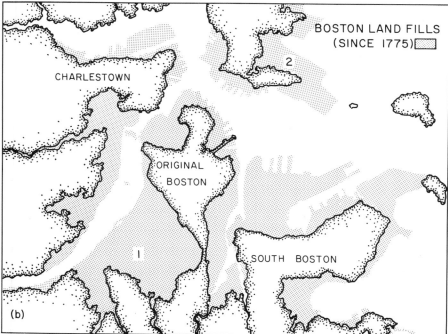

Figure 1.3. Shoreline modification of Boston during the past 210 years. The landfill substances were obtained in part from the Boston Harbor dredging operations. (a) Early map of Boston Harbor. (b) Boston landfills since 1775.

Table 1.4. Classification of Sediment Type by Grain Size (Kuenen, 1950)

Type	Size (mm)
Clay	<0.004
Silt	0.004–0.062
Fine sand	0.062–0.25
Coarse sand	0.25–2.0
Granule	2.0–4.0
Pebble	4.0–64
Cobble	64–256
Boulder	>256

Table 1.5. Range of Concentrations of Selected Constituents in Dredged Material (After Engler, 1981)

Constituent	Range Moles kg^{-1} of sediment (except as noted)
Major ions of seawater	
Sodium	0.5–1.7
Magnesium	0.2–0.5
Calcium	0.01–0.4
Potassium	0.4–0.6
Biologically active constituents	
Organic nitrogen	0.007–0.14
Ammonia	0.007–0.14
Phosphorus	0.02–0.06
Total sulfide	0.003–0.09
Total organic carbon	0.4–4.2
Trace metals	
Iron	0.02–0.90
Manganese	$(0.4–10) \times 10^{-3}$
Zinc	$(0.5–8) \times 10^{-3}$
Copper	$(0.8–9400) \times 10^{-6}$
Nickel	$(0.2–2.6) \times 10^{-3}$
Chromium	$(0.02–3.8) \times 10^{-3}$
Lead	$(5–1900) \times 10^{-6}$
Cadmium	$(0.4–600) \times 10^{-6}$
Mercury	$(1–10) \times 10^{-6}$
Synthetic organic substances	
Chlorinated pesticides	0–10 mg kg^{-1}
Polychlorinated biphenyl compounds	0–10 mg kg^{-1}
Other properties	
pH	6–9
Chemical oxygen demand	0.03–0.4
Oil and grease	0.1–5 g kg^{-1}

A variety of techniques have been used to provide a chemical characterization of dredged material. These include:

1. Bulk chemical analysis.
2. The elutriate test.
3. Selective chemical leaching.
4. Bioassay.

1.2.2. Bulk Chemical Analysis

Bulk chemical analyses are generally performed by a total digestion of the sediment solid phase followed by measurements of individual chemical elements. This generally has been the basis for estimating the mass loads to the marine environment associated with dredged material disposal. The New York Bight provides an example in which the relative magnitudes of ocean-disposed wastes have been estimated (Fig. 1.4). As one might expect, dredged material disposal accounts for the major input of suspended solids and some metals that are abundant in terrigenous and marine sediments. It is surprising, however, that dredged material also is responsible for a major portion of the chemical oxygen demand, total organic carbon, and ammonia which are generally associated with sewage inputs. In this case it is likely that sewage wastes have become incorporated into harbor sediments and they are subsequently transferred to the ocean when these sediments are dredged and dumped into the ocean.

1.2.3. The Elutriate Test

Bulk chemical analysis does not provide a good basis for assessing the quantities of substances that may alter the chemistry and biology of the disposal site for dredged material. The elutriate test provides one approach to a better measure of the amount of a substance that is exchanged between the sediment and the aqueous phase during dredging and disposal. The elutriate test is an operationally defined procedure consisting of vigorously mixing for 30 min one part of sediment to four parts of water on a volume basis. The mixture is allowed to settle for 1 h, the aqueous phase is separated from the solids by centrifugation and/or filtration and then analyzed for prospective contaminants. When this test was initially implemented the sediment was considered to be contaminated if the concentration of a substance in the aqueous phase was 1.5 times greater than prior to mixing with the sediment. Because this 50% increase in the aqueous phase concentration was an arbitrary criterion for contamination, subsequent applications of the elutriate test have been interpreted individually to judge if the sediment should be considered to be contaminated (Lee et al., 1976). There has been some debate as to what is the appropriate source for the water mixed with the sediment. Initially, the water for this test was to come from the disposal site for the sediment, but it also has been argued that the water should come from the dredging site (Lee et al., 1976). This choice may make a substantial difference in the conclusions derived from the test if the sediments and their surrounding waters at the dredging site are polluted relative to the disposal site. The choice of which water is used in the test could

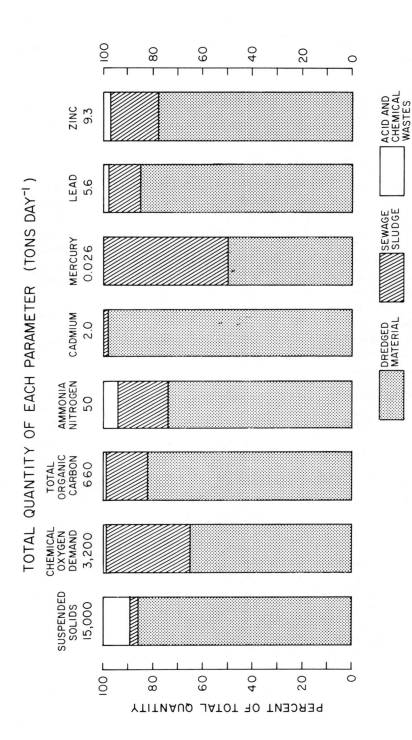

Figure 1.4. Relative contributions of dredged material, sewage sludge, and chemical wastes to the total daily input of eight parameters from ocean-dumped wastes in the New York Bight (data from Stanford et al, 1981).

logically be made by considering whether the concern is about contaminants released at the dredging site or at the disposal site. Lee et al. (1976) indicate that this test is operationally suitable for hydraulic dredging, but not suitable for mechanical dredging. Nevertheless, it has been applied independent of the dredging technique.

Even though the elutriate test seems to be an operationally useful measure of the contaminants that may enter the aquatic environment during dredging, there are a number of chemical complexities that can affect substantially the results. The mobility of metals associated with sediments depends greatly on the pH and the redox conditions of the aqueous phase. O'Connor (1976) conducted a series of experiments with the elutriate test using sediment to be dredged and seawater; he found that the zinc concentrations increased by a factor of 40 as the pH of the supernatant changed from 7.9 to 6.0. In these experiments the suspension became anoxic within 5 min and the iron concentration exceeded 800 μmolar. The iron was oxidized upon aeration over a 4-h period and hydrous ferric oxide precipitated which reduced the zinc in the aqueous phase to values that were 2 to 10 times less than were in the seawater *prior* to mixing with the sediment. It is evident that unless such variables as pH and the redox state of metals are controlled and understood, the elutriate test can show misleadingly that a sediment is contaminated and that its disposal into the ocean will actually reduce the concentrations of metals relative to natural values.

1.2.4. Selective Chemical Leaching

Selective chemical leaching provides a third basis for evaluating the potential degree of contamination of sediments. A variety of operational procedures have been devised to distinguish the chemical reactivity of various phases associated with sediments (Table 1.6). The study by Brannon et al. (1976) provides a good example of how this approach can be applied to dredged material. They determined six fractions of a number of elements in several sediments which were to be dredged. Their data for manganese, cadmium, and nickel in sediment from Mobile Bay, Alabama and from Bridgeport, Connecticut illustrate several points (Fig. 1.5). For this analysis the interstitial water concentrations (which were originally expressed as mg liter^{-1}) and the solid phase concentrations (which were originally expressed as μg g^{-1}) were converted to μg of metal per cm^3 of in situ sediment assuming that the sediment was 50% water by weight (Brannon et al. stated that the water content varied from 31% to 70%). We also took a value of 1.02 g cm^{-3} and 2.60 g cm^{-3} for the densities of the seawater and solid phases respectively, giving a bulk density for the in situ sediment of 1.45 g cm^{-3}. The circular diagrams in Fig. 1.5 begin at the 1200 o'clock position with the residual phase and progress clockwise to the more chemically labile phases with each sector of the circle proportional to that phase in sediment.

The following significance can be associated with the various phases. That portion of the metal in the residual phase (RS) is not likely to be released to the marine environment or biota upon dredging and disposal. The moderately reducible phase (MR) could be mobilized if the redox potential decreases and the organic

Table 1.6. Summary of Three Schemes for Selective Leaching of Solid Phases

Phase	Treatment
Applied to Suspended River Sediment[a]	
Solution	Passage through 0.45-μm pore size filter
Adsorbed	1 N MgCl$_2$ leach at pH 7
Metallic coating	Sodium dithionite leach
Organic	Sodium hypochlorite leach
Crystalline	Fluxed with lithium metaborate at 1000°C and dissolved in HNO$_3$
Applied to Dredged-Material Sediment[b]	
Interstitial water	Centrifugation separation of sediment from water
Exchangeable	1 N ammonium acetate leach
Easily reducible	Hydroxylamine hydrochloride leach
Organic and sulfide	Hydrogen peroxide digestion at 95°C, pH 2.5
Moderately reducible	Sodium dithionite leach
Residual	HF and HNO$_3$ digestion at 95°C
Applied to Marine Sediment[c]	
Easily extractable	0.2 M BaCl$_2$-triethanolamine at pH 8.1
Carbonate	Acidic cation exchanger at pH 5
Easily reducible	0.1 M hydroxylamine hydrochloride and 0.01 N HNO$_3$
HCl soluble	0.3 N HCl
Residual	HF and HClO$_4$ digestion

[a]*Source*: Gibbs (1973).
[b]*Source*: Brannon et al. (1976).
[c]*Source*: Förstner and Stoffers (1981).

plus sulfide phase (OS) could be mobilized by exposure to oxygenated conditions. The interstitial water (IW), exchangeable (EX), and easily reducible (ER) phases are the most labile, with the IW subject to diffusive exchange with benthic organisms and overlying waters. The EX fraction may respond to salinity and pH changes, whereas the ER phase can change with slight reduction of the redox potential. In considering the range of chemical environments that might liberate metals from the solid phase one should include bulk seawater, interstitial water of the sediment, localized environments near the solid-solution interface, and the digestive tracts of particulate-feeding organisms.

For each of the three metals shown in Fig. 1.5 there are large differences between the Mobile Bay and the Bridgeport sediments. Cadmium appears to be particularly significant in the Bridgeport sediment because it has a relatively high total concentration (25.6 μg cm^{-3}) and it is present in mobile or potentially mobile phases. The London Dumping Convention prohibits the ocean dumping of cad-

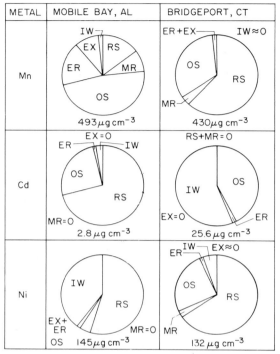

Figure 1.5. Sediment phase speciation of manganese, cadmium, and nickel in dredged material from two locations. RS = residual phase, MR = moderately reducible phase, OS = organic plus sulfide phase, EX = exchangeable phase, IW = interstitial water phase. The total metal concentration per cm^3 of in situ sediment is given also (data from Brannon et al., 1976).

mium and its compounds in all but "trace" amounts. Would it be illegal to dump this Bridgeport dredged material in the ocean because of its cadmium content? We do not have an adequate technical basis to answer this question on the grounds of chemical measurements alone, but the partitioning of an element's total concentration in a sediment into several operationally defined phases provides an improved basis for predicting its possible fate and impact on the environment.

1.2.5. Bioassay Tests

Bioassay tests provide an operational procedure to assess the toxicity of dredged material on test organisms. Bioassay experiments in which one determines a 96-h LC_{50} is one approach to assessing acute toxicity of a substance. This procedure determines the concentration of a contaminant that is lethal to 50% of a population of test organisms after a 96-h exposure. The U.S. Environmental Protection Agency (EPA) criteria for the disposal of dredged material in the ocean without causing unacceptable environmental impacts were presented in the Federal Register of 11 January 1977 (U.S. Environmental Protection Agency, 1977). Biological tests of both the solid and liquid phases of the dredged material were specified and the details of the procedures are discussed in Chapters 2 and 3. The preceding section indicates the uncertainties of the chemical characteristics of these phases. The living organism serves as an integrator of the effects of its environment whether or not we know the specific chemical constituents. The biological tests required include bioassays to evaluate acute toxic effects and evaluation of bioaccumulation.

With regard to the liquid phase of dredged material, the EPA criteria specifically calls for the testing of the most sensitive organism. But what species constitutes the most sensitive organism for the bioassay test? This can only be determined by performing laboratory bioassays on many different species inhabiting each trophic level in the receiving waters. Costs and technical problems associated with maintaining cultures of different species limit the bioassay approach. These tests usually provide a conservative estimate of the effects of contaminants in the aqueous phase because dispersive processes in the ocean dilute the concentrations of contaminants with time.

1.3. IMPACTS OF DREDGED-MATERIAL DISPOSAL ON MARINE BENTHOS

A variety of environmental impacts can be identified from the disposal of either clean or contaminated dredged material. Those impacts that are related to the physical characteristics of the sediment will be common to both types of dredged material whereas the impacts due to chemical characteristics are an issue primarily for contaminated dredged material.

During the period 1973 to 1978 the U.S. Army Corps of Engineers organized and sponsored the Dredged Material Research Program (DMRP) to address many of the problems related to dredging and disposal. This study considered physical, chemical, and biological effects of dredging, criteria for designation of polluted sediment, use of dredged material for habitat development, and a variety of methods for disposal in addition to ocean dumping. The report by Wright (1978) summarizes many of their findings based on investigations at five dredged-material disposal sites. In the fresh and marine aquatic environments dredged-material disposal produced short-term increases in turbidity and there was a release of ammonia, phosphorus, and manganese into the water column. These effects did not appear to influence the pelagic organisms. Deposit mounds were created on the seafloor and they tended to migrate in response to waves, tides, and currents over a period of a year. The dredged material resulted in a reduced number and diversity of benthic organisms at the disposal site. The mounds were readily colonized by benthic organisms, but the population was different from the one originally at the site.

In another summary report from the DMRP, Chen et al. (1978) presented the results of effluents and leachates from a series of active and inactive upland disposal sites for contaminated dredged material. The effluent from these containment sites failed to meet water quality criteria for ammonia, phosphorus, chlorinated hydrocarbons, and for most metals that were tested (iron, manganese, cadmium, zinc, nickel, and copper).   Most of these contaminants could be removed from the effluents by filtration, though ammonia and manganese still exceeded the water quality criteria after filtration.   Chen et al. also indicated that if dredged material from saltwater environments are placed in upland disposal sites, it may render the ground water unfit for drinking due to the soluble salts associated with the sediment.

Engler (1981) presented a number of the conclusions obtained by the DMRP. He particularly emphasized the roles of pH and Eh in determining the fixation or mobility of metals relative to sediments.   He indicated that uptake of metals from the aqueous phase by organisms has been documented, but questions remain concerning the uptake of metals from sediment phases.   In one study about one-fourth of the specimens showed contaminant uptake from solid phases.   Of those that showed uptake, about 80% retained the assimilated metals during an 8-d depuration experiment after removal from the contaminated sediment.   Engler (1981) concluded that field studies by the DMRP found no uptake of metals and chlorinated hydrocarbons by a number of organisms at dredged-material dumpsites relative to control sites.   He did, however, present data that show that the mussel, *Mytilus edulis*, contained 0.2 μg g^{-1} PCBs after two- and three-week exposures at the Duwamish Waterway (State of Washington) dredged-material dumpsite whereas mussels at a control site contained 0.1 μg g^{-1} PCBs.

1.3.1.   Physical Impacts

Perhaps the first-order question concerning dredged-material disposal is whether it will stay at the disposal site or be swept away and dispersed by ocean currents and wave action.   The type of sediment largely determines the speed of a current required to erode, transport, or deposit the particles (Fig. 1.6).   When suspended particles are deposited in a decelerating current they will be graded from sand to silt to clay.   But when sediments consisting of less than 60% water are eroded, the fine sand will be resuspended at lower current speeds than clay or coarse sand. These factors should be considered in selecting disposal sites for dredged material. It is ineffective to deposit dredged material alongside a dredged channel if there is a significant probability that the material will be swept back in and fill the channel.

In many instances dredged material deposited in coastal waters remains at the location where it is dumped.   Substantial mounds of sediment can accumulate at dumpsites that are used over a period of years.   The presently used dredged-material dumpsite in the apex of the New York Bight has become 30 m more shallow (shoaled by 30 m) from 1936 to 1973 (Williams, 1979; also see Chapter 6, Fig. 6.2).   A bathymetric study of a dredged-material dumpsite off Narragansett Bay, Rhode Island, showed that the bottom shoaled by about 6 m after the disposal of about 8×10^6 m^3 of sediment (Saila et al., 1972).   The volume of this mound calculated from bathymetric data agreed to within 2.4% of the volume that was estimated to be dumped.   While in some instances the dredged material forms a mound that remains intact for decades or longer, there are also situations in which

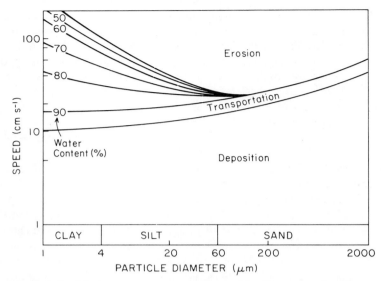

Figure 1.6. Relationship between current speed, particle diameter, and sediment erosion, transport, or deposition (after Kennett, 1982).

the material is dispersed and eroded. Sternberg et al. (1979) found that 61% of the dredged material dumped at a site off the Columbia River remained as an identifiable mound and there was evidence for bedload transport on the order of 0.4 km per year. Other examples of dredged-material dispersion after dumping are provided in Chapters 4 and 5.

The three primary physical effects of dredged-material disposal are water column turbidity, burial of benthic organisms, and possible changes in the grain size or sediment type at the dumpsite. Water column turbidity is a relatively short-term effect. Although the organisms that are buried in a dredged-material mound may not survive, recolonization of the site can occur readily with the cessation of dumping. Changes in sediment type may produce a long-term effect, because the benthic community is often determined by the properties of the sediment. If clay and silt are deposited on an area of the seafloor where sand is prevalent, it cannot be assumed that the sediment will be sorted by currents to reestablish the sand. There are two reasons for this lack of readjustment. As indicated in Fig. 1.6, if the sand was in equilibrium with the prevailing current speeds, the currents may not be adequate to erode the newly deposited clay and silt. Secondly, in many cases the sand presently on the continental shelves are relic deposits from the more recent transgressions of sea level during the present interglacial climatic period. Consequently, some dredged-material mounds are not likely to be redistributed in the marine environment until sea level recedes during the next glacial cycle. One may therefore expect changes in the bottom fauna of a dredged-material dumpsite due to changes in sediment type.

1.3.2. Chemical Considerations

The redox potential (Eh) and the pH are two of the primary variables that control the chemical behavior of metals in marine systems. Gambrell et al. (1976) conducted experiments to measure the concentrations of several metals in sediment-water suspensions when the pH and Eh were adjusted to various values. Their results illustrate that zinc, copper, and mercury in sediment from Mobile Bay, Alabama, each respond differently to changes in Eh and pH (Fig. 1.7).

The following inferences may be drawn from the results presented in Fig. 1.7. These sediments most likely were reducing (Eh $\leq$ 150 mV) with a pH $\approx$ 8 when they were sampled from Mobile Bay. As long as they remain near these Eh–pH conditions the three metals will remain bound to the solid phase. If, upon disposal in the marine or terrestrial environment, they become subjected to changes in Eh or pH the three metals will be released to the solution phase at different rates which are related to their chemical behavior. Copper will be released at all pH as the sediment becomes oxidized (as Eh increases). Mercury requires both an increase in Eh and a decrease in pH to become mobilized. Zinc is not released substantially as Eh increases if the pH $>$ 6, but becomes very mobile when the pH reaches 5. Marine environments that contain dissolved oxygen usually have Eh values greater than 400 mV. Anoxic marine environments containing hydrogen sulfide have Eh values less than – 100 mV. The pH values of these systems generally are in the range 7.2–8.4. For these conditions copper would be expected to be the most mobile of the three metals based on the experiments of Gambrell et al. These ranges of Eh and pH are representative of bulk aqueous conditions. It also may be necessary to consider the Eh and pH of localized environments near solid-phase–aqueous interfaces and in the digestive tracts of organisms for a more complete assessment of metal mobility and availability.

1.3.3. Biological Effects

The biological effects resulting from contaminated sediment disposal may be distinguished as acute or chronic. Acute toxicity is short-term exposure to a contaminant resulting in death. Chronic toxicity is an adverse effect of a pollutant with long-term exposure of more than 10% of the life time of an organism (MITRE Corporation, 1979). In addition to these exposure-related effects it is also necessary to consider the possible bioaccumulation and biomagnification of contaminants by organisms. Bioaccumulation is the concentration of a substance by an organism to levels greater than those in its environment or food supply. This process results from uptake exceeding excretion. Biomagnification is the progressive concentration of a substance among successive levels of a food chain; it has been identified for DDT, PCB, and mercury (MITRE Corporation, 1979).

Table 1.7 illustrates the type of information available on the biological effects, water quality criteria, and natural concentrations of four metals and two synthetic organic substances. Sublethal effects are the most difficult to characterize and in

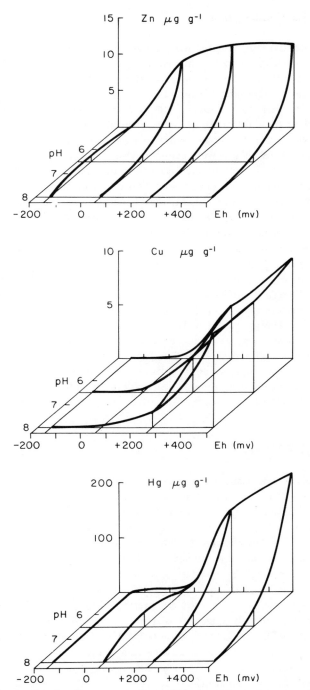

Figure 1.7. Diagram showing the concentrations of zinc, copper, and mercury in suspensions of Mobile Bay dredged material and seawater adjusted to various values of Eh and pH (data from Gambrell et al., 1976).

22

Table 1.7. Summary of Biological Effects of Contaminants in Marine Systems (after MITRE Corporation, 1979)

Substance	Water Quality Criteria[a] ($ng\ kg^{-1}$)	Natural Seawater Concentration[b] ($ng\ kg^{-1}$)	Most Sensitive Response		Maximum Bioaccumulation	
			Concentration ($ng\ kg^{-1}$)	Response	Level Reached ($mg\ kg^{-1}$)	Organism
Cadmium	5000	8	15,000	Retarded sexual development in oysters	1,200	Abalone
Mercury	100	4	5,600	48-h LC_{50} for oyster embryo	7,400	Algae
Copper	$0.1 \times$ 96-h LC_{50}	60	1,000	Reduced phytoplankton growth rate	15,000	Squid
Chromium	$0.01 \times$ 96-h LC_{50}	200	100	Decreased algae growth	260	Zooplankton
DDT	1.0	0	50	Shrimp mortality	$10^7 \times$ ambient	Birds
PCBs	1.0	0	300	Sheepshead minnow mortality	$10^5 \times$ ambient	Oyster

[a]The water quality criteria are based on U.S. EPA guidelines.
[b]The natural seawater concentrations have been updated from Bruland (1980), Mukherji and Kester (1979), and Cranston and Murray (1980). The response for copper is based on Sunda and Guillard (1976).

some cases they depend on the coexistence of two or more contaminants such as cadmium toxicity being synergistic with copper and zinc (MITRE Corporation, 1979).

1.4. STRATEGIES FOR DREDGED-MATERIAL DISPOSAL

The two most common methods of dredged-material disposal in the marine environment are to use the sediment as landfill for shoreline modification and to dump the sediment in a mound on the seafloor at a disposal site. However, when dealing with contaminated sediment a number of other alternatives exist which generally consist of some type of containment of the material. In a study of the dredging requirements for New York Harbor the MITRE Corporation (1979) considered a number of disposal alternatives including filling subaqueous borrow pits, construction of an artificial island, confined upland disposal, and deep-ocean disposal. They considered these and other disposal methods in terms of present knowledge about environmental impacts, capacity to accept the quantities of material anticipated, and cost per unit of material disposed. Considering only the engineering and transportation costs the present method of seafloor mound deposit is among the least expensive disposal alternatives.

1.5. DISCUSSION AND SUMMARY

Dredged-material disposal is a problem of worldwide importance. The problems are greatest when dealing with sediments that have been contaminated with wastes discharged or spilled into harbors and coastal waters. Countries that have experienced extensive industrial development during the past century now face difficulties in maintaining the quality of their coastal regions. As more countries emphasize industrial development the need to dispose of dredged material will increase. Initially the disposal or utilization of new construction dredged material will not be difficult, and if consideration is given to the input and accumulation of pollutants in coastal waters at an early stage, future problems associated with dredged-material disposal can be minimized.

The costs associated with dredging operations can span a large range. In New York the costs in 1976 were about $2 to $3 m^{-3} (MITRE Corporation, 1979). The disposal of contaminated sediments in containment sites on land costs $65 m^{-3} in Japan and in Seattle, Washington (Engler, 1981).

Most economic considerations of dredged-material disposal are woefully incomplete. Certain costs such as capital and operating expenditures related to the dredging and disposal operation can be accounted for directly (MITRE Corporation, 1979). Transportation costs are often put forth as the determining economic factor in selecting a disposal site. There are at least two other costs that should be factored into an economic analysis. If one does not have an acceptable procedure for dredged-material disposal there can be a substantial cost due to reduced marine transportation.   Secondly, if the placement of contaminated dredged material in coastal regions leads to a degradation of marine environmental quality, there can be costs associated with a loss or diminished utilization of other marine resources such as fisheries and recreation.   At the present time our understanding of the linkage between contaminated dredged-material disposal and a loss in marine resources may not be sufficient to calculate costs directly, but these costs can be as real as the cost per kilometer to transport the spoils to the dumpsite.

ACKNOWLEDGMENTS

We would like to express our appreciation to Marilyn A. Maley and Jo-Anne Degidio for their assistance in preparing this manuscript. We also thank Mr. Kenneth Morse for his assistance in locating information on the global magnitudes of dredging. We thank Dr. Manfred Nauke for the information provided by IMCO.   This work was supported by NOAA Grant NA-79-AA-H-00086.

REFERENCES

Brannon, J. M., R. M. Engler, J. R. Rose, P. G. Hunt, and I. Smith. 1976. Distribution of toxic heavy metals in marine and freshwater sediments. *In*: Dredging and Its Environmental Effects, P. A. Krenkel, J. Harrison, and J. C. Burdick III (Eds.).   American Society of Civil Engineers, 345 East 47th Street, New York, pp. 455–495.

Bruland, K. W. 1980. Oceanographic distributions of cadmium, zinc, nickel, and copper in the North Pacific. *Earth and Planetary Science Letters*, **47**, 176–198.

Chen, K. Y., J. L. Mang, B. Eickenberger, and R. E. Hoeppel. 1978. Confined disposal area effluent and leachate control (laboratory and field investigations). Dredged Material Research Program Technical Report DS-78-7, U.S. Army Engineer Waterways Experiment Station, Vicksburg, Mississippi, 94 pp.

Cranston, R. E. and J. W. Murray. 1980. Chromium species in the Columbia River and estuary. *Limnology and Oceanography*, **25**, 1104–1112.

Engler, R. M. 1981. Impacts associated with the discharge of dredged material: Management approaches. *In*: Use of the Ocean for Man's Wastes: Engineering and Scientific Aspects.   Marine Board, National Research Council, National Academy Press, Washington, DC, pp. 129–185.

Förstner, U. and P. Stoffers. 1981. Chemical fractionation of transition elements in Pacific pelagic sediments. *Geochimica et Cosmochimica Acta*, **45**, 1141–1146.

Förstner, U. and G. T. W. Wittmann. 1981. Metal Pollution in the Aquatic Environment, 2nd edition.   Springer-Verlag, Berlin, 486 pp.

Gambrell, R. P., R. A. Khalid, and W. H. Patrick, Jr. 1976. Physicochemical parameters that regulate mobilization and immobilization of toxic heavy metals. *In*: Dredging and Its Environmental Effects, P. A. Krenkel, J. Harrison, and J. C. Burdick III (Eds.).   American Society of Civil Engineers, 345 East 47th Street, New York, pp. 418–434.

Gibbs, R. J. 1973. Mechanisms of trace metal transport in rivers. *Science*, **180**, 71–73.

Inter-Governmental Maritime Consultative Organization (IMCO). 1976. Inter-Governmental Conference on the Convention on the Dumping of Wastes at Sea. (London, 30 October–13 November 1971). Final Act of the Conference with Technical Memorandum and Resolution adopted by the Conference and Convention on the Prevention of Marine Pollution by Dumping of Wastes and Other Matter. Inter-Governmental Maritime Consultative Organization, London, 36 pp. plus Amendments (Publication No. 76.14 E), 6 pp.

Inter-Governmental Maritime Consultative Organization (IMCO). 1979a. Convention on the Prevention of Marine Pollution by Dumping of Wastes and Other Matter, 1972. Reports of permits issued for dumping in 1976. LDC.2/Circ. 31 (19 March 1979), Inter-Governmental Maritime Consultative Organization, London, 25 pp.

Inter-Governmental Maritime Consultative Organization (IMCO). 1979b. Convention on the Prevention of Marine Pollution by Dumping of Wastes and Other Matter, 1972. Reports of permits issued for dumping in 1977. LDC.2/Circ. 33 (10 April 1979), Inter-Governmental Maritime Consultative Organization, London, 23 pp.

Inter-Governmental Maritime Consultative Organization (IMCO). 1980. Convention on the Prevention of Marine Pollution by Dumping of Wastes and Other Matter, 1972. Reports of permits issued for dumping in 1978. LDC.2/Circ. 47 (12 February 1980), Inter-Governmental Maritime Consultative Organization, London, 24 pp.

Inter-Governmental Maritime Consultative Organization (IMCO). 1981. Convention on the Prevention of Marine Pollution by Dumping of Wastes and Other Matter, 1972. Reports of permits issued for dumping in 1979. LDC.2/Circ. 64 (30 April 1981), Inter-Governmental Maritime Consultative Organization, London, 26 pp.

International Association of Ports and Harbors. 1981. A Survey of World Port Practices in the Ocean Disposal of Dredged Material as Related to the London Dumping Convention. Report of the Ad Hoc Dredging Committee, Mr. A. J. Tozzoli, Chairman. Port Authority of New York and New Jersey, One World Trade Center, Room 64W, New York, 38 pp.

Kennett, J. P. 1982. Marine Geology. Prentice-Hall, Englewood Cliffs, New Jersey, 813 pp.

Kuenen, P. H. 1950. Marine Geology. John Wiley and Sons, Inc., New York, 568 pp.

Lee, G. F., J. M. Lopez, and M. D. Piwoni. 1976. Evaluation of the factors influencing the results of the elutriate test for dredged material disposal criteria. *In*: Dredging and Its Environmental Effects, P. A. Krenkel, J. Harrison, and J. C. Burdick III (Eds.). American Society of Civil Engineers, 345 East 47th Street, New York, pp. 253–288.

MITRE Corporation. 1979. Disposal of Dredged Material within the New York District: Volume 1. Present Practices and Candidate Alternatives. MITRE Technical Report MTR-7808, Vol. 1, 1820 Dolley Madison Boulevard, McLean, Virginia, 361 pp.

Mohr, A. W. 1976. Mechanical dredges. *In*: Dredging and Its Environmental Effects, P. A. Krenkel, J. Harrison, and J. C. Burdick III (Eds.). American Society of Civil Engineers, 345 East 47th Street, New York, pp. 125–138.

Mukherji, P. and D. R. Kester. 1979. Mercury distribution in the Gulf Stream. *Science*, **204**, 64–66.

O'Connor, T. P. 1976. Investigation of the elutriate test. *In*: Dredging and Its Environmental Effects, P. A. Krenkel, J. Harrison, and J. C. Burdick III (Eds.). American Society of Civil Engineers, 345 East 47th Street, New York, pp. 299–318.

Saila, S. B., S. D. Pratt, and T. T. Polgar. 1972. Dredge Spoil Disposal in Rhode Island Sound. Marine Technical Report No. 2, University of Rhode Island, Kingston, 48 pp.

Squires, D. F. 1981. The Bight of the Big Apple. New York Sea Grant Institute, State University of New York, Albany, 84 pp.

Stanford, H. M., J. S. O'Connor, and R. L. Swanson. 1981. The effects of ocean dumping on the New York Bight ecosystem. *In*: Ocean Dumping of Industrial Wastes, B. H. Ketchum, D. R. Kester, P. K. Park (Eds.). Plenum Press, New York, pp. 53–86.

Sternberg, R. W., J. S. Creager, J. Johnson, and W. Glassley. 1979. Stability of dredged material deposited seaward of the Columbia River mouth. *In*: Ocean Dumping and Marine Pollution, H. D. Palmer and M. G. Gross (Eds.). Dowden, Hutchinson and Ross, Inc., Stroudsburg, Pennsylvania, pp. 17–49.

Sunda, W. and R. R. L. Guillard. 1976. The relationship between cupric activity and the toxicity of copper to phytoplankton. *Journal of Marine Research*, **34**, 511–529.

U.S. Environmental Protection Agency. 1977. Ocean Dumping, Final Revision of Regulations and Criteria. Federal Register, 11 January 1977, Part VII, **42**, 2476–2489.

Williams, S. J. 1979. Geologic effects of ocean dumping on the New York Bight inner shelf. *In*: Ocean Dumping and Marine Pollution, H. D. Palmer and M. G. Gross (Eds.). Dowden, Hutchinson and Ross, Inc., Stroudsburg, Pennsylvania, pp. 51–72.

Wright, T. D. 1978. Aquatic dredged material disposal impacts. Dredged Material Research Program. Technical Report DS-78-1, U.S. Army Engineer Waterways Experiment Station, Vicksburg, Mississippi, 57 pp.

2

DREDGED-MATERIAL OCEAN DUMPING: PERSPECTIVES ON LEGAL AND ENVIRONMENTAL IMPACTS

Kenneth S. Kamlet

National Wildlife Federation
Washington, D.C.

ABSTRACT

The procedures used by regulatory authorities in the United States to determine the environmental impact potential of contaminated dredged material have changed greatly in recent years. From an early reliance on bulk chemical criteria, dredged-material evaluation has evolved through standard elutriate testing, multiphase bioassay tests, and bioaccumulation assessments. The approach currently in vogue relies on interim guidance matrices for evaluating the significance of the bioaccumulation of dredged-material contaminants. Although the early procedures may have tended to exaggerate the potential impacts of some dredged-material constituents (e.g., heavy metals) because they failed to distinguish between biologically available and nonavailable fractions, there is reason to be concerned that present procedures have perhaps swung too far in the opposite direction. These procedures too often assume that effects that cannot be readily measured in short-term laboratory tests or under field conditions either are not occurring or cannot be of environmental significance. And they frequently underestimate the resourcefulness of living things; for example, the ability of microorganisms to alkylate inorganic forms of heavy metals, with resulting enhancement of their toxicity and biological availability.

    This chapter discusses an array of current and historical dredged-material ocean dumping issues, including the environmental significance of dredged-material disposal in the ocean, alternatives to ocean dumping, research needs, and future problems and prospects.

2.1. INTRODUCTION

The U.S. Congress imposed a 1981 phase-out deadline on the continued ocean dumping of "harmful" sewage sludge. (A mid-1981 court decision has delayed implementation of this deadline.) A similar statutory deadline was also adopted by Congress for "harmful" industrial wastes. No deadline, however, exists or has been proposed for the ocean dumping of dredged material. Given the fact that some 90% of all current U.S. ocean dumping consists of dredged material—contaminated to varying degrees with toxic pollutants—it seems important to focus on the dredged-material component of ocean dumping.

This chapter has five principal objectives: (1) to describe the scope of current dredged-material ocean dumping activities; (2) to discuss applicable legal requirements; (3) to assess the potential environmental significance of these dumping activities; (4) to analyze issues and areas of current controversy; and (5) to outline some of the apparently feasible alternatives to open-water disposal of contaminated dredged material.

2.2. SCOPE OF DREDGED-MATERIAL OCEAN DUMPING

Dredged material is defined in the United States as any material excavated or dredged from the navigable waters. Most dredging is done to enhance navigation, and most navigational dredging in the United States is conducted under the auspices of the U.S. Army Corps of Engineers (ACOE).

The ACOE dates its involvement in navigational dredging back to 1824 when the U.S. Congress directed it to remove the snags and sandbars on the Ohio and Mississippi Rivers (Graves 1976; U.S. Army Corps of Engineers, 1979a). The ACOE is now responsible for maintaining "over 25,000 miles of navigable waterway and improved channels" and "over 155 commercial harbors and ports and more than 400 small boat harbors" (U.S. Army Corps of Engineers, 1979a).

This dredging generates a huge amount of dredged material, a large proportion of which is dumped in the ocean. For example, the U.S. National Oceanic and Atmospheric Administration (NOAA) reported that, of some 305×10^6 m^3 dredged in 1974, approximately 76×10^6 m^3 (25%) were dumped in the ocean (U.S. National Oceanic and Atmospheric Administration, 1975). Smith (1979) puts the proportion of dredged material dumped in the ocean at about 15–20%.

Because of the variable nature of the demand for navigational dredging (i.e., not all harbors need to be dredged every year), there may be considerable fluctuation in the quantities of dredged material dumped from year to year, without there being a meaningful change in long-term trends. For example, due to varying flood and drought conditions in the Mississippi River drainage area, the Lower Mississippi Valley Division's recent ocean disposal volume has fluctuated from a high of 41.7×10^6 m^3 in 1974 because of heavy storm activity in 1973 to a low of only 15.5×10^6 m^3 in 1976 (U.S. Army Corps of Engineers, 1977).

During the period 1973 to 1979, the quantity of dredged material dumped in the ocean ranged from 31.6×10^6 m^3 in 1977 to 75.4×10^6 m^3 in 1974 (Fig. 2.1), averaging 53.1×10^6 m^3 (U.S. Army Corps of Engineers, 1977, 1978, 1979b, 1980). The density of this dredged material varied from 1.85 to 2.13 kg liter^{-1} during the 1976–1979 period (U.S. Army Corps of Engineers, 1977, 1978, 1979b, 1980).

Dredged material is dumped along every U.S. coast, with the heaviest activity

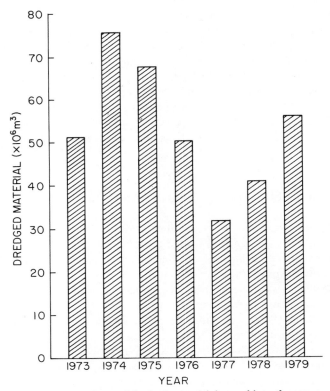

Figure 2.1. Volume of dredged-material dumped into the ocean.

in the Atlantic Ocean and the Gulf of Mexico (Table 2.1). Although there are about as many active ocean dumpsites in a given year in the Pacific Ocean as there are in either the Atlantic or the Gulf, only about half as much dredged material is dumped at these sites.

The EPA has given interim approval to the ocean dumping of dredged material at 131 ocean dumpsites (U.S. Environmental Protection Agency, 1980a), although

Table 2.1. Geographical Distribution of Dredged-Material Ocean Dumping, 1976–1979 (after U.S. Army Corps of Engineers, 1977, 1978, 1979b, 1980)

Coastal Area	Number of Active Dumpsites				Total Volume Ocean-Dumped (10^6 m^3)			
	1976	1977	1978	1979	1976	1977	1978	1979
Atlantic Ocean	28	20	23	20	18	11	17	12
Gulf of Mexico	20	18	23	16	24	10	15	36
Pacific Ocean	24	25	21	14	8	11	8	8
Total	72	63	67	50	50	32	40	56

only a handful of these sites have been studied and a number of them have not been used in recent years.

2.3.   ENVIRONMENTAL SIGNIFICANCE OF DREDGED-MATERIAL OCEAN DUMPING

The bottom sediments of river and harbor areas are a sink for many chemical contaminants. Recent analyses of samples of dredged material from four locations in the New York Harbor region, for example, detected 15 different polynuclear aromatic hydrocarbon compounds, at concentrations (for individual compounds) ranging from 5.2 to 56,400 ng g^{-1} wet weight (O'Connor et al., 1982). Also present in these samples were significant levels of polychlorinated biphenyls (ranging from 188 to 731 ng g^{-1} total PCB) and low levels in some of the samples of various chlorinated hydrocarbon pesticides (O'Connor et al., 1982).

One study of the Hudson River identified 254 industrial and municipal point source discharges which release hundreds of waste chemicals into the Hudson River upstream of the New York Harbor area (Moskowitz et al., 1977). A number of these chemicals, particularly those with an affinity for sediment particles, are probably transported down river into the harbor area. Evidence for this can be found in the fact that fine-grained sediments accumulating in the Hudson estuary in the vicinity of New York Harbor contain radionuclides discharged from a nuclear reactor located more than 60 km upstream (Simpson et al., 1976).

Although the conventional wisdom tends to regard the sediments of river and harbor bottoms, and particularly of offshore coastal areas, as pollutant traps, it has become increasingly apparent in recent years that bottom sediments often operate as pollutant sources and concentrators as well. For example, contaminated bottom sediments appear to have been a principal source of DDT and PCB contamination of Dover sole and other benthic species in the vicinity of wastewater outfalls in the Southern California Bight during and following the period 1974–1975 when wastewater discharges of these compounds had significantly decreased (McDermott et al., 1976; Young et al., 1976). Similarly, the widespread Kepone contamination of fish and shellfish in the James River in Virginia, and similar problems with PCBs in the Hudson River in New York, can be attributed to bottom sediment pollution (Nimmo et al., 1971; Halter and Johnson, 1977; Huggett et al., 1980). Even in the case of toxic heavy metals which, in association with sediments, may have a reduced biological availability, microbial transformations may enhance both their availability and their toxicity (Jensen and Jernelov, 1969; Wood, 1974; Jernelov et al., 1975).

Consequently, when contaminated dredged material is dumped, toxicity and food-chain transfers can be anticipated, particularly when productive fisheries and prey species are located in close proximity to dumping areas. Although contaminated sediments can be a problem in situ, dredging and dumping may expose more sensitive or more ecologically significant biota to toxic contaminants.

In the New York Bight, up to 34% of the input of selected contaminants, such as chromium, lead, copper, oil and grease, and zinc, results from the ocean dumping of dredged material (Mueller et al., 1976a, 1976b, 1976c). Dayal et al. (1981; see also Chapter 6) consider the disposal of dredged material in the New York Bight to perhaps represent "the largest and most concentrated anthropogenic inputs of toxic metals to a coastal environment." A major portion of the PCBs and polynuclear aromatic hydrocarbons entering the New York Bight Apex likewise appears to be contributed by dredged material (O'Connor et al., 1982).

Among the environmental consequences that have been documented in the New York Bight and for which dredged material must bear major or partial responsibility are the following:

1. Reduced benthic species diversity and lower than normal densities of benthic populations in and around the mud dumpsite where dredged materials are ocean-dumped (Pearce, 1970).

2. A high incidence of fin rot in demersal fish and exoskeletal "shell disease" in crabs and lobsters taken from the Bight, with shell erosion effects similar to those caused in large crustaceans subjected to long-term laboratory exposure to dredged material (O'Connor, 1976; Pearce, 1970; Young and Pearce, 1975).

3. An unusual rarity of commercial-size surf clams in an area of about 1550 km^2 surrounding the dredged-material and sewage-sludge dumpsites of the Bight (O'Connor, 1976).

4. Increased incidence of chromosomal abnormalities in developing Atlantic mackerel eggs near the dredged-material and acid-waste dumpsites (Longwell and Hughes, 1980).

5. Levels of PCBs in the water column high enough to alter the structure of phytoplankton communities in ways that may discourage the production of commercially valuable fish and shellfish species (O'Connors et al., 1978).

6. Levels of PCBs high enough to have a significant negative impact on fish reproduction (Freeman and Uthe, 1979).

7. Measurable concentrations of carcinogenic aromatic hydrocarbons in bottom sediments, plankton, and the tissues of fish and lobster from the Bight (O'Connor et al., 1982).

8. Cadmium, lead, PCBs, and petroleum hydrocarbons inputs so high that a panel of marine pollution experts concluded that substantial questions were raised of damage to the public health and endemic marine organisms (O'Connor and Stanford, 1979).

Although conditions in the New York Bight may represent an extreme case in terms of the quantity of contaminated sediments, it is not an isolated situation. For example, in tests of the toxicity of bottom sediments from nine waterways, sediments from the Duwamish Turning Basin and Slip, Washington State and the Houston Ship Channel, Texas, were more toxic than sediments from the Raritan River, New Jersey, which are dumped at the New York Bight mud dumpsite (Swartz et al., 1979).

2.4. FEDERAL OCEAN DUMPING REGULATION

The Ocean Dumping Act, formally known as the Marine Protection, Research, and Sanctuaries Act (MPRSA), was passed on 23 October 1972 and became effective six months later. This legislation was largely in response to environmental concerns expressed by the Council on Environmental Quality (CEQ) in its ocean dumping report to the President (U.S. Council on Environmental Quality, 1970). The CEQ report concluded that:

> If no action is taken and ocean dumping continues to increase, the long-term damage to the marine environment will be great.

With respect to dredged material, the report made the following recommendations:

> Ocean dumping of polluted dredge spoils should be phased out as soon as alternatives can be employed. In the interim, dumping should minimize ecological damage. The current policy of the Corps of Engineers on dredging highly polluted areas only when absolutely necessary should be continued, and even then, navigational benefits should be weighed carefully against damages. Ocean dumping of unpolluted dredge spoils, construction and demolition debris, and similar wastes which are inert and nontoxic should be regulated to prevent damage to estuarine and coastal areas.

The MPRSA committed the U.S.A., for the first time on a national basis,

> ... to regulate the dumping of all types of materials into ocean waters and to prevent or strictly limit the dumping into ocean waters of any material which would adversely affect human health, welfare, or amenities, or the marine environment, ecological systems, or economic potentialities.

Title I of the MPRSA, which is the marine protection part of the statute, requires the EPA Administrator and the U.S. Secretary of the Army to establish permit programs designed to exclude from the ocean all waste materials (dredged materials in the latter case, nondredged wastes in the former) which might result in "unreasonable" degradation or endangerment of the marine environment or human health. The Army is responsible for dredged-material permits, and the EPA is responsible for all other wastes. Project approvals, of both private permit requests and ACOE-initiated project proposals, for the ocean dumping of dredged material are made by the U.S. Secretary of the Army (this responsibility has been delegated to ACOE District Engineers), in accordance with regulatory criteria required to be established by the EPA Administrator (in consultation with the Secretary). If the EPA Administrator and the Secretary disagree as to compliance with the dredged-material criteria, the EPA Administrator's determination prevails and the Secretary may not issue a permit that does not comply with the criteria. The MPRSA authorizes the ocean dumping of nonconforming dredged material only if the Secretary certifies that there is no other economically feasible disposal site or method available and the EPA Administrator grants a waiver based on the absence of certain unacceptable adverse impacts.

The statute provides for the case-by-case evaluation of ocean dumping proposals, with dumping approvals to be granted only where there has been an affirmative showing of no unreasonable degradation. Such a showing must be based on the ocean dumping criteria which, in turn, must consider at minimum the nine evaluation factors specified in Section 102(a) of the MPRSA. These factors are concerned with the short- and long-term effects of ocean dumping on marine life and human health and welfare, as well as with the need for, and availability of, alternatives to ocean dumping.

Complementing and, in some cases, supplementing the MPRSA is the Convention on the Prevention of Marine Pollution by Dumping of Wastes and Other Matter. This international treaty was agreed upon 13 November 1972 by a conference of representatives of 92 nations meeting in London. The Convention, commonly referred to as the London Dumping Convention (LDC), to which the United States is a party, became fully operational in the late summer of 1975 (Park and O'Connor, 1981). As amended on 22 March 1974, the MPRSA requires the domestic ocean dumping criteria, except to the extent that this would relax pre-existing MPRSA requirements, to apply the standards and criteria binding upon the United States under the LDC, including its Annexes.

The EPA administrative regulations, which implement both the MPRSA and the LDC, are known as the Ocean Dumping Criteria. The current criteria were promulgated in 1977 (U.S. Environmental Protection Agency, 1977c). Before discussing present dredged material testing requirements as reflected in the 1977 criteria, it may be of interest to outline briefly the evolution of these requirements. Further details are available elsewhere (Kamlet, 1978).

2.4.1. Bulk Sediment Analysis

The first attempt at regulating dredged material disposal was based on bulk chemical analysis and specified numerical limits on a dry weight basis for volatile solids, chemical oxygen demand, oil and grease, Kjeldahl nitrogen, and three heavy metals: mercury, lead, and zinc (Boyd et al., 1972). This bulk sediment test, which was devised by EPA (and predecessor agencies), specified that if any one or more of the seven covered pollution parameters exceeded the specified limits, "the sediment will be considered polluted in all cases and, therefore, unacceptable for open-water disposal" (Boyd et al., 1972).

On the basis of such factors, as well as chlorine demand, iron, silica content, and color and odor, the ACOE estimated in 1970 that 34% of ocean-dumped dredged material nationwide was "polluted"—with a low of 19% for the Pacific Coast and a high of 45% for the Atlantic Coast (U.S. Council on Environmental Quality, 1970).

Many objections have been voiced over the years to bulk sediment analysis. The concern has been that chemical composition alone is not a true or reliable indicator of the biological activity or availability of contaminants associated with dredged material. Heavy metals are a case in point. All natural sediments contain them as an integral part of their mineral matrix. However, it has been suggested that essentially only the heavy metals associated with pore water or interstitial water are of potential biological significance (Brannon et al., 1976a, 1976b; Jones and Lee, 1978). Bulk chemical analysis may greatly overstate the potential toxicity of a given sample of dredged material. By the time the first Ocean Dumping Criteria were published (U.S. Environmental Protection Agency, 1973b), all official reliance on bulk chemical analysis of dredged material for ocean dumping purposes had terminated.

2.4.2. Standard Elutriate Testing

The second approach to the regulation of dredged material disposal was promulgated in regulations issued by EPA beginning in 1973, to carry out the pollution control requirements of both the MPRSA and the Federal Water Pollution Control Act Amendments of 1972 (U.S. Environmental Protection Agency, 1973a, 1973b; 1975a, 1975b; 1980b). This approach, rather than relying on bulk chemical analysis, focused on so-called standard elutriate testing.

Essentially, the elutriate or "shaker" test requires dredged material, in order to be considered nonpolluting, to produce less than a 50% increase in the dissolved concentration of critical water quality parameters after being mixed in a ratio of 1:4 (volume to volume) with disposal site water. Although the test does provide a basis for categorizing dredged material as polluted versus unpolluted, it specifies no consequences of a finding of pollution. In the words of the 1973 Ocean Dumping Criteria (§227.64): "Polluted dredge material may be disposed of in the ocean if it can be shown that the place, time, and conditions of dumping are such as not to produce an unacceptable adverse impact on [specified] areas of the marine environment. . . ." In this respect, the standard elutriate test differed markedly from the bulk sediment test which definitively designated polluted dredged material as unacceptable for open-water disposal. The success or failure (depending on one's vantage point) of the standard elutriate test can be gauged in part by the fact that no dredge disposal permit has ever been denied on the basis of it.

Apart from a lack of regulatory specificity, the standard elutriate approach has been criticized on the following bases:

1. It is designed to detect the release of chemical contaminants from dredged sediment suspended in a water column. It may not detect the effect of chemical contaminants in dredged sediment on benthic animals.

2. The elutriate test cannot even adequately predict the extent of release of chemical constituents to the water column because of the number and complexity of the factors that govern sediment–water exchange rates, such as sorption, complexation, redox and acid–base reactions (Lee and Plumb, 1974).

2.4.3. Bioassay Testing

The third method for evaluating the environmental impact of polluted dredged material, and the one currently in use for ocean dumping purposes, is bioassay testing. This approach evolved largely in response to a 1975 lawsuit by the National Wildlife Federation (Kamlet, 1976).

Bioassays were first required to be performed on dredged material under proposed revisions to the Ocean Dumping Criteria, announced on 28 June 1976 (U.S. Environmental Protection Agency, 1976), and required to be immediately implemented by the ACOE on an interim basis as a result of two July 1976 directives from the Office of the Chief of Engineers. The 1976 version of the criteria required simply the use of 96-h liquid-phase bioassays on the elutriate derived from dredged material, thereby propagating all of the problems associated with direct elutriate testing, except that the results of a bioassay could be translated into a regulatory limitation and bioassays could detect the effects of contaminants rather than just the release of contaminants.

Ultimately, final revised Ocean Dumping Criteria were promulgated on 11 January 1977, to be applied to all permits issued on or after 10 February 1977 (42 Federal Register 2461) (U.S. Environmental Protection Agency, 1977c). These criteria, which must be complied with before any ocean dumping of dredged material may take place, rely heavily for the first time on solid-phase bioassays (in addition to liquid-phase bioassays which may or may not also be required). Current emphasis on bioassay testing is based on the premise that they will provide a direct measure of the impact which is likely to result from the dumping of the material.

Under the current Ocean Dumping Criteria, dredged material must always be evaluated as to (1) the need for ocean dumping, (2) the impacts of dumping on esthetics, recreation, and economics, and (3) the impacts of dumping on other uses of the ocean. If the dredged material is predominantly sand, if it meets various other preliminary screening criteria, and if it satisfies the preceding requirements, it may be classified as environmentally acceptable for ocean dumping without the need for more detailed testing.

If it does not pass the preliminary screening criteria, the detailed testing procedures must be followed. The first step in this procedure requires the separation of dredged-material samples into three component parts: a liquid phase, which is the supernatant remaining after 1 h undisturbed settling, after centrifugation and filtration through a 0.45-μm filter after vigorous shaking in a 1:4 mixture of sediment:seawater for 30 min (it corresponds to the elutriate in the standard elutriate test); a suspended particulate phase, which is the supernatant obtained after shaking and settling, but prior to centrifugation or filtration; and a solid phase, which is the insoluble material settling to the bottom after 30 min of shaking and 1 h of undisturbed settling.

Separate bioassays must be performed on the liquid, suspended-particulate, and solid phases of dredged material. However, as is noted in the Implementation Manual (U.S. Environmental Protection Agency/U.S. Army Corps of Engineers, 1977):

> It is generally felt that if a dredged material is going to have an environmental impact, the greatest potential for impact lies in the solid phase. This is because it is not mixed and dispersed as rapidly or as greatly as the liquid and suspended particulate phases, and bottom-dwelling animals live and feed in and on the deposited solid phase for extended periods. Therefore, unless

there is reason to do otherwise, the major evaluative efforts should be placed on the solid phase.

The liquid phase must be shown not to contain constituents listed in Annex I of the LDC (i.e., mercury and cadmium compounds, organohalogens, and oil and grease) in more than "trace contaminant" amounts, and must not contain excessive concentrations of other "major constituents." Where marine water quality criteria have been set by the EPA for the constituents in question, the liquid phase must be shown not to contain these constituents at concentrations in excess of applicable criteria limits, "after allowance for initial mixing." Where there are no applicable water quality criteria for constituents of concern, liquid-phase bioassays (usually for 96 h) must also be performed, using "appropriate sensitive marine organisms."

The suspended-particulate phase must be shown not to contain Annex I constituents in more than trace contaminant amounts or to contain other toxic materials in excess of limiting permissible concentrations (LPC), as shown by 96-h suspended-particulate-phase bioassays, using appropriate sensitive marine organisms.

"Appropriate sensitive marine organisms" must be reliable for determining the anticipated impact on the proposed disposal operation, and must include species representing each of the following ecological classifications: (1) phytoplankton or zooplankton, (2) crustacean or mollusk, and (3) fish species.

Finally, the solid phase must be shown not to contain Annex I constituents in more than trace contaminant amounts or to contain other toxic materials in excess of the LPC, as shown by 10-d solid-phase bioassays using appropriate sensitive benthic marine organisms.

The MPRSA sets out a procedure whereby dredged material can be approved for ocean dumping despite a failure to satisfy criteria requirements, based on a demonstrated lack of economically feasible alternative methods or sites for dumping and an overriding need for the dredging project. However, it must be emphasized that this waiver procedure does *not* apply where bioassay and other tests designed to show the absence of more than trace amounts of Annex I constituents have been failed. This is so, because the LDC is binding on the U.S.A. and it contains a nonwaivable prohibition against the dumping of wastes (including dredged material) containing Annex I constituents in more than trace contaminant amounts.

Dredged material may also be deemed environmentally unacceptable for ocean dumping based on the occurrence of significant sublethal effects or the bioaccumulation of toxic materials.

2.4.3a. Rationale for Bioassay Tests

An aquatic bioassay is essentially any test in which aquatic organisms are used to detect or measure the effect of one or more substances, wastes, or environmental factors, alone or in combination, on aquatic organisms. The typical acute, liquid-phase bioassay compares the mortality produced in selected test organisms by different concentrations of a waste material, in relation to the mortality of untreated controls. Commonly, these bioassays are run for 96 h, and the endpoint is the waste dilution that kills 50% of the test population. Such tests are, therefore, referred to as 96-h LC_{50}; "LC" for lethal concentration, "50" for the concentration needed to kill 50% of the test organisms. Since this test provides the waste concentration that kills half of the test animals, it is obvious that this is not a "safe" concentration; one generally multiplies the 96-h LC_{50} by an "application factor" of 0.01. Application factors in effect represent a means of taking into account sublethal and chronic toxicity impacts, including bioaccumulation, which would be difficult to measure directly. Regulatory limits based on short-term bioassays generally also incorporate an initial dilution factor which takes into account the reduction in discharge concentration that occurs as a result of mixing and dispersion processes within the first few hours after a dumping event.

The limiting permissible concentration (LPC) established by the criteria illustrates this approach. The LPC is defined as the concentration of waste or dredged material in the water column that will not exceed 0.01 of a toxic concentration after initial dilution using appropriate sensitive marine organisms.

Solid-phase bioassays differ from the liquid-phase tests in four principal respects: (1) they are conducted for 10 d, rather than 96 h (in recognition of the greater persistence of ocean-dumped solids than liquids); (2) they utilize appropriate sensitive benthic marine organisms (in recognition of the fact that solids which settle to the ocean bottom are likely to exert their greatest impacts on bottom-dwelling organisms); (3) the endpoint of these bioassays is not death of 50% of the test population, but rather the presence or absence of statistically significant differences in survival between the control bioassay and the test bioassay; and (4) since they do not incorporate an application factor to take account of sublethal effects and bioaccumulation, these effects must be evaluated separately.

Although the criteria specify only that solid-phase bioassays be performed on at least three different sensitive benthic species, including representative filter-feeders, deposit-feeders, and burrowers, the Implementation Manual provided a test procedure utilizing five species, each represented by 20 individuals, in each replicate aquarium (U.S. Environmental Protection Agency/U.S. Army Corps of Engineers, 1977). Five replicate tests must be run for each sediment tested and for each control. Therefore, 1000 organisms are required to complete one bioassay experiment.

The number and nature of the test species utilized in solid-phase and other bioassays is of crucial importance for a number of reasons: (1) the greater the number of individuals tested in a bioassay, the more sensitive is the bioassay and the more capable it is of distinguishing toxicity from random variability; (2) since different species of organisms vary markedly in their sensitivities to different toxic materials, and since the array of toxicants present in a given sample of dredged material is generally unknown, the greater the number of different species tested, the less likely it is that the toxicity of the material will go undetected; and (3) for the same reason, the testing of different feeding types of organisms provides a measure of biological impact for a range of assimilative mechanisms to which the waste material might be exposed.

It cannot be emphasized too strongly that the utility and value of a bioassay depends on the sensitivity of the species tested (Murphy et al., 1981). When the purpose of performing the bioassay is to protect marine biota in the vicinity of a dump, it is especially important to use as test organisms the most sensitive important species to the toxicant in the area under consideration.

2.4.3b. *Bioaccumulation Tests*

Closely related to bioassay tests, and often somewhat loosely grouped in the general category of bioassays, are bioaccumulation tests. Whereas bioassays are designed to reveal toxicity to tested organisms, bioaccumulation tests are, in some ways, designed to show the opposite, since only living organisms can accumulate contaminants in their tissues. Of course, once accumulated, these contaminants can cause chronic diseases, impair reproduction, and interfere with normal feeding and behavior patterns. They can also poison higher-level predators with lethal or sublethal effects.

The Ocean Dumping Criteria require testing of bioaccumulation potential under conditions that provide reasonable assurance that when materials containing Annex I constituents are dumped no significant undesirable effects will occur due to bioaccumulation. In explaining this provision, the Final Environmental Impact Statement supporting the Criteria (U.S. Environmental Protection Agency, 1977b) states that these tests "must be sufficiently definitive to determine whether or not [the toxic materials present] . . . will have any chronic adverse effects on marine organisms . . . from bioaccumulation." Dredged material constituents may not exceed concentrations which will cause accumulation of toxic materials in the human food chain.

The EPA-ACOE Implementation Manual (U.S. Environmental Protection Agency/U.S. Army Corps of Engineers, 1977), which specifies bioaccumulation test procedures, recognizes that, "in order to ensure environmental safety, [it must be assumed] that any statistically significant bioaccumulation relative to animals not in dredged material, but living in material of similar sedimentological character, is potentially undesirable . . . [and] a potential cause for concern. . . ." However, noting that at present, tissue concentrations of most constituents in most species cannot be quantitatively related to biological effects, the Manual calls upon EPA and ACOE decision-makers to "objectively consider the magnitude of bioaccumulation shown, the toxicological significance of the material(s) bioaccumulated . . . , the proportion of the sediment sampling sites that produce uptake, the number of different constituents bioaccumulated from the sediments in question, the position in human and nonhuman food webs of the species showing uptake, the presence of motile species at the site that might serve as transportation vectors removing bioaccumulated materials from the disposal area, and other factors relevant to the particular operation in question."

EPA's Region II office in New York City adopted the following position, in a 9 January 1979 letter, on interpreting bioaccumulation test results:

In view of existing FDA criteria limiting the parameters to be tested in the bioaccumulation studies and thereby identifying them as potential threats to public health and welfare, and consistent with the intent of Section 227.6(c) and the COE/EPA manual, paragraph G32, *any* statistically significant bioaccumulation would be considered cause for denial, unless such statistically significant difference is shown to have no significant adverse effect on public health and welfare.

2.5. THE SITE DESIGNATION ISSUE

The MPRSA and the London Dumping Convention prohibit the approval of ocean dumping without prior studies of the dumpsite and without prior consideration of the Ocean Dumping Criteria. The 1977 Ocean Dumping Criteria gave EPA and the ACOE three years in which to complete site studies on 127 dredged material ocean dumpsites. Any sites that had not been redesignated or studied within this period were to be phased out. The three years expired on 11 January 1980. But during that period, site studies were not completed for a single dredged-material ocean dumpsite.   On 16 January EPA published an amendment to the criteria, extending the interim designation of 46 unstudied dredged-material ocean dumpsites for up to three more years (U.S. Environmental Protection Agency, 1980a). The amendment also extended the interim designation of 85 additional unstudied dredged-material ocean dumpsites (total: 131) for an indefinite period of *at least* three years (U.S. Environmental Protection Agency, 1980a).

This extension was further revised in the Federal Register of 9 December 1980. The only justification provided by EPA for its failure to make more progress on ocean dumpsite studies was "current budget priorities and constraints."

In an effort to persuade EPA and the ACOE to give the matter higher priority, the National Wildlife Federation filed suit against EPA and ACOE officials on 11 February 1980, in Federal District Court for the District of Columbia. The Federation indicated to both EPA and the ACOE that it would be willing to withdraw its lawsuit if the agencies would take five modest steps to ensure compliance with at least the spirit (if not the letter) of the MPRSA and the Convention. The five steps were:

1. Limit the time extensions contained in the amendment to those dumpsites known and demonstrated to be unavoidably needed during the period of extension.

2. Specify explicit time deadlines for *all* sites proposed to be kept available on an interim basis.

3. Specify explicit time limits, not only for the completion of draft environmental impact statements, but also for completion of final environmental impact statements, and formal site designations (or site phase-outs).

4. Deny authorization to dump at any site for which EPA has not, at a minimum, made formal (publicly available) written determinations that evaluate, *to the fullest extent possible*, compatibility of the site with the evaluation criteria of Annex III of the LDC and Part 228 of the EPA Ocean Dumping Criteria.

5. Require, as a prerequisite to ocean dumping at any unstudied and undesig-

nated ocean dumpsite, a written (and publicly available) demonstration that (a) use of a studied or designated dumpsite is infeasible, and (b) the delay of ocean dumping until the completion of the site study and designation process will seriously impede navigation and/or cause a serious, otherwise unavoidable, and undue economic hardship to the dumping applicant.

This lawsuit was settled by a "Stipulation of Settlement and Dismissal" approved by the Court on 25 September 1980. The major elements of this settlement can be summarized as follows:

1. The U.S. Army Corps of Engineers agreed to issue a guidance memorandum directed to each ACOE District and Division Engineer specifying procedures to be followed in determining whether to issue an ocean dumping permit for disposal of dredged materials at interim designated dumpsites. The Headquarters' directive would require the District Engineer, before authorizing dumping at an incompletely studied or interim designated site to consider: (a) the feasibility and practicability of using a finally designated ocean dumpsite or a more fully studied dumpsite in lieu of an unstudied one; (b) the feasibility and practicability of deferring the decision on ocean dumping at the proposed site until site study and/or final designation efforts have been completed; and (c) the availability of practicable alternative locations and methods of disposal or recycling (i.e., land-based alternatives). Public notices announcing proposed dumping at interim-approved ocean dumpsites would be required to include the District's preliminary assessment of whether or not there are reasonably available alternatives to dumping at such a site, together with a short explanatory statement.

2. The ACOE agreed that, as a matter of policy, undesignated ocean dumpsites (i.e., sites which are not either interim-approved or finally designated), "will not under normal circumstances be used" (see Code of Federal Regulations, Title 40, Section 228.4e2).

3. The EPA agreed, in promulgating the final version of the 16 January 1980 amendment, to delete from the list of interim approved sites those sites which are no longer in use and for which no future need is anticipated, and those sites which EPA, in consultation with the ACOE, determines are unsuitable for further ocean dumping.

4. The EPA agreed to promulgate regulations which specify an explicit schedule for completing environmental impact statements and final designation or termination of specific dumpsites in 20 coastal areas that account for 90% of all U.S. dredged-material ocean dumping. The EPA and the ACOE separately agreed to discuss further with the National Wildlife Federation the feasibility of setting similar schedules for the remaining interim approved dumpsites. The agreed-upon schedule provides for the completion of final site designations in all 20 areas by the end of March 1983.

5. The EPA agreed to send a letter to all coastal state and Federal fish and game agencies requesting information on the proximity of interim dumpsites to commercial and recreational fishery resources. EPA further agreed that any responses

received "will be considered as part of the administrative record by EPA in assessing the suitability of dumpsites for final designation."

6. The EPA and the ACOE agreed to expeditiously pursue the actions agreed upon, with such actions completed "no later than 24 November 1980."

As of mid-May, 1981, EPA and the ACOE had actually agreed to delete only one site from the interim-approved list. It is to be hoped that the site study process will permit a narrowing of the list of approved sites to those that are truly both suitable and necessary for ocean dumping. Effective and conscientious dumpsite management, including periodic monitoring, would seem to remain unattainable until the more than 10 dozen available dumpsites are reduced to a manageable number that should receive priority attention.

The Settlement Agreement will hopefully promote sound resource management and national regulation by making the use of dumpsites that have never been properly evaluated an option of last rather than first resort.

2.6. THE WAIVER ISSUE

Reference has already been made to the fact that the MPRSA authorizes the EPA Administrator, under specified circumstances, to waive the environmental evaluation requirements. The process is intended to work as follows:

1. The ACOE or EPA determines that dredged material proposed for ocean dumping does not satisfy the tests prescribed by the Ocean Dumping Criteria.

2. The ACOE makes an independent determination as to the need for the dumping—based on an evaluation of the potential effect of a permit denial on navigation, economic and industrial development, and foreign and domestic commerce of the United States. The ACOE also makes an independent determination as to other possible methods of disposal and as to appropriate locations for the dumping.

3. The Secretary of the Army certifies to the EPA Administrator that there is no economically feasible method or site available other than ocean dumping of the material which does not meet the Ocean Dumping Criteria, and a waiver is requested.

4. The EPA Administrator grants the waiver within 30 d of receipt of a complete waiver request, unless he finds that the dumping will result in "an unacceptably adverse impact on municipal water supplies, shellfish beds, wildlife, fisheries (including spawning and breeding areas), or recreational areas. . . ."

This procedure breaks down and confusion results if the dredged material violates the Ocean Dumping Criteria because it cannot satisfy a requirement of the London Dumping Convention; the prohibitions of the LDC are not waivable. A 1974 amendment to the MPRSA requires that U.S. national regulatory policy be at least as stringent as the LDC. Consequently, there is no legal basis for granting a waiver to dump material that does not comply with the LDC. If a dredged material does not meet the Ocean Dumping Criteria, then it must be shown that this failure was not due to LDC Annex I or II constituents before granting a waiver.

As of mid-May 1981, only one formal waiver involving "Annex I" constituents under the LDC has been filed with EPA, although waiver request proposals have made it partially up the chain of command in several other instances. The Calcasieu, Louisiana, waiver request is of sufficient interest to deserve brief discussion.

The Calcasieu River and Pass Project (Fig. 2.2) was first authorized in July 1946. An extension, deepening, and widening of the waterway was authorized in 1960. Currently the total deepwater navigation project is 100 km long and provides ocean vessel navigation access to the port areas of Lake Charles and Cameron, Louisiana.

The ACOE had proposed in mid-April 1978 to perform maintenance dredging in the Gulf of Mexico approach channel of the Calcasieu River and Pass deep-draft navigation project. This approach channel extends 38 km out into the Gulf of Mexico at approximately right angles to the shoreline and has an authorized depth of 14 m and a width of 267 m. The ACOE proposed to dredge the approach channel to its authorized depth, with the removal of approximately 18.3×10^6 m^3 of dredged material, to be disposed of at a dumpsite adjacent to the full length of the channel and extending approximately 500 m to the west (Fig. 2.2).

In support of the proposed ocean dumping, bioassay tests were performed on samples of sedimentary material from three locations along the 38-km channel, at distances of 13, 18, and 30 km. The highest mortalities for the test polychaetes

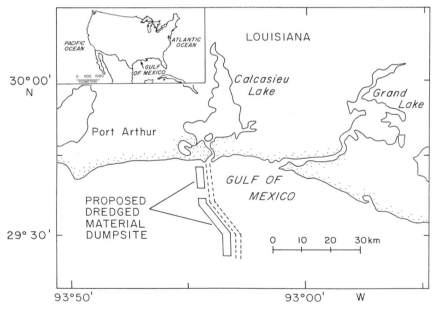

Figure 2.2. Location of the proposed dredged-material dumpsite for the Calcasieu River and Pass Channel Project, Louisiana.

occurred in the two sediments farthest from shore; however, the mysid shrimp tested showed the highest mortality in the two near shore samples. The only statistically significant mortality differences were for the pooled results (for all three test species) at the 18- and 30-km sites.

Bioaccumulation tests were done using clams and oysters. Results showed no significant difference between disposal site and test sediments for Annex I substances. Chemical analyses of dredged sediments conducted several years earlier indicated the presence of the Annex I substances cadmium, mercury, organohalogens, and oil and grease.

Based on the bioassay results, the EPA Regional Administrator was forced to object to the ocean dumping proposal. However, the ACOE was encouraged to seek a waiver from the Administrator. A formal waiver request was submitted by the Secretary of the Army on 7 February 1979.

In his Decision Statement of 28 March, 1979, the Administrator observed that, "while small amounts of Annex I substances are probably present in the material to be dredged and disposed of at sea, I cannot state with certainty that such substances are present in greater than 'trace amounts.'" Accordingly, he found that "no grounds have been shown for denying the waiver on the basis of Annex I." On the other hand, the Administrator also found that the data are not "adequate to assure that Annex I problems are not present." So, the Administrator decided to grant what he called a "conditional waiver."

He authorized immediately the dredging and ocean dumping of that portion of the Calcasieu River and Pass extending from the baseline to kilometer 13, because the sample from kilometer 13 passed the bioassay test. He conditioned his approval of the dredging and associated dumping for the segment extending from 13 to 38 km on the successful completion of further sampling and analyses.

The special supplemental tests were enumerated in 13 numbered paragraphs and included sampling from at least four sites, with required chemical, bioassay, and bioaccumulation analyses.

On 18 April 1979, the Assistant Secretary of the Army (Civil Works) formally requested the EPA Assistant Administrator for Water and Waste Management to reconsider the Administrator's earlier Decision Statement, urging EPA to grant an unconditional waiver. The EPA Assistant Administrator responded on 2 May by indicating that EPA would have "no objection" to ACOE plans to dredge the entire channel provided two sets of tests were completed at the 18, 30, and 38 km locations:

1. Bioaccumulation tests of all Annex I substances found present in the water column or sediments, based on the existing data, and which were not previously tested for bioaccumulation.
2. Chemical characterization of the sediments for oils and greases which were not previously tested and for cadmium for which the test procedures were not sufficiently sensitive.

As of this writing, the results of these supplemental tests were not yet available and no final decision had yet been made on the balance of the project.

The Administrator's Decision Statement on the Calcasieu project included an Appendix which purported to set forth general "Waiver Evaluation Criteria" deemed necessary for EPA to make waiver determinations. These Criteria call for information in the following six categories:

1. Chemical testing of dredged material for Annex I and II constituents, total organic carbon, nutrients, fecal coliform bacteria, additional heavy metals, biological oxygen demand, grain size distribution and geologic origin, settleable solids, and turbidity.

2. Bioassays on all three phases of dredged material; failures to be repeated at least once on the phase that failed; causes of statistically significant mortalities to be determined if possible; if no other cause of mortality can be clearly demonstrated, chemical analysis of tissues to be done for Annex I and II substances where possible.

3. Bioaccumulation evaluation: when done in the laboratory on the solid phase, all organisms used in the tests are to be analyzed to the extent feasible for presence of Annex I and II substances in tissues; when done in the field, at least three species are to be analyzed, or the results supplemented by laboratory tests.

4. Disposal site characteristics using the same chemical and physical characterization as for dredged material; identification of important resident species; location in relation to nearest commercial shellfish beds and other known fishery resources; identification of extent of site use by commercial and recreational fisheries.

5. Sampling stations are to take into account dredge site characteristics and are to be located close enough to permit analysis of gradients; there must be at least two bioassay samples from each homogeneous area, unless there is no statistical difference between sampling stations.

6. Alternative means of disposal are to be considered to determine that no economically feasible alternatives exist for the most highly contaminated material.

These Waiver Evaluation Criteria have not been formally adopted by EPA as regulations and their intended use and legal significance are unclear.

As of this writing the Calcasieu project remains the only one for which a formal waiver has been requested, except for a New York Bight project involving relatively clean sediment. However, several project sponsors in the New York Harbor area did go so far as to invoke the waiver process. Although some of these requests made it part of the way through the U.S. Army Corps of Engineers chain of command, they were never forwarded to the Secretary of the Army for transmittal to the EPA Administrator because other means were found for authorizing the projects in question. In another case, involving a New York Harbor permit application, EPA ultimately ignored a determination that the Ocean Dumping Criteria had been violated—based in large part on economic and hardship considerations—and allowed the ocean dumping to proceed. This action was of highly dubious legality, because it amounted to the grant of a waiver without following the prescribed procedures.

2.7. BIOASSAY TESTING ISSUES

The purpose of bioassays in the context of ocean dumping is to assess whether sensitive species in the vicinity of a dumpsite will be killed or injured by a given dredged material. In recognition of this, the Ocean Dumping Criteria require the use of both "appropriate sensitive" organisms and at least three different sensitive species.

Sensitive species must be tested in the laboratory if protection is to be assured to sensitive species in the field. Multiple species must be tested in the laboratory to decrease the possibility that a particular test species will be insensitive to dredged material contaminants which could be highly toxic to other species in the environment.

2.7.1. "Pooling" and Averaging of Bioassay Results

A number of ACOE District Offices, notably the New York District, have adopted the position that solid-phase bioassay requirements will be regarded as having been violated only when the *pooled* mortality results for all three test species are statistically significant. A statistically significant mortality in one species alone will not require denial of permission to dump.

This position has been widely criticized by the EPA, the U.S. Fish and Wildlife Service, and NOAA on the basis that it ensures, at best, the protection of marine species in the field only of average or below average sensitivity to dredged-material contaminants. Organisms with above average sensitivities will not be protected by a bioassay procedure that relies on average mortality results. This concern is heightened by the fact that highly sensitive species usually can not be cultured and tested in the laboratory in any event—so that the sensitive species tested in the laboratory are likely to be less sensitive than some species in the environment. The pooling approach simply compounds the problem of safeguarding truly sensitive species.

2.7.2. The Ten Percent Factor

Related to the pooling issue is another issue of interpretation of bioassay results. The ACOE points to the fact that a statistically significant effect in a bioassay does not necessarily imply that an ecologically important impact would occur in the field. Consequently, despite the Implementation Manual's caution that, in the face of such uncertainty, environmental protection necessitates treating any statistically significant increase in mortality compared to the controls as potentially undesirable and as indicating a potential for environmental impact, the ACOE has taken the position that only statistically significant differences which *also* exceed 10% in absolute magnitude—for example, 15% mortality in test animals versus 4% in controls—will be regarded as environmentally significant and as requiring permit denial. The only justification given for use of the 10% factor is the cryptic and unsubstantiated statement in the Implementation Manual that "there is a general feeling among many scientists that differences between control and treatment survival of 10% are necessary in most cases before predictions of probable impact can be made" (U.S. Environmental Protection Agency/U.S. Army Corps of Engineer, 1977). Not only is this 10% factor difficult to justify, but it can be argued that a safety factor, in the opposite direction, would be needed to assure adequate protection to marine organisms from the chronic effects of sustained exposure to persistent toxic chemicals.

As a legal matter, the EPA Ocean Dumping Criteria specify that solid-phase bioassays must not indicate occurrence of significant mortality based on considerations of statistical significance of effects at the 95% confidence level (U.S. Environmental Protection Agency, 1977c). Nowhere is authorization given to base determinations of ocean dumping acceptability on factors other than statistical significance.

A number of projects within the New York District of the ACOE as well as elsewhere in the country, were able to be authorized for ocean dumping solely because of ACOE interpretations allowing pooling of solid-phase bioassay results and use of the 10% fudge factor.

2.7.3. *NWF v. Benn* Lawsuit

A National Wildlife Federation (NWF) lawsuit, brought in U.S. District, Court for the Southern District of New York, against the New York District of the ACOE in 1978, challenged the ACOE's approach toward interpreting bioassay test results. A decision was announced on 12 June 1980.

On the bioassay issues, the Court declined to "thrash through this thicket of scientific debate," being confronted with some scientists supporting the NWF's position, and other scientists supporting the ACOE's position. Instead, the Court fell back on the judicial maxim that an agency's interpretation of administrative regulations "becomes of controlling weight unless it is plainly erroneous or inconsistent with the regulation." Applying this standard, the Court was unwilling to conclude that the ACOE's conduct was arbitrary or contrary to regulatory requirements.

This lawsuit, although a disappointment on the bioassay issues, did produce important gains in six other areas:

1. A requirement that ocean disposal of maintenance dredged material may be authorized for no more than three years at a time; that reauthorization decisions must be preceded by new environmental evaluations, notice to the public, and adherence to other applicable procedures; that project evaluation documents must include an analysis of "feasible alternatives to ocean dumping considered by the [permit] applicant or by the Corps of Engineers"; and that dredging sites must be monitored from time to time during the life of each ocean dumping authorization to determine whether changes in conditions have occurred.

2. A requirement that New York District ocean dumping public notices must include such information as the need for and alternatives to ocean dumping; what has been done to assess bioaccumulation potential, sublethal effects, and applicable

marine water quality criteria; and information concerning the performance of applicable bioassay tests, with test results portrayed individually for each series of tests and for each test species.

3. A requirement that bioaccumulation analyses must be conducted on test organisms surviving the 10-d solid-phase bioassay as a prerequisite to ocean dumping. These analyses must be performed for mercury, cadmium, PCBs, DDT, and petroleum hydrocarbons, and are to use *Palaemonetes* (shrimp), *Mercenaria* (clam), and *Nereis* (worm) as test species.

4. A requirement that liquid-phase chemical analyses must be performed for mercury, cadmium, PCBs, DDT, and other chemical contaminants if the permit applicant "has knowledge of nearby sources of contamination which may be affecting the sediments to be dredged." These results are then used by EPA to determine compliance with applicable marine water quality criteria.

5. A requirement that any sublethal effects that occur during the 10-d solid-phase bioassay, such as any physical or behavioral abnormalities, must be recorded on a daily basis and reported by the permit applicant.

6. A requirement that the ACOE prepare a comprehensive Environmental Impact Statement (EIS) covering the extensive ocean dumping of dredged material that occurs at the mud dumpsite. Such an EIS is now underway addressing the cumulative impacts of, and the availability of alternatives to, the longstanding dredged-material ocean dumping that has occurred at the mud dumpsite.

2.7.4. Other Bioassay Issues

Other issues related to bioassay testing have surfaced periodically and are likely to become increasingly important in the future. Among these are the following:

2.7.4a. Number and Distribution of Necessary Sediment Samples

The Implementation Manual specifies that "sediment should be collected from a minimum of three sampling stations within the dredging area" and that the "sampling stations should be located throughout the area to be dredged and should be selected to characterize obviously contaminated as well as uncontaminated areas. . . . " The Manual also points out that the larger the proposed dredging site, the more samples will be required for adequate coverage and characterization. As is apparent from the previous discussion of the Calcasieu project, in which only three sediment samples were taken and tested along a 38-km channel, there could be considerable debate over what constitutes adequate sampling in specific cases. And, although individual samples should obviously be separately bioassayed, there are undoubtedly numerous instances in which multiple samples are pooled and tested only once. Public notices issued by the New York District of the ACOE, for example, seldom present more than one set of bioassay test data for a given dredging and ocean dumping project.

Not only do unsystematic sampling and inappropriate blending of clean and contaminated sediments pose the risk that bioassays will understate the potential harm to the environment, but such practices serve to inhibit efficient sediment management. If, for example, only 10% of all of the dredged material from a given area is sufficiently contaminated to violate the Ocean Dumping Criteria, does it make sense to dispose of all the material at limited or costly upland sites, because the sediments were not fully characterized?

2.7.4b. Selection of Reference and Control Areas

The Implementation Manual specifies that field-caught test species and the reference sediment must be obtained from an uncontaminated area in the vicinity of the disposal site. Similarly, the Manual states, for purposes of field assessment of bioaccumulation, that "at least three stations . . . must be located in an uncontaminated sediment sedimentologically similar to that within the [dump] site, but in a direction opposite that of the net bottom transport." In practice, however, many ACOE Districts utilize reference sediments and organisms which, although collected outside the dumpsite boundaries, cannot in any sense be regarded as uncontaminated, because of multiple polluting activities in the vicinity.

A good case in point is the New York Bight. A bioaccumulation study recently commissioned by the New York District of the ACOE (O'Brien & Gere Engineers, Inc., 1979) utilized as reference sites a location in Lower New York Harbor—a region known to be heavily impacted by contamination from the Hudson River, ship traffic and associated discharges and spills, sewage effluent, and other urban discharges—and a nearshore site located between the New Jersey coast and the mud dumpsite—known and expected to be subject to multiple sources of pollution. A control site was also chosen, in Long Island Sound. However, lobsters collected at this site contained a mean PCB concentration of 78 μg kg^{-1}. Moreover, PCB levels in these lobsters showed a statistically significant correlation with lobster weight and size, which suggests bioaccumulation. One may therefore question the choice of the Long Island Sound site as a reliable control.

This discussion serves only to highlight the significance of careful selection of reference and control sites in bioassay and bioaccumulation testing. On the one hand, use of a contaminated sediment as a "reference" might be defended on the basis that dredged-material dumping should not be held responsible for pollution effects in the dumpsite vicinity unrelated to dredge disposal. On the other hand, however, marine organisms in and around the dumpsite will be harmed or contaminated as a result of the combined inputs of contaminants from dredged-material ocean dumping and from all other nearby sources. If the addition of dredged-material contaminants makes the difference between stressed but healthy organisms and organisms with eroding shells, rotting fins, and impaired reproduction, should the acceptability of dredged-material ocean dumping be judged on the basis of *incremental* impacts in an already dredged environment or on its absolute impacts on a natural environment?

2.7.4c. Use of Flow-Through Versus Static Bioassays

In recognizing the limitations of simple bioassays the U.S. Environmental Protection Agency (1976) states:

> Continuous-flow (often referred to as "flow-through") bioassays have definite advantages over static tests in evaluating certain types of wastes to be disposed of at sea. They are desirable in testing waste chemicals that have high biochemical oxygen demands, and are unstable or volatile. Many test species of fish and macroinvertebrates have high rates of metabolism and are difficult to maintain in jars or tanks of standing sea water. Continous-flow bioassays, conducted under proper conditions, provide for well-oxygenated test solutions, nonfluctuating concentrations of the toxicant, and continual removal of the toxicant, and continual removal of metabolic wastes of the test organisms.

The 1979 edition of Standard Methods defines static bioassays as those in which the test organisms remain in the same test concentration for the duration of the test, and flow-through tests as ones in which "measured quantities of dilution water and the stock toxicant solution are mixed and delivered periodically to the test chambers to give a continuous flow-through of the test toxicants" (American Public Health Association, 1979).

Unfortunately, the Implementation Manual indicates quite a different flow-through bioassay system. The Manual calls for the initial addition of dredged material at the beginning of the solid-phase bioassay, with a continuous flow of clean seawater through the system for the 10 d of the test period at a rate that will replace the aquarium volume at least once every 4 h. No provision is made for the periodic readdition of dredged material—despite the fact that under actual ocean dumping conditions, several dumps frequently occur within a given 10-d period. Indeed, the mud dumpsite in the New York Bight may receive 30 or more dumps within this time period. Although few solid-phase bioassays are currently carried out on dredged material under flow-through conditions, it is likely that the flow-through approach will be used increasingly as the frequency of failure of static tests increases. The concern, of course, is that flow-through tests under the conditions described in the Implementation Manual may greatly understate (particularly at heavily utilized dumpsites) the potential adverse impacts of ocean dumping, because the opportunity exists to wash away the contaminants.

2.7.4d. Use of Field Versus Laboratory Assessments of Bioaccumulation

The Implementation Manual notes that primary attention in connection with bioaccumulation of dredged-material contaminants is usually given to the solid phase that is deposited on the bottom, since concern is focused on the possiblity of gradual uptake over long exposure times. For this reason the Manual indicates that bioaccumulation from the solid phase is best evaluated in the field where possible. Several cautions are stated, however, with respect to reliance on field assessments of bioaccumulation. First, such an approach is permissible only when a historical precedent exists for the proposed operation. That is, it can be used only in the case of maintenance dredging and where the quality of the sediment to be dredged is considered not to have deteriorated or become more contaminated since the last dredging and disposal operation. Also, the disposal must be proposed for the site at which the dredged material in question has been previously disposed or for a site of similar sediment type supporting a similar biological community. Second, the species selected for analysis must occur in sufficient numbers for collection of an adequate sample at all stations. And third, highly mobile epifauna such as crabs, lobsters, shrimp, and fish should not be used, because their location when collected cannot be related to their body burden at the time of collection in any reasonable manner. The most desirable organisms are relatively immobile species that are fairly large, such as bivalves, some gastropods, large polychaetes, and so on. The Manual states that laboratory bioaccumulation tests should be employed *only* in those cases where a true historical precedent for the proposed operation does not exist.

One problem has been that ACOE districts are doing field assessments of bio-accumulation without adhering to the restrictions specified in the Implementation Manual. For example, the two field assessments completed to date under sponsor-ship of the New York District of the ACOE utilized only the very highly mobile eipfaunal species (fish and crabs in one case, lobster in the other) that the Manual says should not be used (Lee and Jones, 1977; O'Brien & Gere Engineers, Inc., 1979). Another is that the Manual provides no real guidance as to the selection of appropriate bioaccumulator species. The organisms should be large and nonmobile. But no preference is expressed for burrowers, deposit feeders, and filter feeders. There is a risk that inappropriate species will be selected.

A further difficulty results from the criterion of "historic precedent." If a dumpsite was used for a particular type of dredged material at some time in the past, and was then subsequently used for other types of dredged material, the present bioaccumulation observations may not be relevant to the "historically" deposited material. For dumpsites used by a multiplicity of dumpers or where long intervals separate successive dumping events, individual laboratory assessments of bioaccumulation potential may be more appropriate than field assessments. Field tests would be appropriate as part of the permit review process only for heavily utilized dumpsites that receive only one type of dredged material over a given, lengthy period of time. Such tests would also have value as an aid to dumpsite management by assisting site managers in evaluating the cumulative uptake and impact of contaminants at continuous use sites.

2.8. BIOACCUMULATION TESTING ISSUES

During the period 24 July 1979 through 24 January 1980, nine public notices were issued by the New York District of the ACOE for projects whose dredged material showed statistically significant elevated levels of PCBs in the tissues of one or more test species under laboratory conditions (Table 2.2). For the five projects prior

Table 2.2 New York District Projects with Dredged Material Showing Significant PCB Bioaccumulation

Applicant	Waterway Dredged	Dredged Material (m^3)	PCB in Test Organism[h] ($\mu g\ g^{-1}$)
U.S. Gypsum Co., New York[a]	Hudson River	76,400	0.29 (worm)
U.S. Navy, Earle, New Jersey	Sandy Hook Bay	5,580,000	0.62 (worm)
Monsanto Co., New Jersey[b]	Passaic River	4,600	0.17 (worm)
Refined Syrups & Sugars, New York[c]	Hudson River	30,600	0.20 (shrimp) 0.07 (worm)
Seatrain Realty Corp., New Jersey[d]	Hudson River	80,200	0.34 (worm)
Port Authority, Newark, New Jersey[e]	Newark Bay	76,400	0.30 (worm)
Port Authority, New York[f]	Hudson River	230,000	0.32 (worm)
Paktank Atlantic Co., New Jersey	Arthur Kill	13,750	0.20 (shrimp) 0.17 (worm) 0.16 (clam)
Jackson Engineering Co., New York[g]	Kill Van Kull	91,700	0.19 (worm)

[a]Permit No. 11323, issued 11 March, 1980.
[b]Permit No. 9590, issued 29 May, 1980.
[c]Permit No. 9104, issued 22 December, 1979.
[d]Permit No. 9244, issued 21 April, 1980.
[e]Permit No. 9232, issued 10 April, 1980.
[f]Permit No. 9372, issued 6 March, 1980.
[g]Permit No. 11392, issued 6 May, 1980.
[h]Only levels exceeding control values to a statistically significant degree are provided.

to September 1979, the Region II office of EPA formally concluded that "the material proposed for ocean dumping . . . is *not* in compliance with the Criteria" and EPA therefore objected to "any determination that the material proposed for ocean dumping [in connection with these projects] complies with the Ocean Dumping Criteria."

A key factor in this EPA position was the level of PCB accumulation in the polychaete worms, because polychaete worms are known to play a significant role in human food webs and it was felt that a potential health hazard might be posed by allowing the dredged material to be dumped in proximity to commercially and recreationally important fisheries.

In fact, measured levels of PCB uptake in the worms were well within an order of magnitude of levels which, if they occurred in fish, would have rendered them unsafe for human consumption based on the U.S. Food and Drug Administration

(FDA) action level of 5 $\mu g\ g^{-1}$. It thus becomes important to assess whether fish that regularly consume worms contaminated with 0.3 $\mu g\ g^{-1}$ of PCB might themselves accumulate levels 10-fold or more higher in their own tissues.

However, notwithstanding these concerns, and without the benefit of a formal waiver, EPA's Acting Assistant Administrator for Water and Waste Management advised the ACOE on 27 December 1979 that EPA would "not object to the one-time authorization of the ocean disposal of the small volume of material associated with the present maintenance dredging operation by Refined Syrups and Sugars." This action was taken despite the lack of any determination that Region II had erred in concluding that the criteria had been violated, and despite EPA's lack of legal authority to withdraw objections to ocean dumping for material that has been found to violate the criteria.

It was argued that Refined Syrups had demonstrated to the satisfaction of the New York District and the North Atlantic Division of the ACOE that the company had no feasible alternative to ocean dumping this material and unless severe shoaling at the company's dock was relieved by dredging, operations at the plant would soon have to terminate, which would result in severe economic hardship for the company and its employees. The overriding of criteria requirements on the basis of economic factors in this way, is an action expressly reserved under the MPRSA for the formal waiver process. The Acting EPA Region II Regional Administrator put it this way in a 11 January 1980 memorandum to the Assistant Administrator for Water and Waste Management at EPA Headquarters;

> We are legally prevented by the Marine Protection, Research, and Sanctuaries Act from taking economic factors into account in our preliminary determination. We may consider economics only if the COE requests a waiver. . . .

Although the 27 December 1979 EPA letter made it clear that the Refined Syrups situation was unique and that it should not be construed as a precedent for future actions, another ocean dumping applicant—U.S. Gypsum Company—quickly sought to take advantage of the Refined Syrups precedent.

The 27 December letter, and a follow-up letter on 16 January 1980 (relating to the U.S. Gypsum Co. request), called for the establishment of a Task Force to evaluate the situation, prepare a list of options available, and submit its recommendations. Specifically, the letters said that the Task Force should "address the nature and extent of the problem in New York Harbor, alternatives to open ocean disposal such as land fill or capping with clean material inside the harbor or in the ocean itself, and make recommendations for a technically and economically feasible solution which will be consistent with domestic law and our international obligations." Recommendations were sought which would "provide an early solution to the U.S. Gypsum problem as well as a long range approach for coping with similar problems in the New York Harbor area."

This Task Force was convened, with one subgroup (chaired by the New York District of the ACOE) addressing short-term alternatives and another (nominally chaired by EPA) addressing ways of interpreting the results of bioaccumulation tests carried out on New York Harbor dredged material.

The alternatives subgroup considered only short-term solutions: (1) a harbor-wide waiver of the Ocean Dumping Criteria (which is illegal because LDC prohibitions cannot be waived); (2) capping at the mud dumpsite (this is technically unproven and probably illegal because material which violates the criteria cannot be ocean-dumped, regardless of any subsequent handling of the material); (3) re-evaluation of the techniques used to interpret criteria requirements (this was addressed by the other subgroup and was the option ultimately adopted); (4) capping in subaqueous borrow pits in New York Harbor (this is not subject to ocean dumping jurisdiction); and (5) continuation of permit processing, with grant of waivers, if necessary, on a case-by-case basis (this too is illegal because the LDC prohibitions cannot be waived).

The alternatives subgroup seemed to favor capping at the mud dumpsite, but the U.S. Fish and Wildlife Service objected to the proposed capping plan unless it could be demonstrated to their satisfaction that the proposed cap would be stable. The subgroup's conclusion as reported in late February 1980 was that "there is no immediately available alternative for the disposal of dredged material that is determined to be in non-compliance with EPA Ocean Dumping Criteria."

2.8.1. The Interim Guidance Matrix for PCBs

The other subgroup—the Working Group on the Development of an Interim Guidance Matrix—forwarded its recommendations to Washington D.C. in March 1981. The matrix recommended can be summarized as follows:

1. If the material proposed for ocean dumping shows statistically significant increases in PCB levels in all three test species—worm, clam, and shrimp—regardless of the magnitude of the uptake, the material is *not* in compliance with the criteria and may not be dumped in the ocean.

2. If the material proposed for ocean dumping shows statistically significant increases in at most two test species, the materials may be dumped when PCB bioaccumulation levels do not exceed 0.4 $\mu g\ g^{-1}$ in the worm, or 0.1 $\mu g\ g^{-1}$ in the clam or shrimp.

3. If statistical significance is shown in at most two of the test species, and the magnitude of the uptake exceeds the matrix value, the material has the potential for being capped. This determination will be made on a case-by-case basis.

Based on this matrix, the U.S. Gypsum Co. project and one of two Port Authority Projects (No. 10062) were cleared by EPA for ocean dumping on 4 March 1980. Four additional projects—Monsanto Co., Seatrain Realty Corp., Port Authority of New York and New Jersey, and Jackson Engineering Co.—were cleared by EPA on 21 March 1980. Of the original nine publicly noticed projects (Table 2.2), only two—U.S. Navy and Paktank Atlantic Co.—remained in violation of the Interim Guidance Matrix and had not been authorized for ocean dumping as of 1981. Although EPA conditioned its approval for the first two of these projects on follow-up capping, no such capping requirement was imposed for the second group of four projects.

In view of the overriding regulatory significance being attached to the Interim Guidance Matrix, a brief discussion of the derivation of the matrix numbers is in order. The 0.1 μg g^{-1} limit for PCBs in shrimp and clams was based on "the most conservative value recommended for PCB levels in fish" by the American Fisheries Society (AFS). The AFS recommendations (Veith et al., 1979) were based on the deliberations of a panel of scientists and were designed to protect fish-eating mammals and birds.

The 0.4 μg g^{-1} limit for PCBs in worms was based on an entirely different rationale. This number was based on levels of PCB in the water column of the New York Bight and the potential for bioconcentration. The working group chose a bioconcentration factor for New York Bight sand worms of 10,000, based upon the known range of 1,350 to 230,000 for PCB bioconcentration among other marine species. No empirical data for sand worms of other polychaetes were employed in making this choice, so the factor chosen may or may not be appropriate.

A more serious shortcoming, however, than the choice of a possibly erroneous bioconcentration factor is the fact that the framers of the matrix assumed that all PCB bioconcentration in polychaetes comes from the water and that direct uptake from contaminated sediments is insignificant and can be disregarded. This is clearly not the case. For example, Fowler et al. (1978) found that 85% of the PCB body burden in sand worms (*Nereis diversicolor*) in both coastal and oceanic habitats could be accounted for by uptake from sediment. Although the PCB concentration factor was much higher in water (800) than sediment (3.5), when Fowler et al. (1978) multiplied these factors by ambient sediment and water concentrations, the dominance of the sediment input became evident. Courtney and Langston (1978) and Elder et al. (1979) provide similar information on PCB uptake from sediment. Consequently, to the extent the Interim Guidance Matrix purports to account for bioconcentration, it may be understating the potential for significant bioaccumulation.

The other basic underpinning of the matrix number for PCBs in worms is the assumption that 44 ng liter^{-1} is representative of present PCB water column levels in the New York Bight. The limited field data available suggest a range of PCB concentrations in the Bight between 10 and 55 ng liter^{-1}. However, measurements within the mud dumpsite have been on the low end of this scale. Since the matrix value of 0.4 μg g^{-1} is derived by multiplying a water concentration of 44 parts per trillion by a bioconcentration factor of 10,000 and then rounding off to the nearest tenth of a part per million, any significant overestimate in either number could result in an excessive and insufficiently protective matrix value. For example, if one used a bioconcentration factor from water for the sand worm of 800 rather than 10,000, one would obtain a matrix value 12.5 times smaller; that is, 0.032 μg g^{-1}. Similarly, if one used an existing water column concentration for PCBs at the dumpsite of 10 ng liter^{-1} rather than 44 ng liter^{-1}, one would obtain a matrix value more than 4 times smaller; that is, 0.1 μg g^{-1}. If either of these choices had been made, *none* of the six projects thus far approved would have satisfied the matrix.

The biggest problem with the matrix approach, however, is the philosophical and legal assumptions that underlie it. The working group has made clear that the matrix value recommended for the sand worm represents a level of PCB bioaccumulation at the mud dumpsite regarded as acceptable based solely on the principle of no *further* degradation at this site.

The premise that ocean dumping can be approved as long as it does not result in *incremental* environmental degradation is highly questionable conceptually and scientifically, and is clearly legally impermissible. The Ocean Dumping Law makes it U.S. policy to prevent or strictly limit the ocean dumping of any material that would adversely affect health or the environment. It does not require strict control only of material that will cause further environmental degradation. To the same effect is the London Dumping Convention which pledges the parties to effectively control all sources of pollution to the marine environment and to prevent dumping that is liable to be hazardous. The goal is prevention of hazard-producing pollution, not merely avoidance of further degradation.

In the New York Bight, which is already severely degraded, and where contaminants are already having a discernible deleterious effect on the marine ecosystem (and a possible impact on human seafood consumers as well, if FDA safety limits are being exceeded), a regulatory strategy that is *designed* to perpetuate the present level of degradation would seem extremely difficult to reconcile with any common-sense notion of what regulators should be attempting to accomplish.

EPA has established a marine water quality criterion for PCBs of 1.0 ng liter^{-1} (U.S. Environmental Protection Agency, 1977a). This reflects the highest level of PCBs in marine waters consistent with assured safety to human health and fish-eating predators. If the working group applied its methodology to this "safe" level, rather than to a claimed existing level 44 times higher, the resulting matrix value for the worm would be 0.01 μg g^{-1}. Even if a bioconcentration factor of 1,000 rather than 10,000 were used, the resulting matrix number would be 0.1 μg g^{-1} — still too low for any of the nine projects to meet. And such a level would still not have considered the significant potential for direct bioaccumulation into the tissues of worms in contact with contaminated bottom sediments. Lest one regard the 1.0 ng liter^{-1} marine water quality criterion for PCBs set by EPA as excessively stringent and unrealistic, it should be noted that a panel of scientists convened by the American Fisheries Society felt that such a criterion was not stringent enough to safeguard fish-eating predators and proposed an alternative level of 0.1 ng liter^{-1} (Veith et al., 1979).

2.8.2. Future Use of Interim Guidance Matrices

Other ACOE Districts—most of which have not yet begun to require bioaccumulation testing—are likely to be increasingly tempted to solve problems which they may encounter with dredged material which fails to pass the Ocean Dumping Criteria, by developing interim guidance matrices that will allow the material to satisfy the criteria. Such an approach, of course, solves nothing as long as the underlying problem of inadequate management of contaminated dredged material remains unsolved.

2.9. ALTERNATIVES TO OCEAN DUMPING

Upland containment of contaminated dredged material has one overriding advantage over ocean disposal: it permits a measure of management and control not possible in the dispersive ocean environment. On the other hand, upland disposal sites tend to be in short supply in the densely populated urbanized areas surrounding most of the ports and harbors that generate contaminated dredged material. And public opposition can usually be anticipated whenever a proposal is made to dispose of wastes in someone's neighborhood. As more than one frustrated government official has remarked in disgust: "Everyone wants you to pick it up, but no one wants you to put it down." Clearly, no alternative is totally risk-free. The most we can hope for and expect is that the best possible decision, in light of all relevant factors, will be made. Managed land disposal of contaminated dredged material will be the best possible decision in many instances.

2.9.1. Management Strategy for Contaminated Dredged Material

A rational management strategy for contaminated dredged material might include the following features:

1. *Inventory the problem.* Determine the proportion and distribution of the bottom sediments in a river or harbor area that are contaminated. Assess the sources of the contaminants and the sediments.

2. *Adopt source control measures.* Stream bank stabilization measures (e.g., revegetation of denuded and eroding bank areas) and controls on shoreline construction can help reduce the siltation and shoaling rate and the need for frequent maintenance dredging. In some cases, selected changes in upstream channel depth or configuration can reduce downstream shoaling and transfer sediments to less obtrusive locations. For example, it has been suggested that the disposal of dredged material from New York Harbor in the Hudson River below the George Washington Bridge during World War II has resulted in a significantly increased shoaling rate in the Harbor (Panuzio, 1965). Removal and relocation of some of this material might have a beneficial effect.

3. *Match the solution to the problem.* If only 10% of dredged material in an area is highly contaminated, the search for upland or other containment alternatives should focus on this portion of the total. Too often, an all-or-nothing approach prevails. Even within a given dredging project, efforts should be made to fully characterize the material into uncontaminated and contaminated components. As part of this, all discrete components of a river or harbor bottom to be dredged should be sampled and tested, in both vertical and horizontal dimensions. Often the upper layers are more contaminated than the layers underneath. Often, too, discontinuities in the waterway bottom, or areas beyond turns or obstructions in the waterway, become areas for deposition of solids and associated pollutants. This should be determined, so that scarce and costly upland or other containment sites are not wasted on dredged sediments that do not require this degree of management.

4. *Beneficially use clean material.* Clean sediments may have resource value. Possible uses include beach nourishment, artificial wetland creation, sanitary land-fill cover, construction aggregate, and fill material. Dredged material should not be dumped in the ocean casually even if all criteria requirements are satisfied, unless no preferable alternative exists.

5. *Isolate and contain contaminated materials.* Dredged materials contaminated with persistent toxic pollutants such as PCBs should be managed to the extent possible to limit the release of these pollutants into ground and surface waters, and their entry into biological systems. It is questionable whether this can be accomplished at all in a dispersive medium like the ocean. On land, use of conventional soil conservation practices, coupled with intelligent site selection (i.e., soils with high cation-exchange capacities, low water tables, minimal slope) and management practices (i.e., suitable buffer areas, containment dikes, leachate collection and monitoring, suitable liners and caps) can reduce pollutant losses to low levels.

2.9.2. Feasible Containment Approaches in New York Harbor Area

In the New York Harbor area, two types of containment approaches are feasible and may be the most acceptable environmentally. One approach would utilize contaminated dredged material to convert two small offshore islands into one large island. This would involve the construction of a containment dike around the outer edges of the two existing islands—Hoffman and Swinburne (Fig. 2.3)—located

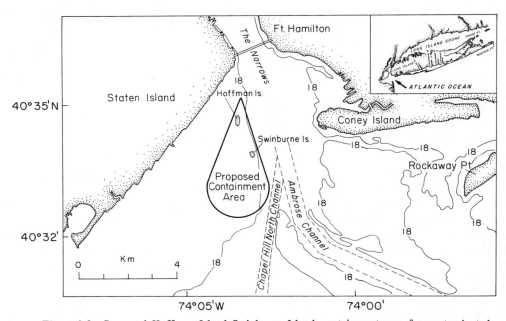

Figure 2.3. Proposed Hoffman Island–Swinburne Island containment area for contaminated dredged material. The 18 foot (5.5 m) depth contour is shown.

near the Staten Island coast. Dredged material would be deposited in the enclosed center area. This alternative, which has been studied by two engineering firms (Howard, Needles, Tammen & Bergendoff 1976; Conner et al., 1979), could accommodate from 20 to 200 years discharge of dredged material from the New York Harbor area depending on whether all or only the most contaminated fraction of the output of the New York District were dumped there. Use of the containment island approach would completely avoid the possibility of groundwater contamination and, if properly carried out, could virtually eliminate risks to health or the environment. The only negative aspects would be loss of several hundred acres of ocean bottom and possible effects on the hydrology of the Staten Island coast; these effects could, however, be estimated and, hopefully, could be minimized.

A second long-term solution for the New York area would be upland containment in selected "barren" areas in New York and New Jersey. The Mitre Corporation, in a two-volume contract study for the New York District of the ACOE (Conner et al., 1979; Leslie et al., 1980) has identified 295 so-called barren areas, collectively comprising about 218 km^2 (54,000 acre), within a 160-km radius of the Statue of Liberty, which might be suitable containment sites for New York Harbor dredged material. Eleven specific barren sites were investigated in depth in the second volume, but only one of these could be rejected as not viable. The 10 sites which survived the initial screening process are listed in Table 2.3. It would take only a few of these sites to accommodate all of the contaminated dredged material produced in the New York Harbor area for many years. One cannot help feeling that, if the New York Harbor area—the most densely populated region in the United States—has access to so much disposal site capacity, few parts of the country can legitimately claim to lack suitable upland sites.

2.9.3. The New York District's Incremental Implementation Plan

On the basis of the evaluations conducted by the Mitre Corporation, the New York District of the ACOE announced on 13 June 1980 (Pub. Notice No. 10314) that it was initating a long-range dredged-material disposal management program for the Port of New York and New Jersey. The stated purpose of the plan is "to incrementally implement the dredged-material disposal alternatives recommended in Volume I and II of the Mitre Report." Although the total program to implement all alternatives will not be completed until 1984, the ACOE stated that alternatives will be implemented to the extent possible as they are determined to be acceptable and feasible for the disposal of dredged material. The ACOE anticipates that the results generated from the overall plan would be incorporated in the review of individual disposal requests on a case-by-case basis.

A Steering Committee consisting of representatives of the EPA, the ACOE, the U.S. Fish and Wildlife Service, the National Marine Fisheries Service, and the States of New York and New Jersey helped to coordinate the development of the Incremental Implementation Plan and will continue to review and make suggestions relating to the plan.

The plan has five discrete components:

Table 2.3. Representative Barren Sites Accessible to New York Harbor Dredging Areas and Regarded as Suitable Sites for Upland Containment of Contaminated Dredged Material

Site Name	Location	Type of Site	Size (km^2)	Distance from Harbor (km)	Capacity ($\times 10^6$ m^3)	Estimated Cost[b] ($ m^{-3})	Comments
North Hempstead[a]	Nassau Co., New York	Active sand and gravel pit	2.4	43	6.5	4.15–5.25	Adjacent to Hempstead Harbor
Cheesquake	Middlesex Co., New Jersey	Former mining area, part is used as a landfill	1.2	43	6.9	1.78–2.95	Adjacent to Garden State Parkway
South Amboy	Middlesex Co., New Jersey	Past sand and gravel mining	2.7	42	1.5	1.63–2.77	Adjacent to Garden State Parkway
Woodbridge	Middlesex Co., New Jersey	Barren sand and clay pits	0.68	31	1.5	2.19–3.50	Adjacent to the Arthur Kill
Fresh Kills	Richmond Co., New York	Part is former sanitary landfill	1.8	18	9.9	3.43–4.28	Near Staten Island Sanitary Landfill (use as cover material)

Elizabeth	Union Co., New Jersey	Vacant	2.4	14	13	1.92–3.06	Located on west shore of Newark Bay
New Windsor	Orange Co., New Jersey	Includes abandoned sand and clay pit.	1.1	101	6.1	3.01–4.16	Within 2 km of Hudson River
Marlboro	Ulster Co., New York	Inactive rock quarry	0.21	108	0.57–5.7	3.77–5.13	Adjacent to Hudson River
Clinton Point	Dutchess Co., New York	Active quarry	1.6	113	4.4–7.6	1.39–4.05	East of Hudson River
Galesville	Ulster Co., New York	Seldom-used military airfield	2.6	98	large	2.03–3.11	About 24 km from the Hudson River

[a]Probably not available until 1995.
[b]Based on disposal of 0.765×10^6 m^3 per year.

1. Subaqueous borrow pit plan.
2. Upland disposal plan.
3. Ocean disposal plan (including investigation of mitigative measures such as capping, monitoring, and criteria review and evaluative changes).
4. Containment islands plan.
5. "Possible in special cases" disposal plan (including selective dredging, Long Island Sound, river/harbor disposal, beach nourishment, environmental enhancement, sanitary landfill cover, and disposal in abandoned piers).

The development of the Incremental Implementation Plan will be coordinated with the preparation of a programmatic EIS by the New York District, as agreed in the aftermath of the *NWF versus Benn* litigation. The ACOE has also initiated a Public Involvement Program to provide a formal means of factoring public input into the incremental planning effort.

2.10. CONCLUSION

The dredging of rivers and harbors to promote commercial navigation shows no signs of abating in the United States. Indeed, interest has been growing in dredging deeper draft ports to accommodate larger tanker and cargo ships. A single such "superport" may produce more dredged material for ocean dumping than all current dredging projects throughout the United States over several years. Fortunately, the dredged material derived from dredging of this kind is likely to be relatively free of contaminants. However, the relocation of massive amounts of even clean sediment, if not carefully managed, can cause significant disruption of ecological habitats.

Clearly, the pressures to dump dredged material in the ocean can be expected to continue and they will not be limited to clean sedimentary material. Unless adequate measures are implemented to avoid it, this expansion will produce further deterioration of the marine environment.

The problem is that the science of measuring, much less predicting, the fate and effect of pollutants in the marine environment is in its infancy. Consequently, all regulatory standards and testing procedures in this area are severely limited. Dredgers view them as oppressively restrictive in the absence of clear and convincing evidence of imminent risk to health or the environment. Environmentalists regard all potential risks as harms to be protected against. Meanwhile, regulators tend to oscillate from one extreme to the other as the political winds shift direction.

The urgent need is for credible procedures to assess dredged materials for environmental impacts before damage has been done to the environment. These procedures must be rigorous enough to ensure environmentalists that significant damage will not go undetected. But the link between laboratory results and impact in the field must also be sufficiently clear to persuade dredgers that the money they are forced to spend on dredged-material disposal will result in definite environmental benefits.

These goals are more easily stated than achieved. However, a beginning could be made by conducting and interpreting laboratory tests in ways that do not give the appearance of muddying the water. If appropriate sensitive bioassay organisms are to be used, results should not be "pooled" and averaged to reduce the apparent impact on the species tested. And, if an adjustment factor of 10% is to be used beyond levels that are statistically significant, a convincing rationale should be presented. Similarly, the number and distribution of sampling stations must reflect more than a grudging choice of the minimum possible number of stations, randomly selected without regard to the probable location of contamination hot spots. Control and reference areas must not turn out to be nearly as contaminated as the area being tested. Flow-through bioassays must not simply be used as a way to flush contaminants out of the test system and thereby minimize negative effects. Field assessments of bioaccumulation years after the last act of dumping or right after the dumping of clean sand are also not likely to win the trust of environmentalists. Nor, finally, are environmentalists likely to eagerly receive the results of 10-d bioaccumulation tests performed on animals allowed to depurate contaminants for 2 or 3 d in clean water before being analyzed for contaminant residues in their tissues.

At the same time, doubtful dredgers must be reassured by designing comprehensive field experiments that are coordinated and correlated with laboratory tests. Sufficient attention must be given in these studies to assessment of sublethal and population effects and to demonstrating a relationship to the food chains of species of direct human significance, to ensure that (1) laboratory and field results can be related to one another and the latter can validate the former, and (2) if adverse effects can be found, they can be related to something of recognized value to skeptical dredgers.

If laboratory tests proved, on the basis of correlative studies of this kind, either too restrictive or too permissive, they could then be adjusted with suitable correction factors or safety margins so they better served their predictive function.

As has been argued elsewhere, however, until the hoped-for accommodation between laboratory and field is achieved, it is necessary to adopt a preventive, precautionary approach to safeguard the ocean from undue harm (Kamlet, 1981). The rational management of contaminated dredged material is a major environmental and resource problem which must be solved. As we begin to clean up effluents and surface waters, the significance of bottom sediments as reservoirs of environmental contamination will become increasingly apparent. We can no longer afford to simply transfer toxic pollutants from one location to another without taking conscious steps to limit the biological availability of these pollutants.

Historical precedent alone is no longer a sufficient basis for tolerating the ocean dumping of contaminated dredged material.

ACKNOWLEDGMENTS

The author gratefully acknowledges the helpful critiques of the manuscript received from Drs. Dana R. Kester, Peter W. Anderson, and Harris H. White.

REFERENCES

American Public Health Association. 1979. Standard Methods for Examination of Water and Wastewater, 14th Edition. American Public Health Association, Washington, D.C., 1193 pp.

Boyd, M. B., R. T. Saucier, J. W. Keeley, R. L. Montgomery, R. D. Brown, D. B. Mathis, and C. J. Guice. 1972. Disposal of Dredge Spoil/Problem Identification and Assessment and Research Program Development. Technical Report H-72-8. U.S. Army Engineer Waterways Experiment Station, Vicksburg, Mississippi, 138 pp.

Brannon, J. M., I. Smith, J. Rose, R. M. Engler, and P. G. Hunt. 1976a. Selective Analytical Partitioning of Sediments to Evaluate Potential Mobility of Chemical Constituents during Dredging and Disposal Operations. Technical Report D-76-7. U.S. Army Engineer Waterways Experiment Station, Vicksburg, Mississippi. 70 pp.

Brannon, J. M., R. M. Engler, J. Rose, and P. G. Hunt. 1976b. Distribution of Manganese, Nickel, Zinc, Cadmium and Arsenic in Sediments and in the Standard Elutriate. Miscellaneous Paper D-76-18. U.S. Army Engineer Waterways Experiment Station, Vicksburg, Mississippi, 39 pp.

Conner, W. G., D. Aurand, M. Leslie, J. Slaughter, A. Amer, and F. I. Ravenscroft. 1979. Disposal of Dredged Material within the New York District: Volume 1, Present Practices and Candidate Alternatives. MITRE Technical Report MTR-7808 Vol. 1. Mitre Corp., McLean, Virginia, 385 pp.

Courtney, W. A. M. and W. J. Langston. 1978. Uptake of polychlorinated biphenyl (Aroclor 1254) from sediment and from seawater in two intertidal polychaetes. *Environmental Pollution*, 15, 303–309.

Dayal, R., M. G. Heaton, M. Fuhrmann, and I. W. Duedall. 1981. A Geochemical Study and Sedimentological Study of the Dredged Material Deposit in the New York Bight. NOAA Technical Memorandum OMPA-3. Office of Marine Pollution Assessment, National Oceanic and Atmospheric Administration, Boulder, Colorado, 174 pp.

Elder, D. L., S. W. Fowler, and G. G. Polikarpov. 1979. Remobilization of sediment-associated PCBs by the worm *Nereis diversicolor*. *Bulletin of Environmental Contamination and Toxicology*, 21, 448–452.

Fowler, S. W., G. G. Polikarpov, D. L. Elder, P. Parsi, and J. P. Villeneuve. 1978. Polychlorinated biphenyls: accumulation from contaminated sediments and water by the polychaete *Nereis diversicolor*. *Marine Biology*, 48, 303–309.

Freeman, H. C. and J. F. Uthe, 1979. Effects of PCB's in Atlantic Cod (*Cadus morhua*). *Marine Pollution Bulletin*, 10, 3.

Graves, E. 1976. U.S. dredging. *In*: Dredging: Environmental Effects & Technology. Proceedings of WODCON VII, San Francisco, California, 10–12 July 1976. Wodcon Association, San Pedro, California, pp. 9–13.

Halter, M. T. and H. E. Johnson. 1977. A model system to study the desorption and biological availability of PCB in hydrosoils. *In*: Aquatic Toxicology and Hazard Evaluation, F. R. Mayer and J. L. Hamelink (Eds.). American Society for Testing and Materials, Philadelphia, Pennsylvania, pp. 178–195.

Howard, Needles, Tammen, and Bergendoff. 1976. Dredged Material Disposal in New York Harbor and the New York Bight. Phase One/Feasibility Study. Report prepared for New York District U.S. Army Corps of Engineers, 74 pp. +2 volumes of appendices.

Huggett, R. J., M. M. Nichols, and M. E. Bender. 1980. Kepone contamination of the James River Estuary. *In*: Proceedings of American Chemical Society Symposium on Contaminants in Sediments, Volume 1, R. A. Baker (Ed.). Ann Arbor Science, Honolulu, Hawaii, pp. 33–52.

Jensen, S. and A. Jernelov. 1969. Biological methylation of mercury in aquatic organisms. *Nature*, **223**, 753–754.

Jernelov, A., L. Landner, and T. Larson. 1975. Swedish perspectives on mercury pollution. *Journal of the Water Pollution Control Federation*, **47**, 810–822.

Jones, R. A. and G. F. Lee. 1978. Evaluation of the Elutriate Test as a Method of Predicting Contaminant Release During Open-Water Disposal of Dredged Sediments and Environmental Impact of Open-Water Dredged Material Disposal. Technical Report D-78-45. U.S. Army Engineer Waterways Experiment Station, Vicksburg, Mississippi, 1936 pp. (3 Volumes).

Kamlet, K. S. 1976. Impact of Public Law 92-532 on dredging and disposal. *In*: Proceedings of the Specialty Conference on Dredging and its Environmental Effects (Mobile, Alabama, 26–28 January 1976), P. A. Krenkel, J. Harrison, and J. D. Burdick III (Eds.). American Society of Civil Engineers, New York, pp. 49–82.

Kamlet, K. S. 1978. Constraints on the off-shore disposal of dredged material. *In*: Summary Report for the Dredging Seminar (Miami, Florida, 9–12 July, 1978). U.S. Army Corps of Engineers, Jacksonville District and State of Florida.

Kamlet, K. S. 1981. The oceans as waste space: a rebuttal. *Oceanus*, **24**(1), 10–17.

Lee, G. F. and R. A. Jones. 1977. An Assessment of the Environmental Significance of Chemical Contaminants Present in Dredged Sediments Dumped in the New York Bight. A Report to the New York District Corps of Engineers. Occasional Paper No. 28. Environmental Chemistry, Center for Environmental Studies, University of Texas at Dallas, Richardson, Texas, 62 pp.

Lee, G. F. and R. H. Plumb. 1974. Literature Review on Research Study for the Development of Dredged Material Disposal Criteria. Contract Report D-74-1. U.S. Army Engineer Waterways Experiment Station, Vicksburg, Mississippi, 145 pp.

Leslie, M., D. Aurand, D. Schultz, and R. Holman. 1980. Disposal of Dredged Material within the New York District: Volume II Preliminary Evaluation of Upland Disposal. MITRE Technical Report MTR-7808 Vol. 2. Mitre Corp., McLean, Virginia, 243 pp.

Longwell, A. C. and J. B. Hughes. 1980. Cytologic, cytogenic, and developmental state of Atlantic mackerel eggs from sea surface waters of the New York Bight, and prospects for biological effects monitoring with ichthyoplankton. *Rapport Proces et Verbaux Reunion Conseil Internationale pour Exploration de la Mer*, **179**, 275–291.

McDermott, D. J., D. R. Young, and T. C. Heesen, 1976. PCB contamination of Southern California marine organisms. *In*: National Conference on Polychlorinated Biphenyls (19–21 November 1975, Chicago, Illinois). EPA-560/6-75-004. Office of Toxic Substances, U.S. Environmental Protection Agency, Washington, D.C., pp. 209–217.

Moskowitz, P., W. Hang, J. Silberman, D. Ross, and J. Highland. 1977. Troubled Waters: Toxic Chemicals in the Hudson River. Environmental Defense Fund and New York Public Interest Research Group, Inc., New York, 205 pp.

Mueller, J. A., J. S. Jeris, A. R. Anderson, and C. F. Hughes. 1976a. Contaminant Inputs to the New York Bight. NOAA Technical Memorandum ERL MESA-6. Marine EcoSystems Analysis Program Office, National Oceanic and Atmospheric Administration, Boulder, Colorado, 347 pp.

Mueller, J. A., A. R. Johnson, and J. S. Jeris. 1976b. Contaminants in the New York Bight. *Journal of the Water Pollution Control Federation*, **48**, 2309–2326.

Mueller, J. A., A. R. Johnson, and J. S. Jeris. 1976c. Contaminants entering the New York Bight: sources, mass loads, significance. *In*: Middle Atlantic Continental Shelf and the New York Bight, M. G. Gross (Ed.). American Society of Limnology and Oceanography, Inc. Lawrence, Kansas, pp. 162–170.

Murphy, L. S., P. R. Hoar, and R. A. Belastock. 1981. The effects of industrial wastes on marine phytoplankton. *In*: Ocean Dumping of Industrial Wastes, B. H. Ketchum, D. R. Kester, and P. K. Park (Eds.). Plenum Press, New York, pp. 399–410.

Nimmo, D. R., R. R. Blackman, A. J. Wilson, Jr., and J. Forester. 1971. Toxicity and distribution of Aroclor 1254 in the pink shrimp *Penaeus duorarum*. *Marine Biology*, **11**, 191–197.

O'Brien & Gere Engineers, Inc. 1979. Bioaccumulation study on *Homarus americanus*. Final Report to U.S. Army Corps of Engineers, New York District. O'Brien & Gere Engineers, Inc., Syracuse, New York, 64 pp.

O'Connor, J. M., J. B. Klotz, and T. J. Kneip. 1982. Sources, sinks and distribution of organic contaminants in the New York Bight ecosystem. *In*: Ecological Stress and the New York Bight: Science and Management, G. F. Mayer, Ed. Estuarine Research Federation, Columbia, South Carolina, pp. 631–653.

O'Connor, J. S. 1976. Contaminant effects on biota of the New York Bight. *In*: Proceedings of the 28th Annual Session of Gulf and Caribbean Fisheries Institute, J. R. Higman (Ed.). University of Miami, Florida, pp. 50–63.

O'Connor, J. S. and H. M. Stanford (Eds.). 1979. Chemical Pollutants of the New York Bight: Priorities for Research. Marine EcoSystems Analysis Project, NOAA/ERL, Boulder, Colorado, 217 pp.

O'Connors, H. B., Jr., C. F. Wurster, C. D. Powers, D. C. Biggs, and R. G. Rowland. 1978. Polychlorinated biphenyls may alter marine trophic pathways by reducing phytoplankton size and production. *Science*, **201**, 737–739.

Panuzio, F. L., 1965. Lower Hudson River siltation. *In*: Proceedings of the Federal Inter-Agency Sedimentation Conference (Jackson, Mississippi, 28 January–1 February 1963). Miscellaneous Publication No. 970. Agriculture Research Service, U.S. Department of Agriculture, Washington, D.C., pp. 512–550.

Park, P. K. and T. P. O'Connor. 1981. Ocean dumping research: historical and international development. *In*: Ocean Dumping of Industrial Wastes, B. H.

Ketchum, D. R. Kester, and P. K. Park (Eds.). Plenum Press, New York, pp. 3–23.

Pearce, J. B. 1970. The effects of solid waste disposal on benthic communities in the New York Bight. FAO Technology Conference on Marine Pollution and its effects on Living Resources and Fishing. United Nations, Food and Agricultural Organization, Rome, Italy, 12 pp.

Simpson, H. J., C. R. Olsen, R. M. Trier, and S. C. Williams. 1976. Manmade radionuclides and sedimentation in the Hudson River estuary. *Science*, **194**, 179–183.

Smith, D. D. 1979. Dredged material, ocean disposal, and the regulatory maze. *In*: Ocean Dumping and Marine Pollution, H. D. Palmer and M. G. Gross (Eds.). Dowden, Hutchinson & Ross, Inc. Stroudsburg, Pennsylvania, pp. 241–262.

Swartz, R. C., W. A. DeBen, and F. A. Cole. 1979. A bioassay for the toxicity of sediment to marine benthos. *Journal of the Water Pollution Control Federation*, **51**, 944–950.

U.S. Army Corps of Engineers. 1977. 1976 Report to Congress on Administration of Ocean Dumping Activities/Public Law 92-532 (Marine Protection, Research and Sanctuaries Act of 1972). U.S. Army Corps of Engineers, Washington, D.C., 69 pp.

U.S. Army Corps of Engineers. 1978. 1977 Report to Congress on Administration of Ocean Dumping Activities/Public Law 92-532 (Marine Protection, Research, and Sanctuaries Act of 1972). U.S. Army Corps of Engineers, Washington, D.C., 47 pp.

U.S. Army Corps of Engineers. 1979a. FY 1978 Annual Report of the Chief of Engineers on Civil Works Activities. Office of the Chief of Engineers, Washington, D.C., 108 pp.

U.S. Army Corps of Engineers. 1979b. 1978 Report to Congress on Administration of Ocean Dumping Activities/Public Law 92-532 (Marine Protection, Research, and Sanctuaries Act of 1972). U.S. Army Corps of Engineers, Washington, D.C., 49 pp.

U.S. Army Corps of Engineers. 1980. 1979 Report to Congress on Administration of Ocean Dumping Activities/Public Law 92-532 (Marine Protection, Research, and Sanctuaries Act of 1972). U.S. Army Corps of Engineers, Washington, D.C., 42 pp.

U.S. Council on Environmental Quality. 1970. Ocean Dumping—A National Policy. A Report to the President. Council on Environmental Quality, Washington, D.C. 45 pp.

U.S. Environmental Protection Agency. 1973a. Interim ocean dumping criteria. U.S. Federal Register, **38**, 12871–12874.

U.S. Environmental Protection Agency. 1973b. Ocean dumping regulations and criteria. U.S. Federal Register, **38**, 28618–28621.

U.S. Environmental Protection Agency. 1975a. Proposed guidelines for the disposal of dredged and fill material. U.S. Federal Register, **40**, 19794–19796.

U.S. Environmental Protection Agency. 1975b. Interim final guidelines for the disposal of dredged and fill material. Code of Federal Regulations, Title 40, Part 230, Washington, D.C., pp. 227–265.

U.S. Environmental Protection Agency. 1976. Bioassay procedures for the ocean disposal permit program. EPA-600/9-76-010. U.S. Environmental Protection Agency, Environmental Research Laboratory, Office of Research and Development, Gulf Breeze, Florida, 96 pp.

U.S. Environmental Protection Agency. 1977a. Quality Criteria for Water. U.S. Environmental Protection Agency, Office of Water and Hazardous Materials, Washington, D.C., 501 pp.

U.S. Environmental Protection Agency. 1977b. Final Environmental Impact Statement on Proposed Revisions to Ocean Dumping Criteria. Oil and Special Materials Control Division, Office of Water Program Operations, Washington, D.C., 2 Volumes.

U.S. Environmental Protection Agency. 1977c. Final revised ocean dumping criteria. U.S. Federal Register, 42, 2476–2489 (also in Code of Federal Regulations, Title 40, Parts 227–228).

U.S. Environmental Protection Agency. 1980a. Criteria for the management of disposal sites for ocean dumping; extension of interim designations. Interim final rule. U.S. Federal Register, 45, 3053–3055.

U.S. Environmental Protection Agency. 1980b. Final guidelines for the disposal of dredged and fill material. U.S. Federal Register, 45, 85336.

U.S. Environmental Protection Agency/Corps of Engineers Technical Committee on Criteria for Dredged and Fill Material. 1977. Ecological Evaluation of Proposed Discharge of Dredged Material into Ocean Waters: Implementation Manual for Section 103 of Public Law 92-532 (Marine Protection, Research, and Sanctuaries Act of 1972). U.S. Army Engineer Waterways Experiment Station, Vicksburg, Mississippi, 122 pp.

U.S. National Oceanic and Atmospheric Administration. 1975. Report to the Congress on Ocean Dumping Research January through December 1974/Public Law 92-532, Title II, Section 201. National Oceanic and Atmospheric Administration, Washington, D.C., 48 pp.

Veith, G. D., T. C. Carver Jr., C. M. Fetterolf, G. F. Lee, D. L. Swanson, W. A. Willford, and M. G. Zeeman. 1979. Polychlorinated biphenyls. In: A Review of the EPA Red Book: Quality Criteria for Water, R. V. Thurston, R. C. Russo, C. M. Fetterolf, Jr., T. A. Edsall, and Y. M. Barber, Jr., Eds. American Fisheries Society (Water Quality Section), Bethesda, Maryland pp. 239–246.

Wood, J. M. 1974. Biological cycles for toxic elements in the environment. Science, 183, 1049–1052.

Young, D. R., J. McDermott, and T. C. Heesen. 1976. DDT in sediments and organisms around southern California outfalls. Journal of the Water Pollution Control Federation, 48, 1919–1928.

Young, J. S. and J. B. Pearce. 1975. Shell disease in crabs and lobsters from New York Bight. Marine Pollution Bulletin, 6, 101–105.

3

TECHNICAL IMPLEMENTATION OF THE REGULATIONS GOVERNING OCEAN DISPOSAL OF DREDGED MATERIAL

Richard K. Peddicord

U.S. Army Engineer Waterways Experiment Station
Vicksburg, Mississippi

John C. Hansen

Marine Bioassay Laboratories
Watsonville, California

ABSTRACT

The 11 January 1977 Federal Register contains criteria regulating the ocean disposal of dredged material which require bioassays and bioaccumulation tests on the solid phase of dredged material as part of an environmental evaluation. An application

71

for an ocean disposal permit for maintenance dredging in Los Angeles Harbor has been evaluated under the criteria. Solid-phase bioassays of *Acanthomysis sculpta*, *Neanthes arenaceodentata* and *Macoma nasuta* showed no statistically significant mortality due to dredged material. Bioaccumulation studies of Cd, Cu, Pb, Hg, Ag, Zn, and PCB in *M. nasuta* showed statistical increases in Cd, Cu, and PCB in clams exposed to some dredged-material samples compared to those in a reference sediment from the vicinity of the disposal site. While the differences were statistically significant, all tissue concentrations were low, and the differences between test and reference animals were small, 0.09 μg g^{-1} for Cd, 0.8 μg g^{-1} for Cu, and 0.04 μg g^{-1} for PCB. Quantitative evaluation of the environmental implications of these increases in tissue contaminant concentrations is difficult to present. Since the criteria require that such evaluations be made, the environmental protection provided by the regulatory program would be enhanced by more involvement from scientists in making these evaluations.

3.1. INTRODUCTION

Section 103 of the Marine Protection, Research, and Sanctuaries Act (MPRSA) of 1972, Public Law (PL) 92-532, specifies that all proposed transportation of dredged material for dumping into ocean waters must be evaluated cooperatively by the U.S. Army Corps of Engineers (ACOE) and the U.S. Environmental Protection Agency (EPA) to determine the potential environmental impact of such activities. Environmental evaluations must be in accordance with criteria published by EPA in the Federal Register (U.S. Environmental Protection Agency, 1977a), referred to hereinafter as the Register. The EPA/ACOE Technical Committee on Criteria for Dredged and Fill Material has published an Implementation Manual of recommended minimum testing procedures for implementing the regulatory program (U.S. Environmental Protection Agency/Corps of Engineers, 1977). The manual also contains a discussion of the regulatory context of the testing and the state-of-the-art limitations in using the tests in routine regulatory applications. The introduction to this chapter, which is in part condensed from the Implementation Manual, briefly summarizes the regulatory context in which the case history studies discussed later were conducted. It cannot be over-emphasized that the case history was part of a regulatory study, directed specifically toward the requirements of the Register and thus its purpose and objectives were different and more limited than those of a research project.

The primary intent of Section 103 of PL 92-532 is to regulate and strictly limit adverse ecological effects of ocean dumping. Consequently, the Register emphasizes evaluative techniques such as bioassays and bioaccumulation studies, which provide relatively direct estimations of the potential for biological changes. However, since the criteria do not prohibit environmental change, but rather they try to avoid unacceptable environmental impact, the decision on granting a permit is ultimately subjective. Consequently, for each permit application, the ACOE District Engineer and the EPA Regional Administrator must decide how much potential impact is acceptable under the environmental, economic, and social conditions related to the operation in question. Technical and scientific evaluations provide necessary but not exclusive input to such decisions.

Dredged material is separated for evaluation into liquid, suspended particulate, and solid phases, as defined in the Register. All three phases must be evaluated for every proposed disposal operation. If a dredged material is going to have an environmental impact, the greatest potential for impact lies in the solid phase, because the bulk of the material settles rapidly with little immediate mixing or dispersion, and bottom-dwelling animals live and feed in and on the deposited solid phase for extended periods. No chemical procedures have been established that will reliably determine the biological availability of specific contaminants or combination of contaminants in the solid phase of dredged material. Therefore, the Register requires that animals be used in a bioassay to provide an integrated measurement of biological availability of the chemicals found in the material.

Exposures must be controlled adequately to minimize nontreatment stresses on test animals. This is one of the most critical and most difficult aspects of sediment bioassays. Each test animal population has its own set of environmental conditions within which stresses are minimized. All such conditions are not always known, especially for some species that have been used in sediment bioassays, and they tend to change upon acclimation of the animals to laboratory conditions. For nontreatment stresses which cannot be relieved prior to testing, additional procedures must be incorporated into the tests to separate their effects from those of the treatments. There is reasonable assurance that an experimental design incorporating such considerations will produce unbiased data. Dredged-material bioassays are at present widely regarded as the best available predictors of environmental effects that would occur in the field if the proposed disposal operation were to take place. However, they must be regarded as qualitative estimators, rather than precise predictors, of those effects, making interpretation somewhat subjective. Although a finding of increased mortality or bioaccumulation in a dredge-material bioassay indicates a potential for impact in the field, laboratory statistical significance, *per se*, cannot be the sole basis to conclude that ecologically important changes will occur in the field. The environmental importance of a statistically significant finding must be determined through professional judgement of persons experienced in environmental evaluations.

The concept is expressed in the environmental impact statement on the Ocean Dumping Criteria that "EPA has chosen to allow some change in sediment characteristics or water chemistry as being reasonable, but no damage to the biota outside the region of initial mixing is allowed under these criteria" (U.S. Environmental Protection Agency, 1977b). Since the primary concern of the criteria is that effects not extend beyond the region of initial mixing, the solid-phase bioassay technique does not evaluate the physical effects of massive sediment deposition immediately under the discharging vessel. Instead the technique generally approximates conditions near the disposal site boundary where sediment dispersion has reduced the thickness of deposited dredged material to a few centimeters. The solid-phase bioassay technique is designed to address the regulatory issue of effects of chemicals associated with this deposited sediment, rather than physical effects of the sediment within the disposal site. It is apparent that there will be a gradient of decreasing sediment deposition with increasing distance away from the disposal site due to dispersion. Since the exact nature of this sediment dispersion gradient can be predicted only on a case-by-case basis, the approach discussed above was adopted for a generally applicable solid-phase bioassay design.

The criteria (U.S. Environmental Protection Agency, 1979a) require that evaluations of the solid phase include an assessment of the potential for contaminants from the dredged material to be bioaccumulated in the tissues of marine organisms. This is intended to assess the potential for accumulation of toxins to concentrations that might ultimately be harmful. Bioaccumulation data are useful in regulatory decisions. They indicate the extent to which there may be a cause-and-effect relationship between the animals' presence in the dredged material and an ecologically meaningful elevation of body burdens of contaminants above those of similar animals in the sediment already present near the disposal site.

The interpretation of bioaccumulation data is difficult because the biological consequences of a particular body burden to the animal whose tissues contain it are often poorly known. Even if consequences to the individual are known, it is often impossible to quantify the ecological consequences of an elevated tissue concentration of a contaminant in a particular species. The only concentrations of contaminants in tissues that are fixed from a regulatory viewpoint are those set by the Food and Drug Administration for fish and shellfish for human consumption (U.S. Department of Health, Education and Welfare, 1980). It should also be kept in mind that at present tissue concentrations of most constituents in most species cannot be quantitatively related to biological effects. Therefore, in order to make an environmentally sound final assessment of bioaccumulation, the ACOE District Engineer and the EPA Regional Administrator must subjectively consider the magnitude of bioaccumulation shown, the toxicological significance of the material(s) bioaccumulated, the proportion of sediment sampling sites that produce uptake, the number of different constituents bioaccumulated, concentrations of that constituent already present in similar species living near the disposal site, and other factors relevant to the particular operation in question.

3.2. CASE HISTORY

The U.S. Army Corps of Engineers, Los Angeles District, received an application from the City of Los Angeles Board of Harbor Commissioners for a permit for ocean disposal of approximately 103,000 m^3 of sediments to be dredged from berthing areas in Los Angeles harbor. The Register requires that a determination be made of the potential for this material to unreasonably degrade or endanger the marine environment. This case history discusses the solid-phase bioassay and bioaccumulation studies conducted for the Board of Harbor Commissioners to assist in making that regulatory determination. The design of the tests and application of the data were dictated by the regulatory framework discussed above. Because the requirements of the regulations are more specific and limited than those of a research program, no attempt was made in this regulatory investigation to address all questions of research interest.

The sediments tested are from eight berthing areas in Los Angeles Harbor, each area consisting of several adjacent berths all used for similar cargoes and considered to have similar sediments. The proposed disposal site is located in the Southern California Bight approximately 13 km due south of Point Fermin on the inland edge of the San Pedro Channel (Fig. 3.1). The depth at the center of the site is approximately 180 m; however, the site has a 910-m radius and the depth of the disposal area varies from 140 m to more than 240 m.

The study objective was to determine whether bioaccumulation of contaminants was likely to be greater from the dredged material than from the sediment already existing in the vicinity of the disposal site. This information would assist the ACOE and EPA in making a regulatory determination of the potential for the dredged material to cause significant undesirable effects on the environment in the vicinity of the disposal site. Potential effects were determined empirically by approximating the disposal activity and the disposal site vicinity with controlled laboratory experimentation.

3.2.1. Experimental Design

The benthic environment in the vicinity of the disposal site was represented in these laboratory studies by sediments collected from a reference site, located approximately 2.5 km due east of the center of the disposal site in approximately 140 m of water (Fig. 3.1). The reference site was sufficiently near the disposal site to be influenced by the same circulation regime, similar in sediment particle size distribution, and free of previous dredged-material disposal activities. In addition, a survey of San Pedro Bay sediments by Chen and Lu (1974) indicates contaminant concentrations in the reference site sediments are representative of those in the surrounding area. These considerations made the reference site an acceptable point of comparison for the regulatory purpose of determining what additional impacts, if any, dredged-material disposal might have on the disposal site vicinity. Because the disposal, and therefore the nearby reference, sites were just off a heavily urbanized coastline, it was considered possible that contaminant levels in reference site sediments might make them inappropriate for use as control sediments for procedural quality assurance. Therefore, a control site well removed from sources of contaminants (Fig. 3.1), was selected on the basis of similarity in sediment particle size distribution to the reference site, and low contaminant levels. The reference and control sediments were characterized in terms of particle size distribution and bulk or total analyses for DDE, cadmium, copper, lead, and zinc in Table 3.1.

The experimental design conformed closely with the Implementation Manual; only those additional measures, changes, or substitutions described herein were made in order to meet the specific needs of this particular evaluation.

Test conditions in the solid-phase bioassays were designed to represent a disposal operation. Test controls functioned only for quality assurance (that is, nontreatment mortality). Survival and bioaccumulation in the test treatments were compared to these responses of animals in the reference sediment. The reference treatment was used as comparative data rather than the control because it was selected to represent the benthic environment in the disposal site vicinity. This must be the

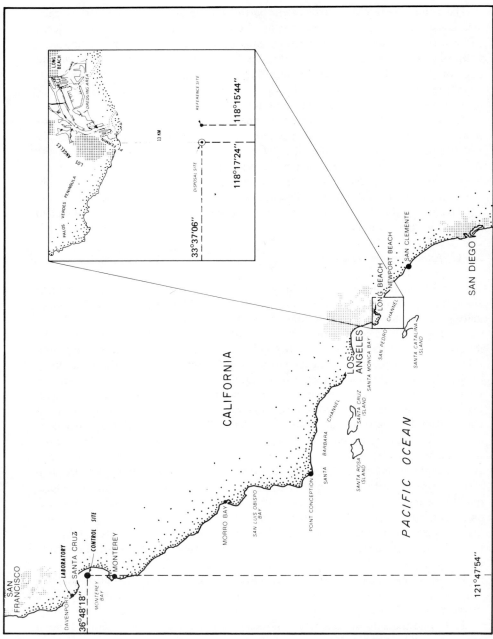

Figure 3.1. Location of dredging, disposal, reference, and control sites along the coast of California.

Table 3.1. Concentration of Selected Chemical Constituents and Sediment Particle
Size Distribution in Sediments from the Reference and Control Sites

Parameter (Total Sediment Content)	Concentration[a]	
	Reference Site Sediment	Control Site Sediment
DDE	1.25	<0.01
Cadmium	4.2	0.8
Copper	58.0	4.1
Lead	40.0	2.2
Zinc	56.0	20.0
Sand	31.2%	34.5%
Silt	64.2%	63.6%
Clay	4.6%	1.9%

[a] $mg\ kg^{-1}$ dry weight unless other units indicated.

basis for comparison in order to make the regulatory determination of what additional effect, if any, the proposed discharge would have on the dumpsite vicinity in light of possible incremental effects already occurring in the area unrelated to dredged-material discharge.

Clams surviving the solid-phase bioassays were used in bioaccumulation studies. Immediately upon termination of the bioassays, survivors were placed in sediment-free seawater for 3 d to allow complete emptying of the gut as evidenced by absence of fecal pellet formation. This was necessary since sediment remaining in the guts might contain contaminants in biologically unavailable forms and thus give an incorrectly high indication of bioaccumulation potential if it were included in the tissue analysis. Conversely, the dense sediment would add weight of inert material, thus tending to lower the apparent concentration of contaminant on a weight basis. After considering the available data, the international Mussel Watch program recommended emptying guts prior to metals analysis and considered it acceptable for chlorinated hydrocarbons (National Academy of Sciences, 1980). In neither case was the possible loss of contaminants incorporated in tissues considered to be a major concern during the short time required for gut voiding.

Bioaccumulation potential was determined by successively addressing the following questions: (1) What is the tissue burden of each constituent? (2) Does the measured tissue burden represent a bioaccumulation of the constituent? (3) Is bioaccumulation of the constituent greater than the level in reference animals? After analytically determining tissue burden, treatment data were compared statistically to reference data to determine bioaccumulation. Bioaccumulation potentials were evidenced when tissue burdens from treatments were significantly greater than tissue burdens from animals in reference sediment.

Bioassay procedures were conducted in a laboratory at Davenport Landing, California. Nearshore water from this site, well removed from important sources of contamination, was delivered by an all cast iron pump through a 30-cm polyvinyl chloride (PVC) intake line extending 180 m seaward from the beach. A continuous flow of seawater passed through a sand filter and was heated or cooled to within

$0.3°C$ of the $15°C$ test temperature. Air temperature in the laboratory was controlled to similar tolerances and circulated to effect uniformity. Cool-white fluorescent light at an approximately uniform intensity of 1.5×10^{15} quanta cm^{-2} s^{-1} was regulated to produce a 14-h light/10-h dark photoperiod during animal acclimation and testing periods. Aeration, when required, was provided by an oil-less air pump. Bioassay test containers were of all-glass construction. Test containers were all thoroughly acid-washed prior to each use.

Test dredged materials representing each sampling area consisted of 1- to 2-liter samples from random locations over the entire area; these samples were composited until a sufficient volume was obtained from each area. This task was accomplished by a team of scuba divers.

Reference and control site samples were collected by use of an all-plastic pipe dredge. All sediments were placed in cleaned 20-liter polyethylene buckets and covered with leak-proof closures for transportation. In every case, samples were delivered to the laboratory for processing within 12 h after collection.

3.2.2. Test Organisms

Solid phase bioassays were conducted on:

1. *Acanthomysis sculpta*, mysid shrimp.
2. *Macoma nasuta*, bent-nose macoma clam (also used in bioaccumulation studies).
3. *Neanthes arenaceodentata*, polychaete.

Mysids were collected from kelp beds just north of Goleta, California (60 km east of Point Conception, Fig. 3.1). The animals were gently concentrated with a dip net into a submerged bucket without removing them from the water. In transit to the laboratory, holding-tank temperatures were maintained within $2°C$ of the ambient temperature at sampling. Gentle aeration was supplied from a bottle of compressed air. Upon arrival at the laboratory, holding-tank temperature was adjusted to within $2°C$ of the collection water temperature. Acclimation to test temperature was accomplished at a maximum rate of $2°C$ d^{-1}. Mysids were held 3–4 d after temperature acclimation prior to testing. During this time and throughout testing, mysids were fed 20–30 brine shrimp *Artemia salina* nauplii per day per mysid to prevent mortality from starvation and cannibalism. The day prior to test initiation, mysids were presorted into groups of 20. The next day animals injured in the sorting process were readily found and carefully replaced. Presorting and feeding were both found to be necessary to minimize mortality caused by handling mysids during testing.

Macoma nasuta were collected from near the mouth of Elkhorn Slough in Monterey Bay, California (Fig. 3.1), with a modified hydraulic-lift dredge. Animals 4–6 cm in length were retained for bioassay and bioaccumulation use. Animals were held for 5–7 d prior to testing. During the holding period, clams were fed rehydrated brewer's yeast and *Thalassiosira pseudonana* cultures. Feeding was discontinued 48 h prior to test initiation. Clams were not fed during testing.

Neanthes arenaceodentata test populations were purchased from Dr. Don Reisch, California State University at Long Beach. Animals were received 5–7 d before scheduled tests to allow sufficient time for laboratory acclimation. During the holding period, animals were fed suspensions of dried *Enteromorpha* sp. All handling and transfer of worms was done with the use of small watercolor brushes rather than with rigid utensils to prevent damaging the soft-bodied animals.

3.2.3. Bioassay Procedures

Bioassays of solid-phase materials were performed simultaneously on the eight samples, each composited from one of the berthing areas. Five replicates of station, control, and reference treatments were randomly assigned to test tanks by a random numbers computer program. Control and reference sediments were sieved through a 1-mm screen to remove indigenous fauna and a 3-cm layer of each was placed in the bottom of the respective tanks. Control sediment was placed in each control tank. Tanks were filled with water, and 20 each *M. nasuta* and *N. arenaceodentata* were added. These animals were allowed 48 h to adapt to the sediments in the aquaria.

After the 48-h acclimation period, freshly screened samples of dredged material were added to the test tanks to a depth of 1.5 cm. Reference and control tanks were treated with additional layers of reference sediment and control sediment respectively. After a 1-h settling time, the flow-through seawater system was activated and adjusted to a flow rate equivalent to four tank volumes per day.

Immediately after flow was begun a screen was placed over the overflow of the tanks and 20 presorted *A. sculpta* were placed into each tank. Mysids were not added with clams and worms, because the mysids are not infaunal and might be harmed by the direct physical impact of dredged material addition. This would interfere with the objective of determining the chemical toxicity of the dredged material.

Solid-phase bioassays continued for 10 d. Once each day, the salinity and temperature of the system, and the dissolved oxygen of each tank were measured. Salinity remained nearly constant at $30.8 \pm 0.1\%_{00}$ over the 10-d period. Temperatures ranged from 15.0 to 15.2°C. Dissolved oxygen was maintained between 6.5 mg liter^{-1} and saturation by aeration when necessary.

After the 10-d bioassay period, the contents of each tank were washed through a 0.5-mm Nytex screen with seawater. The animals were retrieved from the screen and counted. Test data were the number of survivors of each species.

3.2.4. Bioaccumulation Procedures

Macoma nasuta surviving the solid-phase bioassay were placed in clean, sediment-free water for 3 d to void their guts of sediment. The clams were then shucked and the soft tissues homogenized for chemical analyses, which were performed in triplicate.

Chemical analyses determined the concentrations of the following groups of constituents:

1. *Polychlorinated biphenyls (PCB)* were extracted from 20-g aliquots of each sample with petroleum ether/dichloromethane. The solvent phase was separated,

concentrated, partitioned into acetonitrile, and reextracted with petroleum ether. Extracts were then adsorbed onto florisil-packed columns and subsequently eluted with 6% (v/v) diethyl/petroleum ether followed by 15% (v/v) diethyl/petroleum ether. Eluents were then analyzed by gas-liquid chromatography using electron-capture detection (U.S. Environmental Protection Agency, 1973, 1974).

   2. *Mercury* was determined by the method of Goldberg (1976). In this method sample aliquots are digested in aqua regia, potassium persulfate, and potassium permanganate. Analysis was by "cold vapor" atomic absorption spectrophotometry.

   3. *Cadmium, copper, silver, zinc, and lead* concentrations were determined by the method of Goldberg (1976). Atomic absorption spectrophotometry with both flameless graphite furnace and flame atomization was used for analysis. Samples were first charred at $325°C$, then digested in concentrated HNO_3 and H_2O_2 to decomplex and dissolve trace metals.

3.2.5. Data Analysis

The statistical treatment of bioassay and bioaccumulation data was the same for each data set. Once the fundamental assumption of variance homogeneity was tested, the appropriate parametric or nonparametric test was followed. Variance homogeneity was tested with both *Cochran's C-test* and *Bartlett's test* (Zar, 1974), an analogous procedure for testing this same assumption. A modification of the analytical procedure was necessary when a deviation from this assumption existed. Significant results for this and all subsequent parametric tests were determined by the critical values ($\alpha = 0.05$) of the appropriate distributions.

   If homogeneity of variances could be established, the data were subjected to single factor analysis of variance (*ANOVA*), testing the difference between means of two or more samples simultaneously. Following a significant *ANOVA* for a given species and parameter, *Dunnett's test* was employed to analyze data. A one-tailed hypothesis was used with *Dunnett's test* to identify those treatments which differed significantly from the comparative datum in the appropriate direction. That is, only increases in mortality or tissue concentration in the test animals, not decreases, were considered critical by the regulatory agency in evaluating this permit application.

   When sample variances did not exhibit homogeneity as determined by *Cochran's C-test* and *Bartlett's test*, an arcsin $x^{1/2}$ data-transformation and a subsequent reduction in degrees of freedom were employed. If this procedure did not compensate for the deviation from homogeneity, then nonparametric *Kruskal–Wallis tests* were employed.

3.3. RESULTS

The solid phase bioassay data for all species are summarized in Table 3.2, and statistical analyses are presented in Table 3.3. A data transformation was applied to *A. sculpta* results but was unsuccessful in correcting heterogeneous variances.

Table 3.2. Survival of Test Organisms in the Solid-Phase Bioassay[a]

| Sediment | Number of Survivors (Mean ± One Standard Deviation) | | |
	Mysid *Acanthomysis sculpta*	Clam *Macoma nasuta*	Polychaete *Neanthes arenaceodentata*
Control	18.2 ± 0.4	19.2 ± 0.4	19.8 ± 0.4
Reference	17.4 ± 1.3	18.8 ± 0.8	14.4 ± 3.0
Dredged Material			
Site 1	17.0 ± 0.7	19.6 ± 0.6	16.0 ± 2.6
2	16.2 ± 3.4	18.6 ± 1.1	15.8 ± 4.7
3	14.2 ± 3.0	18.4 ± 1.1	17.0 ± 2.6
4	15.0 ± 4.8	19.8 ± 0.4	19.8 ± 0.4
5	17.0 ± 2.2	19.0 ± 0.7	15.3 ± 2.2
6	17.0 ± 1.2	19.4 ± 0.9	13.0 ± 4.4
7	17.6 ± 1.3	18.8 ± 0.8	19.0 ± 1.2
8	15.8 ± 2.8	19.0 ± 1.4	18.2 ± 1.6

[a]All species were exposed to every sediment in five replicates of 20 organisms each.

The subsequent nonparametric *Kruskal–Wallis* analysis was nonsignificant. The transformation was also applied to *N. arenaceodentata* data to correct for variance heterogeneity. *ANOVA* was applied to the transformed data and yielded a significant result. The transformed means were then compared by *Dunnett's* analysis. Differences among means were significant, but not in the direction of regulatory concern (i.e. mean survival in dredged-material samples was greater than mean survival of each comparative datum, in this case reference material). An *ANOVA* showed no significant differences within the *M. nasuta* survival data, which were homogeneous.

The results of the analyses of *M. nasuta* tissue for Hg are presented in Table 3.4. There were no statistically significant differences within the data at the α-0.05 probability level (Table 3.5). Thus, exposure to none of the dredged material samples caused changes in Hg concentrations in *M. nasuta* compared to clams in either the control or the reference sediments.

An *ANOVA* showed statistically significant differences in tissue concentrations of Pb in *M. nasuta* in the various treatments (Table 3.5). Station 5 was the only dredged material producing a numerically higher tissue concentration of Pb than the reference (Table 3.4). However, examination of *Dunnett's q-values* revealed that even this station mean did not statistically exceed the reference mean at the α-0.05 level, although test organisms in some dredged-material samples showed significantly less Pb than the reference animals. Thus, there was no statistical indication of bioaccumulation for Pb from the test sediments by *M. nasuta*.

The magnitude and pattern of tissue concentrations of Ag were similar to those for Pb. There were statistically significant differences within the data (Table 3.5), but only station 4 numerically exceeded the reference mean and this difference was not statistically significant (Table 3.4). All significant differences involved dredged-material stations producing Ag concentrations lower than the reference substrate.

Table 3.3. Analysis of Survival of Test Species in Solid-Phase Bioassays

Species	Homogeneity of Variances		Test of Significance		Mean Comparison	
	Cochran's Test	Bartlett's Test	ANOVA F-Value	Kruskal–Wallis H-Value	Difference between Means (Transformed Data)	Dunnett's q-Value[c]
Mysid shrimp *Acanthomysis sculpta*	0.37[a]	4.40[a]	—	12.65 n.s.		
Clam *Macoma nasuta*	0.25 n.s.	1.06 n.s.	1.23 n.s.	—		
Polychaete *Neanthes arenaceodentata*	0.30 n.s.	1.01 n.s.	5.34[b]	—	$\bar{x}_R - \bar{x}_1 = -5.71$	-0.81
					$\bar{x}_R - \bar{x}_2 = -8.16$	-1.16
					$\bar{x}_R - \bar{x}_3 = -9.84$	-1.40
					$\bar{x}_R - \bar{x}_4 = -28.68$	-4.09
					$\bar{x}_R - \bar{x}_5 = -2.64$	-0.38
					$\bar{x}_R - \bar{x}_6 = 3.63$	0.52
					$\bar{x}_R - \bar{x}_7 = -21.53$	-3.07
					$\bar{x}_R - \bar{x}_8 = -16.22$	-2.31
					$\bar{x}_R - \bar{x}_C = -28.68$	-4.09

— Test not performed.

n.s. Not statistically significant at the α-0.05 level.

[a]Significant nonhomogeneity of variances at the α-0.05 level. Nonparametric test of significance used.

[b]Statistically/significant differences at the α-0.05 level.

[c]No sample mean is less than the reference mean at the α-0.05 level, although some means are significantly greater than the reference mean.

82

Table 3.4. Bioaccumulation in the Clam *Macoma nasuta* in the Solid-Phase Bioassay[a]

Sediment	Contaminant Concentration (wet wt: mean ± 1 std. dev.)						
	μg g⁻¹				μg kg⁻¹		
	Zn	Cu	Hg	Pb	Ag	Cd	PCB
Control	27 ± 0.6	2.1 ± 0.3	21 ± 18	127 ± 31	70 ± 20	257 ± 58	7.3 ± 0.5
Reference	33 ± 1.0	1.9 ± 0.3	21 ± 2	180 ± 26	193 ± 74	280 ± 26	15.0 ± 1.0
Dredged material							
Site 1	29 ± 0.6	2.7 ± 0.2[b]	62 ± 32	160 ± 17	53 ± 15	257 ± 6	7.3 ± 1.5
2	29 ± 1.2	2.5 ± 0.2[b]	29 ± 15	117 ± 32	107 ± 40	367 ± 45[b]	12.0 ± 2.0
3	28 ± 2.9	2.2 ± 0.2	42 ± 26	177 ± 50	67 ± 12	293 ± 15	8.7 ± 1.5
4	28 ± 0.6	2.3 ± 0.3	27 ± 14	127 ± 25	260 ± 131	270 ± 30	9.7 ± 2.1
5	28 ± 0.6	2.1 ± 0.3	21 ± 5	220 ± 36	150 ± 36	277 ± 21	5.3 ± 2.1
6	32 ± 0.6	2.1 ± 0.1	30 ± 16	153 ± 32	193 ± 32	277 ± 6	54.3 ± 6.0[b]
7	29 ± 1.0	1.8 ± 0.1	18 ± 5	173 ± 15	137 ± 31	273 ± 32	8.3 ± 1.5
8	29 ± 1.2	1.7 ± 0.2	26 ± 17	187 ± 6	170 ± 62	307 ± 6	4.3 ± 1.5

[a]Each mean represents three replicates.
[b]Sample mean exceeds the reference mean at the α-0.05 level. See Table 3.5 for statistical analysis.

Table 3.5. Statistical Analyses of *Macoma nasuta* Bioaccumulation Data Presented in Table 3.4

Contaminant	Homogeneity of Variances		Test of Significance	
	Cochran's Test	*Bartlett's Test*	*ANOVA F-Value*	*Kruskal–Wallis H-Value*
Hg	0.34 n.s.	1.50 n.s.	1.75 n.s.	
Pb	0.29 n.s.	0.81 n.s.	3.54[a]	
Ag	0.35 n.s.	1.14 n.s.	3.68[a]	
Zn	0.57[b]	1.25 n.s.	6.78[a]	19.76[a]
Cu	0.20 n.s.	0.66 n.s.	5.66[c]	
Cd	0.38 n.s.	1.86 n.s.	3.55[c]	
PCB	0.39 n.s.	1.11 n.s.	28.70[c]	

n.s. Not significant at the α-0.05 level.
[a]Statistical differences exist within the data at the α-0.05 level. No sample mean was found to exceed the reference mean at the α-0.05 level, although some means were significantly less than the reference mean.
[b]Heterogeneity of variances significant at the α-0.05 level.
[c]Statistical differences exist within the data at the α-0.05 level. See Table 3.4 for means that statistically exceed the reference mean.

The two tests for homogeneity of variances in the Zn data produced conflicting results (Table 3.5). Therefore, both nonparametric and parametric analyses of transformed data were performed. Both showed statistically significant differences among the data. However, none of the dredged-material station data numerically exceeded the reference substrate data (Table 3.4), and all significant differences represented decreases in tissue Zn concentration relative to clams in the reference substrate.

Copper concentrations in tissues of *M. nasuta* exposed to the control sediment and six of the eight dredged-material samples numerically exceeded concentrations in the reference animals (Table 3.4). However, only dredged-material stations 1 and 2 produced Cu concentrations statistically higher than the reference sediment.

Concentrations of Cd in *M. nasuta* numerically exceeded the reference values in three of the dredged material samples (Table 3.4). Of these, only station 2 produced a statistically significant increase in Cd concentration.

Concentrations of PCB in tissues of test animals numerically exceeded the reference value only at station 6, an increase that was statistically significant (Table 3.4).

3.4. DISCUSSION

Six metals and one chlorinated hydrocarbon were analyzed in the tissues of *M. nasuta* exposed to dredged material from eight stations, for a total of 56 contaminant–sediment combinations in which uptake might have been measured. Of these, statistically significant increases in tissue concentrations above the reference animals occurred four times, or 7% of the possible cases. Statistically significant uptake of Cu occurred from station 1 dredged material, Cu and Cd from station 2, and PCB from station 6. Five of the eight stations showed no significant uptake of any contaminant measured relative to the reference animals.

In the scientific literature data quantitatively relating tissue concentration of PCB in a cause-and-effect manner to responses of aquatic organisms are generally lacking, particularly in the case of *M. nasuta*. Faced with this lack of adequate specific data on effects of bioaccumulation, regulatory personnel must turn to more indirect interpretations of the ecological importance of the concentrations produced by exposure to the dredged material. One approach is to compare the data to concentrations regarded to be environmentally acceptable by at least a segment of environmental scientists. For example, the National Academy of Sciences (1973) recommended that PCB concentrations in fish species consumed by birds or mammals not exceed 0.5 μg g^{-1} wet weight. A group of scientists convened by the American Fisheries Society recommended that PCB concentrations in fish not exceed 0.1 μg g^{-1} for the protection of marine life and animals which consume it (Veith et al., 1979).

Another approach is to compare the concentrations in test organisms to those in the same species living in areas well removed from inputs of the contaminants in question, and therefore representing "background" or "ambient" concentrations in apparently healthy populations. Concentrations in test animals below these might be regarded as having a relatively low potential for ecological harm, whereas concentrations above these levels could be regarded as having a higher potential for adverse effects. Reference stations in field monitoring studies can provide such "background" or "ambient" values, but for many species bioaccumulation data are lacking in the scientific literature. Regulatory personnel must then turn to such data on species other than those tested for assistance in assessing the ecological importance of the bioaccumulation found in the tests. The difficulties inherent in such interspecific comparisons are recognized, but if data on the species in question do not exist in the literature, regulatory personnel must use those data that are available.

Dredged material from station 6 produced a mean PCB concentration in *M. nasuta* of 0.054 μg g^{-1} wet weight, which was 0.039 μg g^{-1}, or 3.6 times, greater than the mean reference concentration. At a reference station in a field study of pollution effects in San Francisco Bay, Risebrough et al. (1976) reported 47 samples of *Mytilus edulis* as having a mean PCB concentration of 0.068 μg g^{-1} wet weight. McDermott et al. (1975) reported mean PCB concentrations in *Mytilus californianus* from 10 Southern California Bight sites in coastal areas well away from urban centers. Nine of these stations had PCB values between 0.014 and 0.026 μg g^{-1} wet weight, with a concentration of 0.069 μg g^{-1} at the tenth site. The PCB concentrations produced in *M. nasuta* by station 6 dredged material in this study were in the same range as those found in *Mytilus* spp. at reference stations in the two studies of West Coast bivalves cited. In comparison to recommended PCB concentrations, *M. nasuta* contained 0.11 of the National Academy of Sciences (1973) value and 0.54 of that recommended by Veith et al. (1979).

The mean value in station 6 clams was 0.011 of the U.S. Food and Drug Administration action level of 5 μg g^{-1} wet weight for PCB in fish and shellfish for human consumption (U.S. Department of Health, Education and Welfare, 1980).

The only statistically significant increases in Cu concentration were produced by dredged material from stations 1 and 2, where the mean values were 2.7 and 2.5 μg g^{-1} wet weight, respectively. These values were 0.8 and 0.6 μg g^{-1} (or about 1.4 times) greater than the mean reference concentration. Wenzloff et al. (1979) reported background metals levels in the foot muscle of the bivalves *Spisula solidissima* and *Arctica islandica* at 151 stations in the Mid-Atlantic Bight. When the stations were grouped by latitude, the authors found mean Cu levels between 2.87 and 3.83 μg g^{-1} wet weight in *S. solidissima* and 2.84–7.16 μg g^{-1} in *A. islandica*. The mean Cu values of *M. nasuta* in dredged-material samples 1 and 2 in this study were slightly below the range reported by Wenzloff et al. (1979) for other bivalve species in areas well removed from major sources of pollution. The U.S. Food and Drug Administration had established no action level for Cu in human food, but its Australian counterpart, the National Health and Medical Research Council, has recommended a maximum Cu concentration of 30 μg g^{-1} wet weight in seafoods, according to Wenzloff et al. (1979). This is more than a factor of 10 above the levels in *M. nasuta* exposed to dredged material from stations 1 and 2.

Dredged material from station 2 also produced a statistically significant increase in Cd over the reference value. The mean value in *M. nasuta* in station 2 material was 0.37 μg g^{-1} wet weight, which was 0.09 μg g^{-1}, or 1.3 times greater than the reference mean. Wenzloff et al. (1979) reported mean background Cd levels in the foot of *S. solidissima* from the Mid-Atlantic Bight as <0.11 to 0.15 μg g^{-1} wet weight. Values for *A. islandica* were between 0.39 and 0.54 μg g^{-1}. The mean Cd value of 0.37 μg g^{-1} in dredged material from station 2 was above the reported background for *S. solidissma*, but below that for *A. islandica* both of which are bivalves, as is *M. nasuta*. The station 2 value is five times less than the Australian National Health and Medical Research Council recommendation of a maximum of 2.0 μg g^{-1} Cd on a wet weight basis in seafood, as reported by Wenzloff et al. (1979). The U.S. Food and Drug Administration has established no action level for Cd in fish and shellfish.

The Register requires that dredged material proposed for ocean disposal be evaluated for, among other things, its potential to cause bioaccumulation to levels resulting in environmental or human health impacts. In this study statistically significant bioaccumulation of Cd, Cu, and PCB was shown in *M. nasuta*. The increases were small in terms of both percentage and magnitude of increase, and the resulting concentrations were within the range reported for the same contaminants in other bivalve species from areas well removed from direct sources of contamination. The levels in exposed clams were also well below limits established for seafood for human consumption, and in the case of PCB, below levels recommended as environmentally protective by two groups of environmental scientists. Yet very little scientific literature exists documenting a direct cause-and-effect relationship between a specified body burden of a particular contaminant and direct biological response in the aquatic organism harboring it. There is essentially no scientific information quantifying cause-and-effect relationships between a given tissue concentration and a specific biological response at the population level, let alone at the ecosystem level. Therefore, one could argue that no bioaccumulation should be allowed, because no particular concentration can be shown to be inconsequential.

The intent of this chapter has not been the traditional presentation and evaluation of research data. Rather the intent is to outline the context within which dredged-material bioassays are conducted under the Ocean Dumping Criteria, and to illustrate the difficulties of making regulatory decisions lacking an adequate data base. Due to a lack of adequate information regulatory personnel must often draw conclusions indirectly on the basis of data on similar species and contaminants. Usually data must be evaluated in relation to "background" or "ambient" concentrations. For many contaminants we do not know what concentrations are "safe," nor have protective values been recommended, such as the PCB values of the National Academy of Sciences (1973) or Veith et al. (1979).

Regulatory personnel often lack the expertise and familiarity with the scientific literature that is necessary to make the best evaluations under these conditions. Yet decisions allowing or not allowing disposal operations are made daily under the existing criteria, often without benefit of adequate input from the scientific community. Scientists can improve the implementation of environmental regulations by applying their judgmental expertise to answering such basic questions as: does an increase in PCB concentration in $M.$ $nasuta$ from 0.015 μg g^{-1} to 0.054 μg g^{-1} wet weight in a 10-d laboratory exposure to dredged material indicate that if the material were dumped, significant undesirable effects due to bioaccumulation would occur near the dumpsite? Environmental protection can be enhanced today by scientists who will assist in implementing scientific aspects of the existing regulations. Future protection will be enhanced to the extent that scientists participate in revisions of the regulatory criteria to ensure due consideration of the information, based on research, scientists can actually provide.

ACKNOWLEDGMENTS

This chapter was possible only due to the cooperation of the Los Angeles Board of Harbor Commissioners, particularly Mr. Michael Martin. The research described in the case history was performed under contract to the Board by Dr. John C. Hansen and the staff of Marine Bioassay Laboratories, Watsonville, California. Appreciation is also extended to the reviewers of the manuscript for their constructive suggestions.

REFERENCES

Chen, K. Y. and J. C. S. Lu. 1974. Sediment compositions in Los Angeles-Long Beach harbors and San Pedro Basin. *In*: Marine Studies of San Pedro Bay, California, Part VII—Sediment Investigations, D. F. Soule and M. Oguri (Eds.). The Allan Hancock Foundation, Los Angeles, California, pp. 1–177.

Goldberg, E. D. (Ed.). 1976. Strategies for Marine Pollution Monitoring. Wiley-Interscience, New York, 310 pp.

McDermott, D. J., D. R. Young, and T. C. Heesen. 1975. Polychlorinated Biphenyls in Marine Organisms off Southern California. Southern California Coastal Water Resources Project, TM233. Los Angeles, California 45 pp.

National Academy of Sciences. 1980. The International Mussel Watch. Report of a workshop sponsored by the Environmental Studies Board, Commission on Natural Resources, National Research Council. National Academy of Sciences, Washington, D.C. 248 pp.

National Academy of Sciences–National Academy of Engineering. 1973. Water Quality Criteria, 1972. EPA Ecology Research Series EPA-R3-73-033, U.S. Environmental Protection Agency, Washington, D.C. 594 pp.

Risebrough, R. W., B. W. DeLappe, and T. T. Schmidt. 1976. Bioaccumulation factors of chlorinated hydrocarbons between mussels and seawater. *Marine Pollution Bulletin*, 7, 225–228.

U.S. Department of Health, Education and Welfare. 1980. Action Levels for Poisonous or Deleterious Substances in Human Food and Animal Feed. Food and Drug Administration, Industry Programs Branch, Bureau of Foods, Washinton, D.C., 13 pp.

U.S. Environmental Protection Agency. 1973. Method for Organochlorine Pesticides in Industrial Effluents. Environmental Monitoring and Support Laboratory, Cincinnati, Ohio, pages unnumbered.

U.S. Environmental Protection Agency. 1974. Analysis of Pesticide Residues in Human and Environmental Samples. Environmental Toxicology Division, Research Triangle Park, North Carolina, pages unnumbered.

U.S. Environmental Protection Agency. 1977a. Ocean Dumping–Final Revision of Regulations and Criteria. U.S. Federal Register, 11 January 1977, Part VI, 42, 2462–2490.

U.S. Environmental Protection Agency. 1977b. Proposed Revision to Ocean Dumping Criteria: Final Environmental Impact Statement. Office of Water Program Operations, Washington, D.C., 128 pp.

U.S. Environmental Protection Agency/Corps of Engineers Technical Committee on Criteria for Dredged and Fill Material. 1977. Ecological Evaluation of Proposed Discharge of Dredged Material into Ocean Waters; Implementation Manual for Section 103 of Public Law 92-532 (Marine Protection, Research, and Sanctuaries Act of 1972), (Second Printing, April 1978). Environmental Effects Laboratory, U.S. Army Engineer Waterways Experiment Station, Vicksburg, Mississippi, 244 pp. + 8 appendices.

Veith, G. D., T. C. Carver Jr., C. M. Fetterolf, G. F. Lee, D. L. Swanson, W. A. Willford, and M. G. Zeeman. 1979. Polychlorinated Biphenyls. *In*: A Review of the EPA Red Book: Quality Criteria for Water, R. V. Thurston, R. C. Russo, C. M. Fetterolf, Jr., T. A. Edsall, and Y. M. Barber, Jr. (Eds.). Water Quality Section, American Fisheries Society, Bethesda, Maryland, pp. 239–246.

Wenzloff, D. R., R. A. Greig, A. S. Merrill, and J. W. Ropes. 1979. A survey of heavy metals in the surf clam, *Spisula solidissima*, and the ocean quahog, *Arctica islandica*, of the Mid-Atlantic coast of the United States. *Fishery Bulletin*, 77, 280–285.

Zar, J. H. Biostatistical Analysis. 1974.. Prentice-Hall, Inc., Englewood Cliffs, New Jersey, 620 pp.

PART II: CASE STUDIES OF DREDGED-MATERIAL DISPOSAL IN THE OCEAN

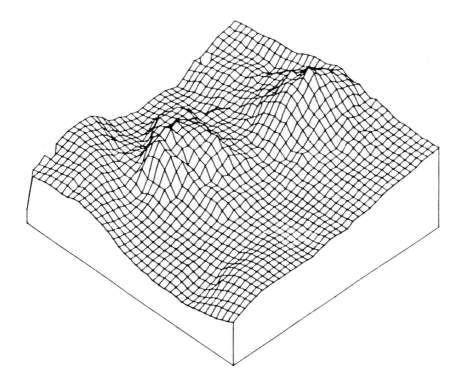

4

PEARL HARBOR
DREDGED-MATERIAL DISPOSAL

Keith E. Chave and Jacquelin N. Miller

University of Hawaii
Honolulu, Hawaii

ABSTRACT

Between 11 April and 31 May 1977, 637,000 m^3 of material dredged from the channels and turning basins of Pearl Harbor, Hawaii were dumped at a site approximately 4.6 km south of the entrance to the harbor in 410 m of water. The environmental effects of the dumping were monitored before, during, and after disposal.

The bottom at the disposal site is essentially featureless with a slope of about 1:100 to the southeast. Sediments are relatively pure carbonate sands. The water column has a 60–80-m mixed layer with a thermocline, and it ranges from 25 to 9°C. Water quality is typical of open ocean waters. Zooplankton are typical for Hawaiian waters, being dominated by copepods. The only potentially economic resource in the area is the benthic shrimp *Heterocarpus ensifer*. The dredged material itself is about 80% silt and clay, the remainder being sand, gravel, and coral rubble. The material is rich in Cu, Zn, Cr, Ni, and Pb with lesser amounts of other heavy metals.

During the dump period small amounts of fine material could be detected over a widespread area, whereas coarser materials were limited to within 2 km of the dumpsite. No buildup of dumped material on the bottom could be detected. A surface plume was observed shortly after each dump, but it dispersed rapidly, and an increase in turbidity was observed near the top of the thermocline. Zooplankton and benthic shrimp were more abundant during dumping than before.

In the period of 6 months following the material dumping the fine sediments were dispersed further. The water column was normal. Zooplankton increased in abundance (probably as a result of relocation of the nearby Honolulu sewer outfall). Shrimp abundance was slightly higher also. At no time during the study were elevated concentrations of heavy metals found in either the zooplankton or the benthic shrimp.

In summary, the dumping of 637,000 m^3 of dredged material, 4.6 km offshore, in 410 m of water had no significant environmental effects.

4.1. INTRODUCTION

Between 11 April and 31 May 1977, 637,000 m^3 of material dredged from the channels and turning basins of Pearl Harbor, Hawaii, were dumped by the hopper dredge *Harding* at a site approximately 4.6 km south of the entrance to the harbor, in 410 m of water (Fig. 4.1). Effects of this disposal on the ocean environment were monitored by a team from the University of Hawaii before, during, and after the disposal.

4.2. PREDUMPING SURVEY

Before the dumping, conditions in the water column at the dumpsite were typically oceanic. During August 1976 the mixed layer was approximately 50 m deep; below 50 m the temperature decreased linearly to 10°C at 300 m (Fig. 4.2). By October 1976 the mixed layer had deepened to about 80 m. Salinity and oxygen were nearly constant throughout the water column, averaging 34.5‰ and 5.5 ml liter^{-1}, respectively. Total nitrogen and total phosphorus were always less than 0.1 mg liter^{-1} and 0.03 mg liter^{-1}, respectively. Of the heavy metals analyzed only Cu and Zn could be detected, and these, only occasionally. The currents in the area are largely tidal with a dominant south and west flow. Mean current velocities measured over a 30-d period at 356 m (just above the bottom) ranged from 3.7 cm s^{-1} (south) to 7.9 cm s^{-1} (west).

Night oblique zooplankton tows showed that copepods dominate, with lesser numbers of chaetognaths, euphausiids, and ostracods. The zooplankton were typical of open-water populations near the Hawaiian Islands, both in composition and abundance.

The bottom in the vicinity of the dumpsite is smooth and slopes gently to the southeast, as indicated by bottom photographs and fathometer traces (Fig. 4.3). A hard substrate of unknown composition is covered by a thin veneer of predominantly calcareous sand (90% sand and gravel). Numerous attempts at coring were largely unsuccessful apparently due to the absence of fine-grained materials. The

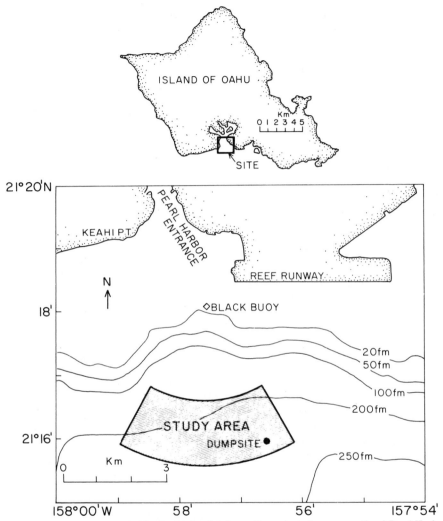

Figure 4.1. Location of the dredged-material dumpsite and study area south of Pearl Harbor, Hawaii.

bottom was studied for species and abundance of foraminifera (in sediments), occurrence of macrobenthos (in bottom photos and grabs), and abundance and size of the potentially economically valuable benthic shrimp *Heterocarpus ensifer* (by trapping).

4.3. IMMEDIATE EFFECTS OF DUMPING

Dredging in Pearl Harbor was conducted on a 24-h schedule. Each dumping deposited approximately 2000 m^3 of material. The Pearl Harbor sediments sampled from the *Harding* were approximately 80% silt and clay, physically quite different

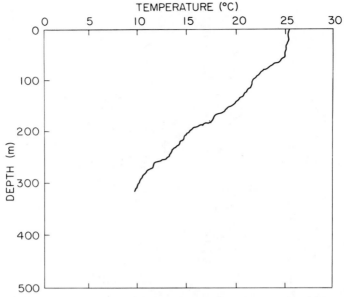

Figure 4.2. Temperature profile at the dumpsite in August 1976 showing a thermally stratified water column with a 50-m mixed layer.

from the sediments at the dumpsite. The solid content of the dredged material averaged 67%. Heavy metals in the dredged material were determined by atomic absorption spectrophotometry following nitric acid–hydrogen peroxide digestions and gave a combined average concentration of 541 mg kg^{-1} for Ag + Cd + Cr + Cu + Ni + Pb + Zn. The predominant metals were Cr, Ni, and Zn (Table 4.1). Lindane was the only pesticide occurring above the 10 ng kg^{-1} range.

During the dumping, samples taken in the water column between 14 min and 1 h

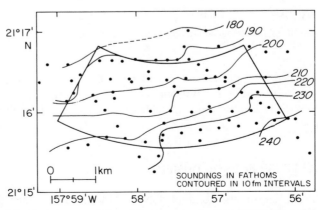

Figure 4.3. Bathymetry of the study area prior to the 1977 disposal operations.

Table 4.1. Characterization of Dredged Material from the *Harding* for Extractable Metals (mg kg^{-1} Dry Weight) and for Pesticide Residues (ng kg^{-1})

Date[a]	Extractable Metals							
	Ag	Cd	Cr	Cu	Ni	Pb	Zn	Total
3 May 1977	4	3	165	69	77	44	160	522
16 May 1977	4	4	187	66	113	51	104	529
31 May 1977	2	2	258	66	127	25	93	573
							Average	541

	Pesticide Residues				
	Dieldrin	Lindane	Chlordane	DDD	DDT[b]
3 May 1977	0.208	41.870	2.603	2.493	ND
6 May 1977	0.575	6.847	0.381	1.195	ND
9 May 1977	0.284	35.430	0.670	1.118	ND

[a] All samples dredged from Ford Island Channel, NE.
[b] ND = not detectable.

38 min after a dump, both at the dumpsite and in the plume 1 km downstream from the dumpsite, showed normal salinity, temperature, and dissolved oxygen. Suspended solids and turbidity showed maxima at the surface and at 150 m, within the thermocline. Values at other depths were near predump values after 1 h 38 min. One day after all dumping ceased, on 1 June 1977, all values were within the range of predump values. Fourteen minutes after a dump, Cu (20 ng liter^{-1}) and Zn (48 ng liter^{-1}) were measured in surface water. Their values decreased significantly within 1 h 38 min, and one day after dumping ceased, the values were back to predump values.

Zooplankton were three times more abundant during dumping than in the baseline survey. It is not known whether this increase is caused by normal seasonal variation, increased land runoff, or the seaward extension of the Honolulu sewer outfall 6–7 km south of the dumpsite which was placed into operation between the predump and dump surveys. No effects of suspended dredged material were noted microscopically on the respiration or feeding parts of species of euphausiids.

Benthic surveys with a grab sampler showed detectable but relatively insignificant Pearl Harbor materials. There was no indication of mounding, or even thickening of soft sediments. Grain sizes were, within measurement error, the same as before dumping.

Shells of organisms restricted to shallow water environments such as are found in Pearl Harbor were collected in the grab samples. Large species (> 64 mm) of molluscs and echinoderms could be found less than 1 km from the dumpsite. Small dredged-material indicators (< 2 mm) including seven species of foraminifera and pyrite framboids were more widespread, but were nowhere a significant portion of the sediments. Small fecal pellets typical of those taken in Pearl Harbor sediments were also found 2–3 km from the dumpsite.

Table 4.2.   Heavy Metals in Shrimp (*Heterocarpus ensifer*) Collected on 15 July 1977 (mg kg^{-1} Wet Weight)[a]

Location	Ag	Cd	Cr	Cu	Ni	Pb	Zn	Total
Dumpsite	ND	ND	ND	12	ND	ND	12	24
Control site	ND	ND	ND	19	ND	ND	12	31

[a]ND represents nondetectable.

Trapping of the benthic shrimp *Heterocarpus ensifer* was conducted for one night during dumping. (For this night the *Harding* dumped at an alternate site 1.5 km to the north.) Trapping lines were set at the dumpsite and at a control site 3.3 km to the southwest. Catches at the dumpsite and control site both were significantly larger in weight and body size than the predump catches. Evidently the natural variability is greater than any effects associated with dredged-material disposal.

Heavy metals in the shrimp muscle at the dumpsite and control site were limited to a few mg kg^{-1} Cu and Zn (see Table 4.2). Both of these metals are necessary for the normal metabolism of the shrimp.

4.4. LONG-TERM EFFECTS OF DUMPING

Dumping ceased on 31 May 1977. Sediment samples were taken throughout the area in September, October, and December. Water samples were taken in September. Zooplankton were sampled in June, July, September, and December. Shrimp were trapped in July, September, and December.

Most of the water-column chemistry returned to predump conditions within 24 h of the cessation of dumping.

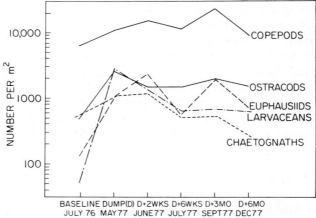

Figure 4.4. Temporal variation of five groups of zooplankton prior to, and up to six months after, the disposal of dredged material.

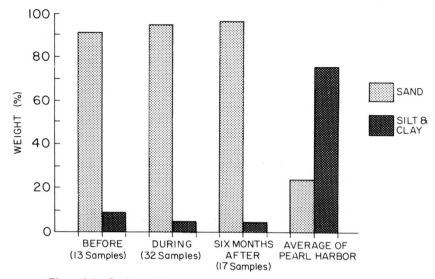

Figure 4.5. Surface sediment type in the study area and in Pearl Harbor.

Zooplankton abundance, which had increased during dumping, decreased after dumping but remained well above the abundance found in the predump survey (Fig. 4.4). We conclude that the higher standing crop relative to the predump conditions results from increased nutrient loadings from the Honolulu sewer outfall extension and clearly not from any effects of dumping of dredged material.

The average grain size of 17 sediment samples taken at the disposal site and in the surrounding area was significantly coarser than previous to dumping (Figs. 4.5 and 4.6). Although the difference may be due to minor changes in sampling locations, it is clear that dispersal of the fine-grained material by currents precluded significant accumulation within the disposal site.

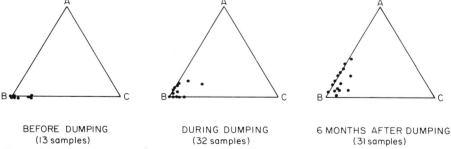

Figure 4.6. Bulk mineralogy of surface sediments in the study area before, during, and six months after the dredged material disposal. Carbonate is aragonite + calcite; other includes magnetite and halloysite. Key: A, 50% carbonate, 50% other; B, 100% carbonate; C, 50% plagioclase, 50% carbonate.

Trace foraminiferal species, pyrite framboids, and fecal pellets decreased in abundance by a factor of 10 within four months, and the area containing them decreased by approximately one-half. Except in the immediate area of the dumping, the benthic foraminifera showed a trend toward recovery to predisposal populations, based on a comparison of pre- and postdisposal species lists.

The total number of benthic shrimp trapped increased in the dumpsite area relative to predump catches, whereas catches decreased at the control site. Possible explanations for the observed population changes include seasonal fluctuations or variations in specific trap locations.

4.5. CONCLUSIONS

On the basis of extensive analysis of the physical, chemical, and biological properties of the water column and bottom, before, during, and after the dumping of 637,000 m^3 of Pearl Harbor dredged material in 410 m of water, we conclude that this dumping had no significant effect on the ocean environment. Effects of changes in the Honolulu primary treated sewage outfall 6–7 km away had more effect.

Ocean dumping in deep water (hundreds of meters) is very different from dumping in shallow water (tens of meters) in terms of dispersion of the dredged material. This difference is because of such factors as time in the water column, density stratification of the water column, and effects of currents, plus the paucity of marine life at deeper depths. Thus, governmental regulation of deepwater ocean dumping should be handled differently from that of shallow-water dumping.

ACKNOWLEDGMENTS

The University of Hawaii Pearl Harbor dredged-material disposal study team included M. H. Allen, Oceanography; A. L. Char, Oceanography/Public Health; E. H. Chave, Zoology; K. E. Chave, Oceanography/Hawaii Institute of Geophysics; E. A. Kay, Zoology; J. N. Miller, Environmental Center; R. Moberly, Geology and Geophysics; and J. F. Walters, Oceanography. This work was supported by the Department of the Navy, Pacific Division, Naval Facilities Engineering Command. This chapter is Hawaii Institute of Geophysics contribution number 1043.

5

PRECISION BATHYMETRIC STUDY OF DREDGED-MATERIAL CAPPING EXPERIMENT IN LONG ISLAND SOUND

Robert W. Morton

Science Applications, Inc.
Ocean Science and Technology Division
Newport, Rhode Island

ABSTRACT

Dredged-material disposal procedures have been employed recently at the Central Long Island Sound Disposal Site to cap heavy-metal enriched material from Stamford, Connecticut with silt and sands from inner and outer New Haven Harbor. Monitoring of the disposal operation consisted of precision bathymetric mapping, visual observations of the sediment surface and margins, chemical comparisons of the dredged material and natural sediment, and sampling of benthic populations for recolonization and bioaccumulation studies.

Prior to the dredging operation, two disposal sites for Stamford sediment were designated, one to be capped with sand, the other with silt. A survey grid for each site (25-m lane spacing) was programmed into a computerized navigation and bathymetric data acquisition system. Volume difference calculations between replicate surveys were made with errors less than $\pm$ 1000 m^3.

Profiles across both dredged-material mounds indicate that the Stamford sediment was concentrated in a low mound with rough topography and that both silt and sand provided adequate cover for the enriched material. However, the sand produced a thin (2 m) dense blanket of material that spread over a larger area, whereas silt produced a thick (4 m) cohesive cap with steeper sides and less spreading on the flanks. Contour plots and associated volume calculations accounted for more than 97% of the estimated volume of material transported to the area. The dredged material was confined to discrete mounds at the designated disposal points. This configuration was substantiated by diver observations which revealed a sharp demarcation between natural bottom and dredged material after disposal.

Postdisposal monitoring over a six-month period revealed no significant changes in the sand cap. After two months, the silt cap had settled approximately 30 cm and slumping had occurred along the steep flanks. Six months after disposal, the silt cap was substantially altered with extensive slumping of the flanks, flattening of the top of the mound, and loss of material from the disposal site. However, the silt continued to provide adequate cover (2 m) for the Stamford material. The sand cap was more successful in terms of coverage and stability. The cohesive nature of the silt material resulted in a dredged-material mound that was thicker and steeper than expected.

5.1. INTRODUCTION

The disposal of dredged material in Long Island Sound has been a controversial and sensitive issue for several years. The extreme shoaling conditions that exist in some harbors bordering the Sound emphasize the need for a solution to this controversy that will allow dredging of these harbors in a safe and cost-effective manner. Because of the large volumes to be dredged, the lack of suitable land sites, and the prohibitive costs of diking or transporting dredged material to the continental shelf, the New England Division of the U.S. Army Corps of Engineers undertook a carefully managed and monitored program of disposal at two sites within the Sound beginning in 1977. Under this program, dredged materials from the Thames River were deposited at the New London Disposal Site; sediments from Stamford and New Haven harbors were placed at the Central Long Island Sound Disposal Site (Fig. 5.1).

Because bulk sediment analyses indicated that dredged material originating from Stamford Harbor was enriched in heavy metals, management procedures were initiated to cap the Stamford material with silt and sand from New Haven Harbor. The objectives of the capping procedures were to isolate the polluted material from the benthic fauna and the overlying water column; to evaluate the relative merits of sand and silt as capping materials in terms of coverage, stability, and effectiveness in isolating contaminants; and to estimate recolonization potential.

Monitoring of the disposal operation was conducted as part of the Disposal Area Monitoring System (DAMOS) and consisted of precision bathymetric mapping of dredged-material distribution, visual observations of the disposal mound surface and

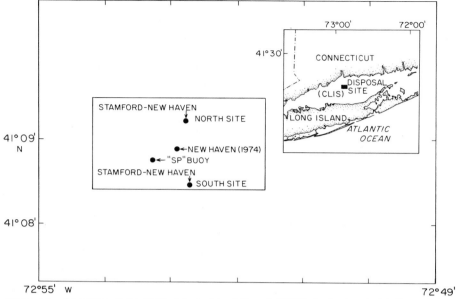

Figure 5.1. Location of the Central Long Island Sound (CLIS) dredged-material disposal site. The location of three dredged-material mounds within the CLIS are shown.

margins, chemical comparisons of dredged and natural sediment, and sampling of benthic populations for recolonization and bioaccumulation studies.

This chapter is concerned primarily with the results and implications of the bathymetric monitoring procedures. Replicate precision bathymetric surveys were performed during the disposal and capping operations to monitor the volume and distribution of exposed Stamford material at the disposal site. Following the completion of the capping operation, additional replicate surveys were made to monitor the long-term stability of the capping material.

5.2. INSTRUMENTATION AND PROCEDURES

Application of bathymetric data to monitoring small changes in topography which resulted from either accumulation or loss of dredged material, required that measurements be made with extreme precision. To achieve this precision, a computerized navigation and data acquisition system was used with carefully controlled range and depth measurement sensors.

This system consisted of a Hewlett Packard 9825A computer and 9872A plotter interfaced with a Del Norte Trisponder system, an EDO 4034A fathometer and an EDO 261C Digitrak unit (Edo Western Corp., Salt Lake City, Utah). The computer and plotter were also used to obtain report quality charts of bathymetric data within a short time after completion of a survey. Data quality was assured by a careful calibration program to provide accurate measurements of range and depth. All shore stations were surveyed to an accuracy of ±1 m, and the fathometer was calibrated with a bar check prior to each survey. Because a computer was used for data acquisition, all corrections for ship's draft, sound velocity, and tidal height were made after completion of the survey; all adjustments on the fathometer were set to zero.

Earlier measurements of tidal height at the Central Long Island Sound Disposal Site have indicated close agreement with predicted tidal heights under normal weather conditions. Because this relationship was previously established and because additional corrections were applied that reduce tidal errors in the survey data, predicted tidal correction values were used for all surveys in this study.

Prior to the disposal of dredged material at this site, a survey grid was established (Fig. 5.2) consisting of 25 transects, 600 m long oriented in the east–west direction and spaced 25 m apart. While conducting the survey, range data were input to the computer which provided steering information to assist the helmsman in maintaining the ship's position relative to the survey grid. Because precision data were required for this work, surveys were only made on calm days and the errors in steering the ship were generally less than 5 m either side of a given transect (Fig. 5.2). This navigational precision was necessary for comparing replicate surveys because slight errors in position can cause large errors in depth over sloping bottoms.

Data acquisition was controlled by the sampling rate of the Del Norte Trisponder unit which was nominally one range measurement per second. Depths were averaged over this one second interval and recorded on cassette tape with corresponding time and position information.

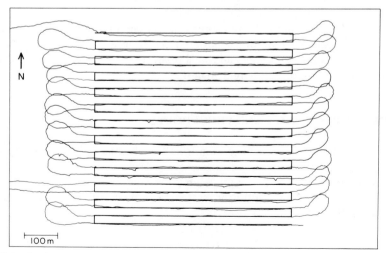

Figure 5.2. Bathymetric survey grid 600 m long with 25-m spacing (heavy lines with rectangular limits) and the computer-plotted track of the survey vessel (light lines with rounded limits at turning points of the grid). After Shonting and Morton (1982).

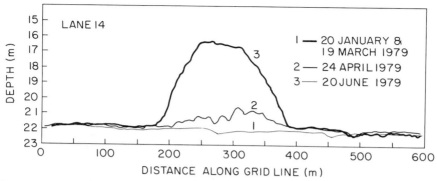

Figure 5.3. Three depth transects along one of the survey grid lines through the Stamford–New Haven South dredged-material mound before, during, and after disposal operations. Vertical exaggeration is 25 times the horizontal scale. The contaminated sediment was deposited between surveys 1 and 2, and the silt cap was added between surveys 2 and 3.

Analysis of bathymetric data was first accomplished through the generation of depth sections along the transect lanes. Since each transect was reproducible with a positional accuracy of better than 5 m, these sections provided a means of evaluating the precision of the survey technique as well as small-scale changes in topography. All depths on these sections were corrected for sound velocity, draft, and tidal height.

Figure 5.3 presents a section for a representative transect across the dredged-material mound at the Stamford–New Haven South Disposal Site. Assuming no significant change (i.e., deposition or erosion) in the depth of the ambient bottom at some distance from the dredged-material mound, the precision of the depth measurements between successive surveys can be evaluated by comparing the depths at the extremeties of the transect. In Fig. 5.3 it is apparent that there are no significant depth differences beyond the disposal mound between sequential surveys.

Following the development of the vertical sections, the data were inserted into a grid pattern for further analysis. This grid pattern was established such that each grid block was centered on a transect lane, each had a north–south length equal to the lane spacing (25 m) and an east–west length equal to one-half the lane spacing (12.5 m). This convention has applied to all surveys even though it was possible to establish a finer grid pattern by sampling more frequently along the transect direction. The finer grid pattern would, however, introduce a bias into the data because the resolution between lanes cannot be improved. All depth measurements falling within the area of each grid block were averaged and a mean depth was assigned to each grid location. This matrix of depths was then used to develop a contour chart of the entire survey area.

Calculations were performed to compute volume differences between successive surveys. The difference in depth (Δz_i) of each cell between successive surveys was determined by subtraction and was then multiplied by the area of the cell to determine the net change in volume. These volume changes were then summed along transects and over the entire grid to determine the total volume change.

The precision of the depth measurement had to be extremely high to achieve an accurate volume, because small changes in depth were multiplied by the area of the survey. In order to increase this precision, additional corrections were made based on the assumption that no significant changes in depth occur on the natural bottom beyond the extremeties of the disposal mound. This assumption was fully supported by the data presented in Fig. 5.3. To make these corrections the average depth changes (Δz_i) for all grid locations in the first and last five lanes were determined. If these Δz_i were different from zero a correction was applied to the third and twenty-third lanes to set those differences to zero. Correction factors for each transect were then determined by linear interpolation between adjacent lanes.

Small differences resulting from errors in tide, sound velocity, or draft corrections were thus accounted for and the baselines of both surveys were accurately aligned with each other. Corrections of this type, while always less than 10 cm, were important for increasing the resolution of the volume difference technique.

The errors in determining the topographic volume relative to a baseline were evaluated through a calculation of the standard error based on the standard deviation of the depth measurement. A conservative estimate of the precision in depth measurement by echo sounding which accounts for navigation, correction factors, topographic changes and so on, is ± 20 cm. Using this value for the standard deviation of all depths measured within a grid cell, the standard error for a given cell was

$$\epsilon_i = \frac{\sigma_i}{\sqrt{n_i - 1}}$$

where n_i is the number of measurements in the cell. For the entire survey, the average depth was calculated by

$$\bar{z} = \frac{1}{M} \sum_{i=1}^{M} \bar{z}_i$$

where M is the number of cells. Therefore, the standard deviation of $\bar{z}$ resulting from errors in the depth measurement can be expressed as

$$\sigma_{\bar{z}}^2 = \frac{1}{M^2} \sum_{i=1}^{M} \bar{\epsilon}_i^2$$

$$\sigma_{\bar{z}}^2 = \frac{1}{M} \bar{\epsilon}_i^2$$

$$\sigma_{\bar{z}} = \frac{\sqrt{\bar{\epsilon}_i^2}}{\sqrt{M}}$$

Since the volume difference approach was used for this computation, the calculation was actually made on the amount of water over the site and the difference could be expressed as

$$\Delta V = A\bar{z}_1 - A\bar{z}_2$$

where A is the area of the survey region and $\bar{z}_1$ and $\bar{z}_2$ are average depths at survey times 1 and 2.

Therefore, the standard error of the volume calculation for each survey is

$$\epsilon_v = A\sigma_{\bar{z}} = \frac{A\sqrt{\bar{\epsilon}_i^2}}{\sqrt{M}}$$

Assuming that the standard deviations of all cells were approximately equal, this equation reduced to

$$\epsilon_v = \frac{A\sigma_i}{\sqrt{M(n-1)}}$$

For each New Haven survey

$$A = 600 \times 600 = 3.6 \times 10^5 \text{ m}^2$$
$$M = 48 \times 25 = 1200$$
$$\sigma_i = 0.2 \text{ m}$$

therefore,

$$\epsilon_v = 1200 \text{ m}^3$$

Since two surveys were required to accomplish a volume difference calculation, the total error could be as much as 2400 m^3.

Because a depth difference Δz_i between successive surveys was determined for each grid cell, a contour program was applied to the difference data and a contour difference plot was generated. This chart provided information on the distribution of changes in depth resulting from the accumulation or loss of material. A contour interval of 0.25 m was used on these charts with consistent results due to the correction procedures described.

These techniques were applied to the monitoring of disposal operations at the Central Long Island Sound Site from January to June 1979, and to postdisposal conditions through November 1979. The data obtained during this study represent a significant improvement over previous disposal monitoring efforts for several reasons, including (1) use of precision navigation control to maintain 25-m lane spacing, (2) the nearly flat bottom available to provide a baseline datum, (3) the application of computer software to complete data sets to provide better calibration between surveys, and (4) the careful management of the disposal operation in order to create a discrete disposal mound that could be evaluated for small topographic changes. This study provided a unique opportunity to accurately measure dredged-material volumes and to evaluate the importance of such parameters as compaction, stability, and capping.

5.3. MANAGEMENT OF DISPOSAL OPERATIONS

There were two major objectives to be achieved through disposal of dredged material at the Central Long Island Site. These were: (1) containment and isolation of Stamford dredged material by capping with New Haven sediment; and (2) a general evaluation of the viability of the procedure with particular emphasis on the effectiveness of sand versus silt as a capping material. In order to compare the sand and silt caps two disposal points were designated. They were located north and south of the mound created by the New Haven project in 1974 (Fig. 5.1). The south site was designated for capping with silt from the inner harbor and the north site was designated for capping with sand from the outer breakwater area of New Haven Harbor. The north–south orientation was selected because tidal flow through the site is in an east–west direction, thus potential effects resulting from the older mound would be minimized.

Precision disposal of Stamford material was essential in order to create discrete mounds prior to capping. To accomplish this, two taut-wire moored buoys were installed at the designated disposal points using the trisponder system for navigation control. Towboat operators were then instructed to dispose of material near the south side of each buoy. Even under adverse conditions disposal generally took place within 25 m of the designated point.

Initial disposal of Stamford material took place between 25 March and 22 April 1979 at the southern disposal point. After 23 April, silt from New Haven was dumped at the south site to provide capping material. This continued until 15 June when dredging was halted to avoid impact to oyster larvae by siltation generated from the dredging operation. Disposal of Stamford material was restricted to the north site from 23 April until 15 June when dredging of Stamford Harbor and associated disposal at the north site was halted. Between 15 June and 21 June the hopper dredge *Essayons* removed sandy sediment from the mouth of the New Haven harbor and used this material to cap the north site.

5.4. BATHYMETRIC MONITORING PROCEDURES

A survey grid similar to that shown in Fig. 5.2 was established at both the north and south disposal sites with the disposal buoy centered in the 600 m² area. Prior to disposal, background surveys were run on these tracks. Two baseline surveys were made at the south site on 20 January and 19 March 1979, and a single survey was made at the north site on 22 March. An estimate of the precision of the volume calculation technique was made by comparing the difference between the two southern surveys. This volume difference was approximately 2700 m³ which is only marginally greater than the error expected from the analysis presented in Section 5.2. Furthermore, the contour difference chart generated from the two surveys indicated that the errors were small and randomly distributed because all contours were either ± 0.2 m or zero and showed no consistent pattern over the survey area.

Disposal of dredged material from Stamford Harbor at the southern site reached a total of 37,800 m³ (based on scow load records) on 22 April 1979. A survey of the site was conducted on 24 April to determine the distribution of dredged material prior to capping (Fig. 5.4). This survey indicated that the disposal procedure was successful in developing a small, discrete mound approximately 100 m in diameter and 1.2 m thick.

Close examination of the vertical depth sections for lanes 13–16 (Fig. 5.5) indicates that the topography of this mound was quite variable, and thicknesses of 2 m relative to the initial bottom are present. The contouring procedure smooths and decreases the topographic signature of the mound. Although overall volumes are

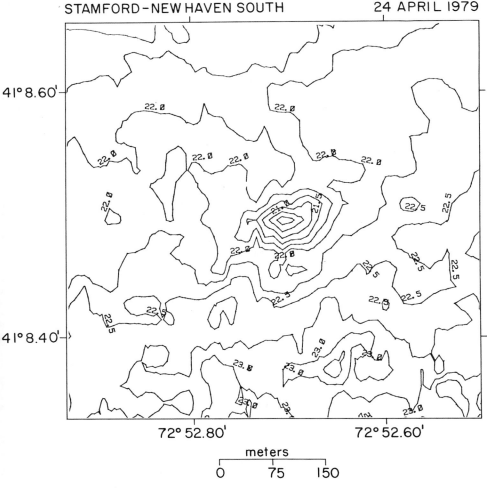

Figure 5.4. High precision bathymetric survey of the contaminated dredged-material mound (in meters) at the Stamford–New Haven South Site prior to capping with silt.

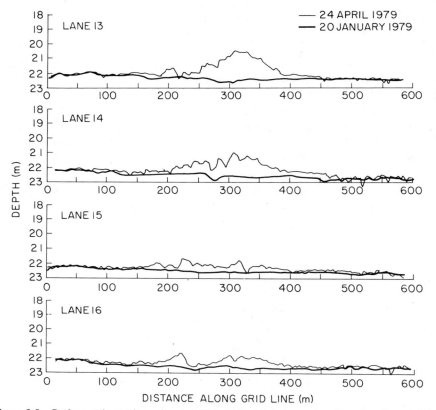

Figure 5.5. Bathymetric sections showing the small-scale topography along four lanes of the survey grid passing across the Stamford–New Haven South dredged-material mound. The interval between lanes is 25 m and the vertical exaggeration is 25 times the horizontal scale.

accurate due to averaging of all depths measured, specific features smaller than the grid size cannot be resolved. These features can, however, be seen in the vertical sections, but only within the accuracy of navigation between successive surveys. The rough topography exhibited in the vertical sections was substantiated by diving observations and attributed to the cohesive nature of the dredged material. Toward the margins of the mound, specific scow loads could be identified as separate topographic features.

Calculations of total Stamford sediment detected relative to the January baseline survey resulted in a volume of 34,300 m^3 or approximately 90% of the estimated volume deposited. The contour difference chart (Fig. 5.6) indicated that there was additional material present beyond the immediate mound, and that it was possible for significant amounts of dredged material to be undetected by acoustic measurements.

This problem was addressed through a combination of visual diver observations and precision (50-m spacing) remote sampling of the fringes of the mound with a

CONTOUR DIFFERENCE
STAMFORD-NEW HAVEN SOUTH   24 APRIL - JANUARY 1979

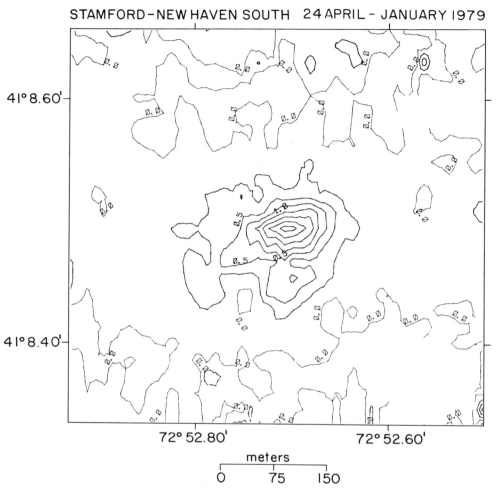

Figure 5.6. Contour difference chart (in meters) at the Stamford–New Haven South Site. The 0.25-m contour interval shows the difference in bottom depth after disposal of the contaminated Stamford dredged material.

Smith–McIntyre grab. During the period of disposal, an extensive population of the stalked hydroid *Corymorpha* was growing over the entire bottom. Wherever dredge material was present, these hydroids were covered or destroyed. Consequently, the boundary of the Stamford sediment could be readily defined by the presence or absence of these animals. Furthermore, the dark, organic dredged material provided a sharp contrast to the natural, brown, oxidized muds of the disposal site so that the thickness of the margins of the mound could be directly measured in the grab sampler.

The most striking result of these measurements was the rapid decrease in dredged material thickness at the margins of the mound. In the east and west directions the change from thickness greater than 50 cm to less than 5 cm occurred between 100 and 150 m from the disposal point. In the north–south direction, the change occurred between 50 and 100 m. It was apparent that the cohesive nature of the dredged material was creating a definite mound with discernable boundaries that could be acoustically detected with spatial accuracy certainly better than 50 m.

Volume calculations along the periphery of the mound were made by assuming that beyond the immediate disposal point the material flowed uniformly outward and was, therefore, of uniform thickness at a given radius from the center of the mound. This assumption was supported by the observation that the coarseness of the particles in the fringe areas decrease inversely with distance from the disposal point. The evidence indicated that when cohesive sediments are dredged and dumped in shallow water on a flat bottom, approximately 80% of the sediment is transferred to the bottom as a cohesive unit and forms a mound, while most of the remaining material forms a turbidite type deposit spreading radially from the disposal point.

The volume of dredged material in the fringe area was estimated by contouring the measured thickness in the grab sample and measuring the major and minor axes of the resulting ellipse. The area of each ellipse was multiplied by the difference thickness and summed to calculate the total volume. This volume measured 1980 m^3 or approximately 5% of the estimated dredged-material volume.

Since the bathymetric and sampling procedures accounted for more than 95% of the estimated material dumped at the site and because the error of estimating volume in the scows must be relatively large, it was concluded that the bathymetric survey technique was adequate for monitoring disposal operations. Furthermore, these data indicated that the initial disposal of Stamford material was tightly controlled by the taut-wire buoy, and subsequent capping with New Haven material should be successful. Disposal of additional Stamford material at the north site was also accomplished successfully and a monitoring survey conducted on 21 May (Fig. 5.7) indicated the development of a small mound similar to that observed at the south site. About 26,000 m^3 of Stamford material were deposited at this location prior to capping.

Silt from New Haven Harbor was dumped on the Stamford material at the south site, and sand from the breakwater area was used to cap the northern site. Capping was completed on 15 June at the south site and on 22 June at the north site. On 20 June a survey was made of the southern site to determine the success of the silt capping operation. The contour chart and the depth sections indicated that a distinct mound had developed with a minimum water depth of 16 m and a thickness of up to 4 m over the Stamford dredged material (Fig. 5.8). Because the silt material from New Haven was cohesive, the resulting mound did not display extensive spreading. Although the sections indicated that all Stamford material was capped, future operations with silt should be designed to spread the capping sediment and reduce the thickness to some extent. The volume of New Haven sediment dumped as capping material at the south site was estimated at 76,000 m^3

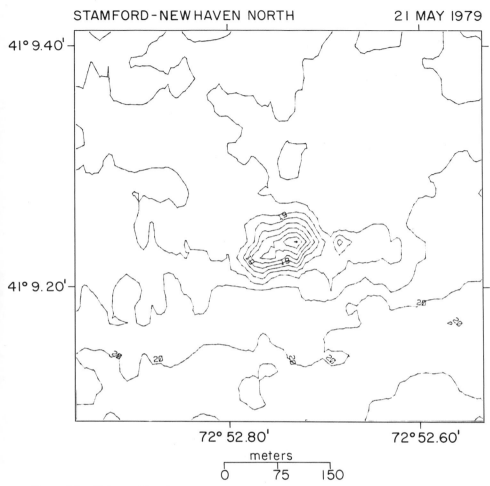

Figure 5.7. High precision bathymetric survey of the contaminated dredged-material mound (in meters) at the Stamford–New Haven North Site prior to capping with sand.

from scow load measurements, of which 72,000 m³, or 95%, was accounted for by the volume calculations.

Capping of Stamford material at the northern disposal site was accomplished in 6 days using the hopper dredge *Essayons* to create a sand layer. Management of this operation was aided by a bathymetry survey on 19 June to determine any areas that were not covered by sand, and the dredge was directed to dump additional material east of the disposal buoy to insure complete coverage. A final survey was conducted on 22 June after completion of the capping operation (Fig. 5.8). This survey and the associated sections indicated that all Stamford sediments were capped by the sand material. However, since the sand was less cohesive, it tended

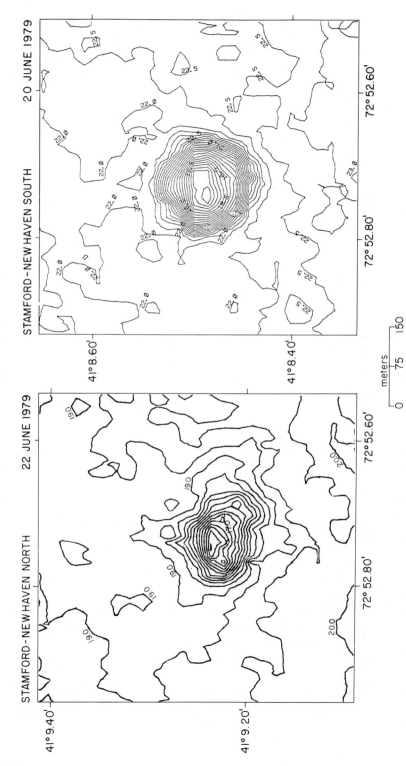

Figure 5.8. High precision bathymetric surveys at the Stamford–New Haven North and South Disposal sites shortly after dumping of the cap material. (Contour interval = 0.25 m.)

to flow during deposition thus creating a broader, flatter mound than that developed by silt at the southern site.

At the time of the 22 June survey the capping layer had a maximum thickness of 3.5 m over the Stamford material. This cap was a smooth blanket of sand that divers were unable to penetrate more than 10–15 cm by digging with their hands. A calculation of the volume of sediments deposited since the 21 May survey indicated an increase of 33,000 m³. This volume compared favorably with dredge volumes specified by the *Essayons*. However, large correction factors based on density and water content of the sand make comparisons tenuous, and calculations of volume and percentage lost to the water column were meaningless.

The results of these surveys indicate that the capping procedures employed during the Stamford and New Haven disposal operations were successful. The precision disposal of Stamford sediment resulted in two small compact mounds that were readily covered with New Haven material. There was little apparent difference in the ability of sand or silt to accomplish the desired capping. In the case of sand, the capping layer was not as thick, but the smooth, dense nature of the deposit should act as a barrier over the contaminated dredged material. Silt deposits, on the other hand, derive their capping ability from the cohesive nature of the sediment, developing a thicker deposit with rougher microtopography. Several recommendations for future capping operations can be made based on the data obtained from this study:

1. The dredged material to be capped must be cohesive. This would normally be the case since higher concentrations of contaminants are generally found in fine-grained cohesive sediments. However, dredging procedures must be conducted in a manner to preserve this cohesiveness in order to achieve a confined mound.

2. Point dumping of the material to be covered should be done as accurately as possible, preferably with a taut-wire moored buoy as a disposal marker.

3. Disposal of the capping material should be accomplished as soon as possible, also using the buoy as a marker.

4. After disposal of approximately two-thirds of the capping material at the disposal point, the remainder should be dumped in a circle with a radius equal to that of the initial dredged-material mound to insure capping of the flanks.

5. Monitoring of the capping operation with bathymetric techniques should be done during disposal to allow modifications in disposal operations to insure coverage.

5.5. POSTDISPOSAL MONITORING

Although the operational techniques for capping Stamford sediment with silt and sand from New Haven Harbor were successful, the effectiveness of the procedure depends on the stability of the resulting cap and its success in isolating the contaminated material from the biota and the water column. Therefore, following deposition of the capping material the monitoring effort evaluated the stability of the resulting mounds with time. This was a multidisciplinary effort involving physical, chemical, and biological measurements. However, the emphasis in this chapter is placed on the results of the bathymetric monitoring and their implications for understanding physical processes acting on the disposal mounds.

Evaluation of long-term changes in the shape and volume of the dredged-material mounds required an initial baseline for comparison similar to that used in the operational monitoring phase of the project. For postdisposal studies the 20 June survey of the southern site and the 22 June survey of the northern site were used (Fig. 5.8).

On 7 August 1979, a bathymetric survey of the north disposal site was conducted that indicated there were no significant changes in the topography of the mound. Examination of the depth sections supports this conclusion (Fig. 5.9). In all cases except lane 13, the small-scale topographic features were unchanged although the mound had settled or compressed slightly, increasing the water depth by approximately 20 cm. Calculation of volume differences between the 22 June and

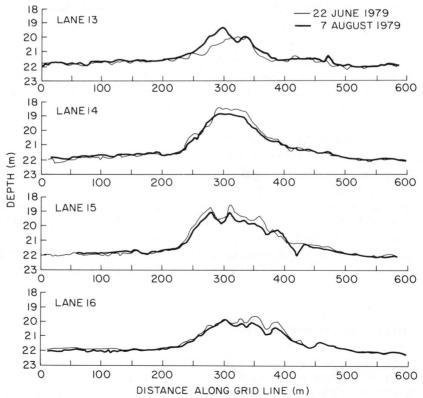

Figure 5.9. Comparison of bathymetric sections within two months after deposition of the Stamford–New Haven North capped dredged-material mound.

7 August surveys indicated that only lane 13 had an increase in volume while the other lanes over the mound showed a slight decrease. Total loss for the entire survey area was approximately 1700 m^3 which was less than the 2400 m^3 resolution of the survey procedure.

No explanation is readily available for the increase in volume for lane 13. Examination of the survey track shows no deviation from the specified lane at this location eliminating the possibility of navigation error. However, the location of the increase in material is immediately west of the disposal buoy and it is possible that a permit contractor who should have been dumping west of the "SP" buoy could have mistakenly dumped at the north disposal buoy.

A survey of the southern site was also run on 7 August 1979 which, similarly, indicated no major differences in topography of the disposal mound. Calculation of the volume difference indicated the total volume change for the entire survey was a decrease of 900 m^3 which is well within the precision of the analysis. There was some indication of slumping on the north margin of the mound where a broad decrease in depth from 20 through 40 cm occurred.

In summary, the results of the August surveys indicated no significant changes in the disposal mounds or the capping material. Slight settling or consolidation of both mounds did occur resulting in a 20–40-cm increase in depth on the tops of the piles. The persistence of these mounds was expected because the mound from the 1974 dredging operation has been stable for several years.

Following the August surveys an additional 6000 m^3 of material from Stamford Harbor was deposited at the southern site and a survey was conducted on 7 November 1979 to evaluate changes resulting from the addition of these sediments (Fig. 5.10). The results of this survey showed a major change in the topography of the mound consisting of the loss of approximately 10,000 m^3 of material from the top of the mound. Depth sections across the center of the mound revealed a flat surface at 19 m indicating that approximately 2 m of sediment had been removed (Fig. 5.11). Some of that material was present, particularly on the northeast margin of the mound, where slumping had occurred. However, the build-up of material in that area cannot account for all the missing sediment. This loss did not expose the initially deposited contaminated Stamford material.

The flat topography of the sediment surface at a constant depth suggested that wave action was most likely responsible for the movement of material. The passage of Hurricane David through the area on 6 September provided a possible energy source to create the wave motion required. Consequently, additional work was conducted to survey the other disposal sites and to determine the potential stress exerted on the mounds as a result of the hurricane. Surveys were made of the north disposal site and the 1974 New Haven mound on 15 November 1979. Both of these surveys were conducted using the same precision techniques, replicating previous 25-m lanes. Both surveys indicated that no significant changes had occurred in either mound during the period in which the southern site was affected.

It is important to note that both the Stamford–New Haven North and the 1974 New Haven deposit have minimum water depths that are less than the southern site, and thus should have been more susceptible to wave motion. Because these three mounds are all within 1.6 km of each other, on comparatively flat bottom, it is

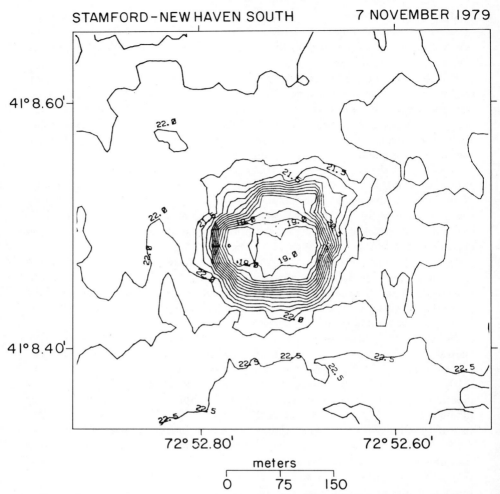

Figure 5.10. Bathymetric survey at the Stamford–New Haven South capped dredged-material dumpsite on 7 November 1979. Comparison with Fig. 5.8 reveals partial removal of cap. (Contour interval = 0.25 m.) After Shonting and Morton (1982).

highly unlikely that one site would experience markedly different environmental stress exerted by currents or wave action than would be expected at the other sites. Therefore, an explanation for the loss of material from the southern mound must account for the lack of movement at shallower depths. Differences in the physical and lithological properties of the sediments composing the mounds are likely to be important.

The Stamford–New Haven North and the 1974 New Haven mounds are characterized by a surface of fine sand material which is probably thicker on the newer mound. This lithology is in sharp contrast to the cohesive silt surface of the southern mound which is characterized by clumps of cohesive clay interspersed within a

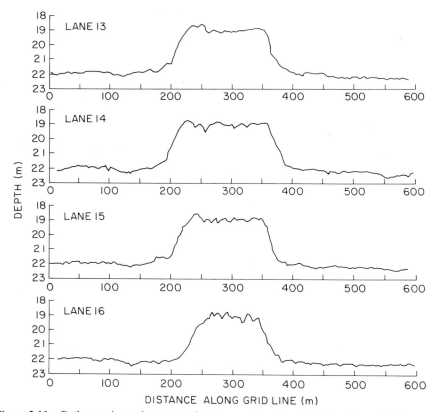

Figure 5.11. Bathymetric sections across four lanes of the Stamford–New Haven South capped dredged mound on 7 November 1979. Compare with Fig. 5.3 which shows lane 14 at earlier times.

fine, silty matrix. Furthermore, the slopes of the sand-covered mounds are more gentle than those of the southern site, although all three sites exhibit angles less than 5° and should be within a stable angle of repose for the sediment.

There are several reasons to suggest that normal tidal currents are not responsible for the movement of disposed material in this case. First, there has never been any previous indication of significant movement in this area, either on earlier disposal mounds or during this disposal operation. Second, although the motion of the tidal currents is in an east–west direction, the only observed shift of material is in a north and south direction. Finally, a subsequent survey of the disposal site conducted on 19 December 1979 indicated that no further changes in the topography had occurred.

Because tidal currents are not likely to initiate sediment motion, the most logical explanation would be the stress exerted on the mound by wave action or a combination of waves and currents. Because Long Island Sound is a relatively protected area, the generation of long-period waves that are capable of affecting sediment at depths greater than 18 m must be a rare occurrence. However, the passage of Hurricane David may have been such an event and may have provided sufficient stress to initiate sediment motion.

To examine this possibility, calculations were made of theoretical shear stress developed by hurricane waves over the rough surface of the south site and were compared with stress developed over a smooth surface. These theoretical stresses were then compared with estimates of critical shear stress to determine the potential for sediment motion. For unconsolidated fine sand similar to that present on the north mound and the 1974 New Haven mound, the critical threshold could be exceeded in water depths of 14 and 16 m by waves with a 5-s period and height greater than 1.5 m. The wave height in 18-m depth (southern site) must, however, exceed 2 m with a period of 5 s to meet the nominal threshold condition. To estimate stress due to wave motion, it was necessary to hindcast waves based on wind data and fetch distance. The wave hindcast data generated for Hurricane David indicated that development of such long-period waves would be unlikely. However, because failure of the top of the 18-m southern mound was observed, estimates of the developed shear stress were made and compared.

The dredged-material mounds differ in depth of water, composition, shape, and surface roughness. The southern mound is composed of clumps of consolidated clay material surrounded by a fine, silty clay matrix. These clumps protrude into the near-bottom flow and will, therefore, develop shear stress due to form drag as well as skin friction. The size of these elements, estimated from bottom photographs and relatively undisturbed grab samples, is approximately 20 cm. The other mounds were covered with fine-to-medium sand and have a roughness, estimated from the grain size analysis, of about 0.025 cm.

The Shields Criterion (ψ), which expresses the threshold of sediment motion as a function of sediment properties, was calculated for a grain diameter of $D = 0.025$ cm for waves of 4-s period. Shear stresses were then calculated as a function of wave height for both bottom roughness factors (Table 5.1).

The calculated shear stress values for large roughness height are near or exceed the critical value of 0.045 for all tested wave heights. In contrast, the shear stress developed over the surface of smaller roughness never exceed the critical value. Consequently, we can conclude that the high roughness factor resulting from the clumps of cohesive sediment on the south site created a greater stress and caused sediment motion under storm wave conditions, while the smoother surfaces of the other mounds produced significantly smaller stress values, thus insuring the stability of the dredged material even at shallower depths.

Though the calculations show that this difference could have been the cause of the preferential erosion of the southern mound, some factors affecting the accuracy of the results must also be considered. The calculation of shear stress due to waves over the relatively smooth surfaces may be done with some confidence since the relative roughness values are within the range of experimental observation. However, the determination of the stress over a surface with relatively large roughness must be considered only an estimate. Without field observations under these conditions, it is unknown how the stress is partitioned between skin friction, which may cause erosive failure of the block, and form drag, which may physically move the

Table 5.1. Stress Parameters at 18-m Depths with a Wave Period of 4.5 s and Roughness Elements of 0.025 and 20 cm[a]

H (m)	d_o (cm)	U_m (cm s^{-1})	$\dfrac{U_m d_o/2}{\nu}$	$\dfrac{d_o/2}{k_1}$	f_1	$\dfrac{d_o/2}{k_2}$	f_2	t_1	t_2	ψ_1	ψ_2
1.0	5.54	3.87	1.07×10^3	111	0.06	0.14	0.5	0.46	3.85	0.011	0.09
1.5	8.31	5.80	2.41×10^3	166	0.04	0.21	0.5	0.69	8.64	0.017	0.20
2.0	11.08	7.74	4.29×10^3	222	0.035	0.28	0.49	1.078	15.07	0.026	0.36
2.5	13.85	9.67	6.70×10^3	277	0.024	0.35	0.49	1.152	23.53	0.028	0.56
3.0	16.62	11.60	9.64×10^3	332	0.020	0.42	0.49	1.382	33.86	0.033	0.81
3.5	19.39	13.54	1.31×10^4	388	0.016	0.48	0.49	1.506	46.13	0.044	1.11

[a] $h = 1800$ cm; $L_o = 3158$; $h/L = 0.5709$; $T = 4.5$; $h/L_o = 0.57$; $k_1 = 0.025$ cm; $k_2 = 20$ cm.

block or cause eddies that entrain interstitial material. Furthermore, actual Shields Criteria for consolidated sediments can only be estimated to be substantially greater than unconsolidated sediments.

Further investigation should be pursued in order to determine:

1. The mode of failure of the cohesive material under conditions of high shear stress.
2. The degree of consolidation and cohesion of the bottom sediments (dredge pile, sand cover, block) and the effect of these parameters on erodability of dredged material.
3. The partitioning of shear stress over beds of large roughness under waves and currents.

5.6. SUMMARY

The precision bathymetric survey procedures employed to monitor the Stamford–New Haven disposal operation have been successful in managing the capping operation and in monitoring changes that have occurred after disposal. With proper control of the disposal operation, these procedures can readily be applied at other locations.

The effectiveness of capping contaminated dredged material with cleaner sediments has not yet been completely determined because the loss of silty clay material from the Stamford–New Haven South Site amounted to 10,000 m^3 or approximately 12% of the total capping material. However, since all of this material was lost from the upper surface of the mound no exposure of Stamford sediment occurred.

Observations of the sand-capped mounds in the Central Long Island Sound Site have indicated successful capping because they have shown no measureable changes in volume or distribution, even though these deposits have more shallow minimum water depths than the southern site. An explanation for the selective movement of sediment on the southern site has been proposed based on the interaction of storm waves resulting from Hurricane David and the roughness parameters of the cohesive New Haven material.

The implications of these conclusions are important to future disposal and/or capping operations. Consolidated, cohesive sediments are common in the New England area, and clamshell dredges which preserve the cohesive nature of the material must be used to reduce suspended load and spreading of material at both the dredging and disposal sites. Consequently, while these properties aid in reducing the area of coverage, most mounds will have surface roughness comparable to the southern site after disposal. These features have been observed at the New London Site, but the cohesive clumps have broken down over a period of time primarily due to biological activity, but also as a result of fracturing and erosion.

From the results of this study, it is apparent that the stress created by the roughness factor associated with these clumps under storm wave conditions is more important than the depth of the mound surface, the strength of currents, or the cohesive nature of the sediment in determining the stability of disposal material. The occurrence of a major storm such as Hurricane David before the surface of the mound has been smoothed by other natural forces thus creates a potential for large-scale erosion and transport of material.

Future disposal operations might, therefore, consider methods to produce a smooth surface at the conclusion of the dumping procedure. Such methods could include:

1. Capping with sand material, as was done at the north Stamford–New Haven sites.
2. Dredging and disposal of less cohesive sediments near the end of the operation.
3. Disposal of cleaner material from the mouth of the estuary after artificially increasing the water content of these sediments to break down cohesion.
4. Artificially smoothing the surface through dragging.

Additional work is needed to determine if these procedures are in fact necessary and to more accurately evaluate and predict the reoccurrence of the effects observed at the Stamford–New Haven South Site. The problem of stability is being addressed to some extent under the DAMOS program through a combination of bottom turbulence and erosion studies. However, the phenomena observed at the Central Long Island South Site emphasize the importance of monitoring disposal areas and of understanding the interaction of the energy regime with dredged material.

REFERENCES

Shonting, D. and R. W. Morton. 1982. The New England Disposal Area Monitoring System and the Stamford–New Haven Capping Experiment. *In*: Impact of Marine Pollution on Society, V. K. Tippie and D. R. Kester (Eds.). Bergin Publishers, South Hadley, Massachusetts, pp. 137–172.

6

A GEOCHEMICAL STUDY OF THE DREDGED-MATERIAL DEPOSIT IN THE NEW YORK BIGHT

R. Dayal, M. G. Heaton, M. Fuhrmann, and I. W. Duedall

Marine Sciences Research Center
State University of New York
Stony Brook, New York

Dr. Dayal's and Mr. Fuhrmann's present address: Department of Nuclear Energy, Brookhaven National Laboratory, Upton, New York.
Mr. Heaton's present address: Interstate Electronics Corporation, Anaheim, California.
Dr. Duedall's present address: Department of Oceanography and Ocean Engineering, Florida Institute of Technology, Melbourne, Florida.

ABSTRACT

The sediments of the New York Bight dredged-material deposit are composed of a wide variety of sediment types which can be classified as quartzose and glauconitic sands, muds, sandy muds, gravel intermixed with muds, and artifact material such as coal and fly ash, wood, slag, metal flakes, glass, and so on. Black, sandy mud is characteristic of dumped dredged material whereas glauconitic and gravelly quartzose sands are typical of the natural sediment underlying the deposit and in surrounding areas.

Geochemical investigations of the deposit reveal that heavy metals such as Pb, Cu, Ag, Hg, Cd, Fe, and Mn in dredged-material sediments are highly variable and considerably elevated over concentrations observed in sediment outside the deposit and in underlying natural sediment. Compared to metal enrichments reported for other coastal deposits, the enrichments observed in dredged-material sediments are significantly greater. The calculated rates and magnitudes of inputs of metals and organic matter to the New York Bight, via dredged-material dumping, are two to three orders of magnitude higher for Cd and Ag and more than an order of magnitude higher for Pb and Cu than those reported for other naturally deposited coastal sediments. Even Fe and Mn have significant anthropogenic inputs at the dumpsite. Organic matter and, to a lesser extent, iron and manganese phases appear to control the distribution of Cu, Pb, Mn, Hg, Cd, and Ag in dredged-material sediments.

6.1. INTRODUCTION

The most prominent sedimentological feature of the New York Bight is the dredged-material deposit, centered in the Bight apex approximately 8 km east of the New Jersey coast. This unique topographic feature is a cumulative effect of continual disposal of dredged material in the Bight apex since at least the year 1900. The deposit has a peak elevation of 14 m and covers an area of 36 km^2 (Freeland and Merrill, 1977). On an annual basis, the dumpsite receives approximately 4.5×10^6 m^3 of material dredged principally from the New York Harbor. This amount is three times greater than the annual sediment load carried by the Hudson River to the harbor area (Panuzio, 1965; Meade, 1972). The total mass of material contained in the deposit corresponds to approximately 250 times the annual sediment discharge of the Hudson River (Panuzio, 1965). When compared to the total annual load of suspended sediment delivered by rivers to the entire east coast of the United States (Meade, 1972), the dredged-material deposit has a mass that is 10 times greater.

To evaluate the magnitude of dredged-material dumping, in terms of sediment and metal inputs, it is essential to compare the dredged-material input with natural sediment accumulation in a coastal area. The deposition of dredged material essentially represents an accelerated sedimentation process, similar to episodic sedimentation that is periodically interrupted by accumulation of natural sediment. The deposition of dredged material is highly localized in time and space whereas episodic deposition, which occurs under flood conditions, involves accumulation of homogeneously dispersed material over a large area in a relatively longer period of time.

The sediments discharged at the mud dumpsite have been dredged primarily from the Hudson River, particularly from around the dockage areas and from the channels of the inner harbor, with smaller volumes taken from the Newark Bay and Raritan River areas (Fig. 6.1). Much of the sediment in the harbor areas has been contaminated with heavy metals and hydrocarbons, frequently as a result of raw sewage disposal and wastewater discharges into these waters (Gross, 1976; Mueller et al., 1976). Therefore, associated with dredged-material dumping there is an input of heavy metals and organic substances into the New York Bight.

The disposal of dredged material in the New York Bight represents perhaps the largest and most concentrated anthropogenic input of heavy metals to a coastal environment. The resultant dredged-material deposit represents a sedimentary record of the dumping activities for the last 100 years.

The primary objectives of our investigation were: (1) to identify the metal contaminants and their spatial distributions in the dredged-material deposit; (2) to describe the major sediment types and develop an overall stratigraphy of the deposit, defining the natural sediment basement; (3) to estimate rates and magnitudes of metal inputs to the Bight via dredged-material dumping; and (4) to compare the record of accumulation of metals at the dumpsite with those recorded in coastal deposits from other regions. In addition, sedimentological and interstitial water chemistry investigations were conducted as part of this investigation. Further details regarding the data obtained from these investigations have been given by Fuhrmann (1980) and Dayal et al. (1981).

6.2. EXPERIMENTAL

6.2.1. Field Sampling

Ten vibracores, varying in length from 3.0 to 8.4 m, were collected at the study site at stations located on the northwest and southeast transects intersecting at the apex of the dredged-material dumpsite (Fig. 6.1). Information on the vibracores collected in the study area is summarized in Table 6.1. Coring was performed during three days, 30 May to 1 June 1978 aboard the *R V Atlantic Twin*. Each station was fixed by navigation with a Motorola Mini-Ranger®.

The vibracorer consists of a steel pipe with plastic liner (9 cm i.d.) which is essentially hammered into the sediment by a pile driver located on top of the core assembly. The corer is supported on the sediment surface by a pyramid-shaped

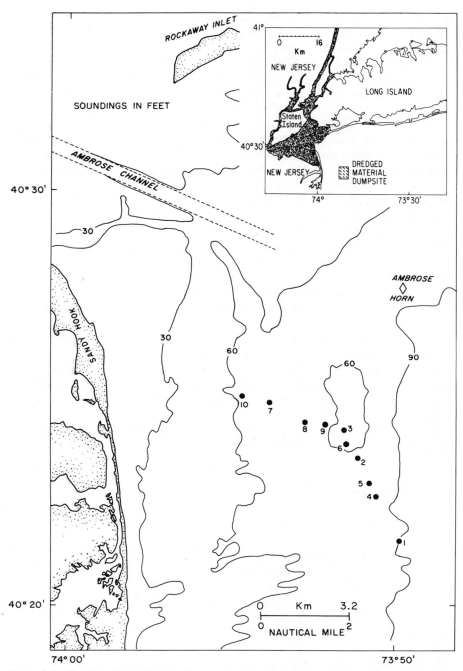

Figure 6.1. The New York Bight study area showing the location of vibracoring stations. The inset shows location of the dredged-material dumpsite relative to the dredging sites (shaded area; 30 feet = 9.2 m).

metal framework. The core barrel slid along an I-beam passing through the center of the pyramid. Affixed to the top of the barrel was the pneumatically powered vibratory head. The cored material was retained in a 9-cm plastic core liner. It is likely that some disturbance of the sediment occurred during the coring operation.

After the corer was brought on board and the liner was withdrawn from the barrel the two ends were immediately capped. The liner and cored material were cut into 1-m sections, capped, labeled, and stored in a vertical position. Upon completion of the cruise the meter lengths were returned to the laboratory and refrigerated prior to further subsectioning.

6.2.2. Methodology

In the laboratory, the cores were bisected longitudinally with a circular saw which had been adjusted to allow the tungsten carbide blade to cut only the plastic core liner. The sediment itself was separated into the two longitudinal sections with a plastic spatula. The two halves provided identical samples for detailed geochemical and sedimentological analyses. The split cores were immediately photographed and color-coded and the general sediment types were described. Sedimentological analyses of the cores are reported by Fuhrmann (1980).

6.2.2a. Sample Preparation

Sediment samples for geochemical analyses were carefully removed with a plastic spatula from the center of the split core to avoid potentially contaminated material which may have come in contact with the saw blade. These samples were generally

Table 6.1. Schedule and Location of Vibracores Collected at the Dredged-Material Dumpsite, New York Bight[a]

Station No.	Date Collected	Water Depth (m)	Length of Core (m)	Latitude[b]	Longitude[b]
1	31 May 1978	28.0	5.7	40°21.50'N	73°50.30'W
2	31 May 1978	17.4	6.6	23.50'	51.45'
3	30 May 1978	16.8	7.9	24.25'	51.80'
4	31 May 1978	26.5	7.6	22.58'	50.95'
5	31 May 1978	22.3	5.4	22.98'	51.13'
6	30 May 1978	15.9	8.4	23.95'	51.75'
7	1 June 1978	23.8	3.0	24.97'	54.00'
8	1 June 1978	24.1	4.6	24.47'	52.97'
9	1 June 1978	21.0	6.1	24.40'	52.39'
10	1 June 1978	20.7	3.2	25.18'	54.83'

[a]The cores were collected from the *RV Atlantic Twin* operated by Ocean Seismic Survey, New Jersey.
[b]Provided by Motorola Mini-Ranger® (Motorola Inc., Tempe, Arizona) with Loran-C backup.

taken at 30-cm intervals. Dried sediment samples were sieved through 2-mm Nitex[®] screen to remove the > 2-mm gravel fraction. The gravel-free fraction was ground to an approximately uniform grain size in an alumina–ceramic container. The ground sample was carefully homogenized and subsampled for analysis.

6.2.2b. Sediment Digestion

Ten ml each of concentrated reagent grade HCl and HNO_3 were slowly added to a 3–10 g sediment sample contained in a Bel-Art[R] (Pequannock, New Jersey) poly-ethylene bottle. The loosely capped bottle was placed on an 85°C (±3°C) sand bath in a fume hood for about 4 h. The digest was then vacuum filtered, while still hot, through an acid-washed Gelman Type A (Gelman Instrument Co., Ann Arbor, Michigan) glass fiber filter into a 50-ml volumetric flask. The bottle and filter were rinsed with small quantities of HCl and deionized distilled water which, after passing through the filter, were added to the volumetric flask. The digest solution and rinses were then brought to volume with deionized distilled water. The solutions were transferred to acid-cleaned polyethylene bottles and placed in a refrigerator for storage prior to analysis.

6.2.2c. Metal Analysis

The acid digests were analyzed for Fe, Mn, Pb, Cu, Cd, and Ag by direct aspiration of the sample into the air-acetylene flame using a Perkin-Elmer Model 403 (Perkin-Elmer, Inc., Norwalk, Connecticut) atomic absorption spectrophotometer (AAS). Standards were serial dilutions of Fisher Scientific (Fair Lawn, New Jersey) atomic absorption standards. Mercury determinations were performed by the cold vapor technique using the Perkin-Elmer MHS-10 Mercury Hydride System attached to the AAS. Precision for the acid-leach method described was determined by analyzing four subsamples of sediment derived from four separate core sections with differing grain size characteristics. The precision of the analysis was generally better than 4% with one exception which was due to the presence of inhomogeneities in the sample such as metal flakes.

6.2.2d. Organic Matter Analysis

Subsamples of the sediments used for total metal analyses were weighed and combusted at 550°C for 5 h, allowed to cool in a desiccator to room temperature and reweighed. Percent weight loss on ignition (LOI) was calculated and is reported as percent combustible organic matter. This analysis is easily performed and has been found to correlate well with total carbon by dry combustion in CO_2-free oxygen at 1500°C followed by gasometric analysis of the evolved CO_2 (Gross, 1970). High clay content in sediment may cause a positive error in the analysis due to water trapped in the clay lattice during drying and released during combustion.

Further details concerning methods used for water content, bulk density, and sediment grain size are given by Fuhrmann (1980) and Dayal et al. (1981).

6.3. RESULTS AND DISCUSSION

6.3.1. Sediment Types and Stratigraphy

Four major sediment types were found in the cores taken at the dredged-material dumpsite: (1) black mud and black sandy mud; (2) yellow and white coarse-grained sands; (3) red and gray plastic clays; and (4) glauconitic green sand. These sediment types were classified according to their color, grain size, and mineralogy. Significant quantities of artifact materials such as coal and cinders were associated with the black mud. Further details regarding the description of these sediment types is given by Fuhrmann (1980).

Based on the spatial distributions of sediment types observed, an overall stratigraphy of the deposit has been developed, defining the boundary between the dredged materials and the underlying sediment basement. A schematic cross-section, along the northwest–southeast transect, showing the lithology of the deposit is given in Fig. 6.2. Also shown in Fig. 6.2 are the core station locations.

The quartzose sands, observed in cores 7 and 10 and, to the southeast in core 1, are materials typical of the inner continental shelf. The gravelly sand in these cores is part of a lobe of sediment that extends outward from the New Jersey coast immediately south of Sandy Hook (Freeland and Swift, 1978). The green sand stratum underlies the entire dumpsite deposit. Shallow seismic reflection profiling has indicated that this bed may extend as far inshore as station 10. The dumpsite rests directly on the once exposed green sand bed. The broken line in Fig. 6.2 indicates uncertainty in the exact position of dredged material-natural sediment boundary. Core 4 penetrated both the dredged material and the underlying natural sediment, providing the greatest penetration of the natural sediment in any of the 10 cores. This core also revealed the presence of a trough in the green sand stratum

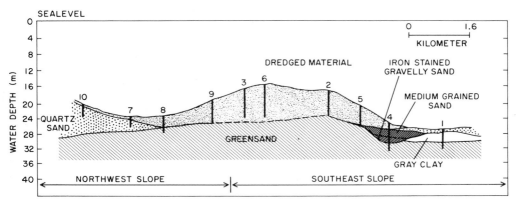

Figure 6.2. Cross-sectional profile of the dumpsite area along the northwest–southeast transect, illustrating the lithology of the deposit. Vertical lines represent actual lengths of the cores collected at the locations shown. Broken lines indicate the uncertainty in the exact position of the dredged-material–natural-sediment boundary. The various sediment types found at the dumpsites are also shown.

that was later filled with a yellow, gravelly sand overlain by a bed of medium-grained sand that contained significant amounts of echinoid (sand dollar) shells. This material was also observed, overlying the green sand, in an adjacent core at station 5. A bed of gray clay, believed to be part of a back bay deposit, was observed in core 1, located downslope southeast of core 4.

6.3.2. Depth Profiles of Metals and Organic Matter

The depth profiles of metals and organic matter in cores 1 through 10 are displayed in Figs. 6.3 through 6.7. The main features of the depth profiles are: (1) the highly variable and considerably elevated concentrations of metals and organic matter in dredged material over those observed in naturally occurring sediments in the region (Carmody et al., 1973; Gross, 1976) and in natural sediment underlying the deposit; (2) the dredged-material part of the depth profiles is characterized by a highly erratic, sawtooth form of distribution, whereas the underlying natural sediment exhibits a relatively less varied, smooth profile; (3) for most metals and organic matter, cores 4, 5, 7, 8, and 10 exhibit with increasing depth a sharp drop in the concentrations to less varied and relatively lower values, reflecting the position of the dredged material–natural sediment boundary; (4) the depth profiles of cores 2, 3, 6, and 9 do not display such a transitional feature, indicating that these cores are comprised entirely of dredged material.

Based on the overall stratigraphy of the deposit displayed in Fig. 6.2 and other sedimentological features of the cores (Fuhrmann, 1980) and the depth profiles of metals and organic matter, we are able to determine that cores 1, 5, 7, 8, and 10 contain both dredged material and underlying natural sediment, while cores 2, 3, 6, and 9 are comprised entirely of dredged material. It is important to note that cores 1, 7, and 10 were collected well outside the perimeter of the designated dumpsite. The presence of dredged material in the core tops at these stations may reflect the extent of lateral dispersion of dumped material in the area. "Short dumping" also could have contributed to the presence of dredged material in cores 7 and 10.

Using geochemical and sedimentological information, we have established that the dredged-material–natural-sediment boundary occurs at depths of 2.6 m in core 4, 4.8 m in core 5, and 3.5 m in core 8. Cores 1, 7, and 10 were not considered here because they lie outside the designated area of the dumpsite. The extent to which dredged material, present in cores 2, 3, 4, 5, 6, 8, and 9, is enriched in metals and organic matter relative to the underlying natural sediment was calculated from the relationship

$$EF = \frac{C_d}{C_n} \tag{1}$$

where EF is the enrichment factor; C_d is the average concentration of metal or organic matter in dredged material present in a core and C_n is the mean concentration in the underlying natural sediment. For sediment samples having undetectably low metal concentrations, the analytical detection limit for a given element was

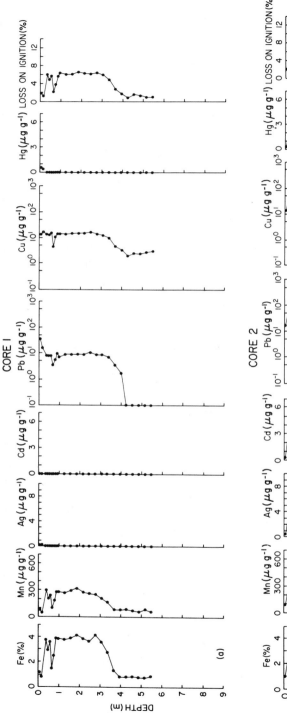

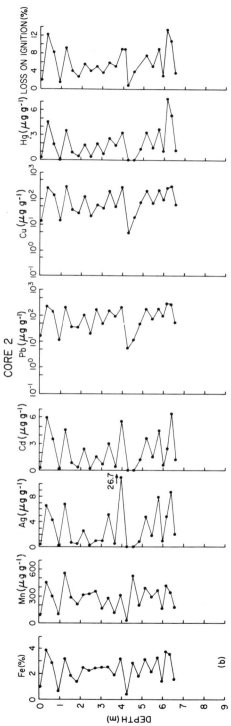

Figure 6.3. Depth distributions of metals and organic matter. (*a*) Core 1. (*b*) Core 2.

131

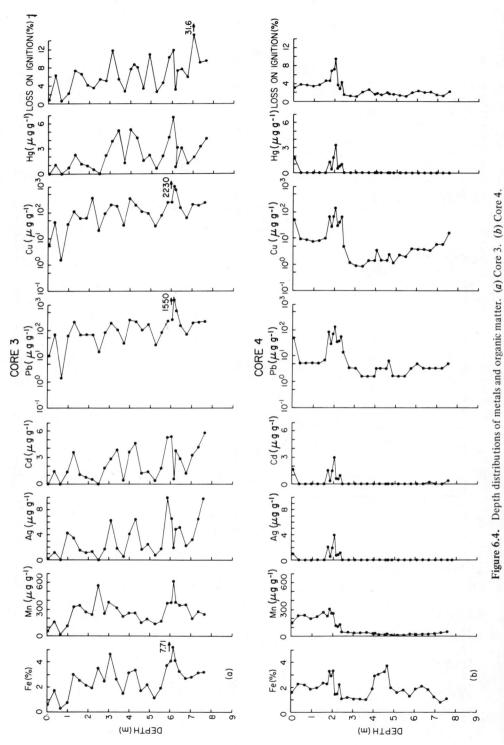

Figure 6.4. Depth distributions of metals and organic matter. (*a*) Core 3. (*b*) Core 4.

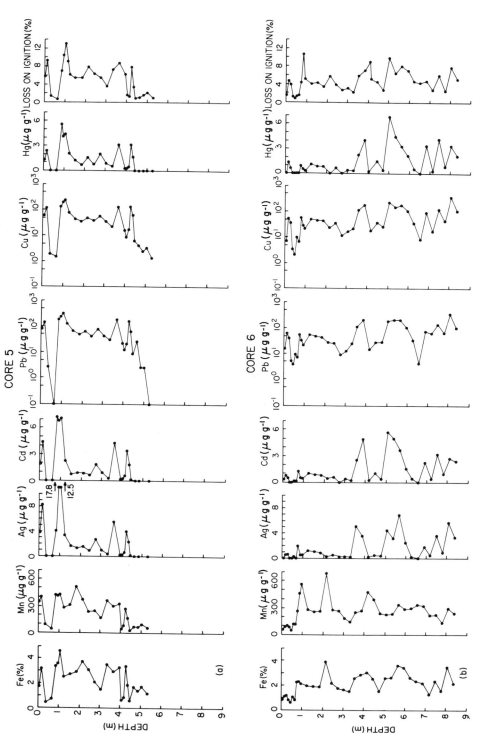

Figure 6.5. Depth distributions of metals and organic matter. (*a*) Core 5. (*b*) Core 6.

133

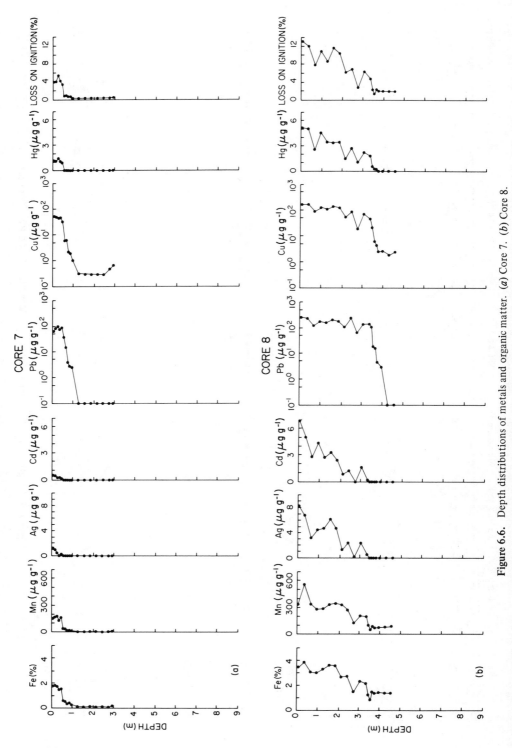

Figure 6.6. Depth distributions of metals and organic matter. (*a*) Core 7. (*b*) Core 8.

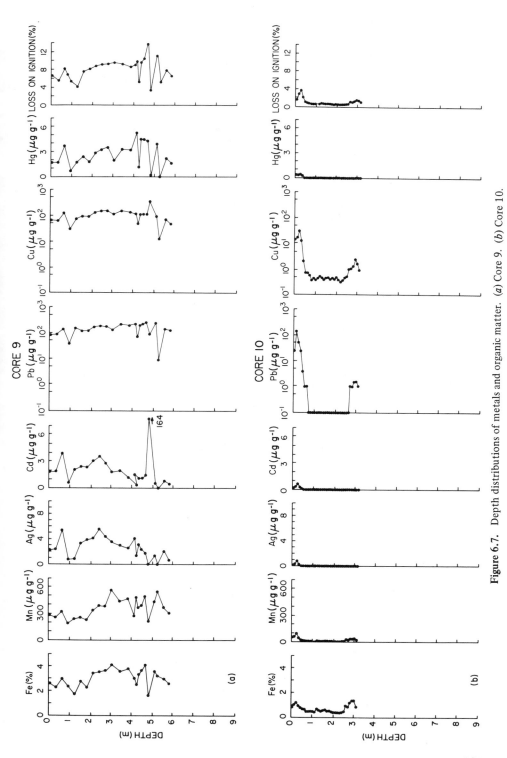

Figure 6.7. Depth distributions of metals and organic matter. (*a*) Core 9. (*b*) Core 10.

used as its concentration value for estimating enrichment factors. For example, the analytical detection limit of 0.2 μg g^{-1} was used for Cd, Hg, and Ag for C_n in equation 1. This approach provided a lower limit for *EF* for these three metals. The metal and organic matter data for natural sediment, sampled in cores 4, 5, and 8, were combined to obtain a mean and standard deviation for each metal and organic matter. These values were used for C_n in equation 1 to compute enrichments of metals and organic matter in dredged material sampled in cores 2, 3, 4, 5, 6, 8, and 9. Table 6.2 gives the mean enrichments and standard deviations, showing the extent to which the dredged material is enriched relative to natural sediment in Pb, Cu, Ag, Hg, Cd, Fe, and Mn and organic matter. The magnitude of the standard deviation for each metal reflects the degree of variability in enrichments estimated for the various cores. For example, Cd enrichment in dredged material exhibits up to 100% lateral variation within the deposit. The large variations in metals and organic matter enrichments can be attributed to the multiplicity of sources of dredged material as compared with the underlying naturally accumulated sediment. The dredged material in the deposit also exhibits significant enrichment in Fe and Mn, indicating that dumping of dredged material does indeed contribute to anthropogenic inputs of Fe and Mn.

The mean and standard deviation values listed in Table 6.3 were compared to evaluate the variability in the observed distributions of metals and organic matter in dredged material within the deposit. Also included in Table 6.3 are the values for the range of concentrations observed for the metals and organic matter in each core.

The depth distribution of metals varies widely for individual metals and from

Table 6.2. Mean Enrichments and Standard Deviations of Metals and Organic Matter in Dredged Material Relative to Underlying Natural Sediment

Component	Enrichment Factors[a]
Fe	1.7 ± 0.2
Mn	4.7 ± 0.5
Cu	22 ± 13
Pb	16 ± 8
Cd	14 ± 14
Ag	13 ± 6
Hg	9 ± 4
Organic matter	3.2 ± 0.9

[a]The values used for C_n in Equation 1 are: Fe—1.4 ± 0.2%; Mn—56 ± 21 μg g^{-1}; Cu—4.4 ± 0.3 μg g^{-1}; Pb—6 ± 2 μg g^{-1}; organic matter—1.7 ± 0.3%; since the natural sediment concentrations of Cd, Ag, and Hg were below detection, their analytical detection limits of 0.2 μg g^{-1} were used. The enrichments were calculated for dredged material in cores 2–6, 8, and 9.

Table 6.3. Mean, Standard Deviation (SD), and Range of Concentrations of Metals and Organic Matter for Dredged Material in the Cores Collected at the New York Bight Dumpsite

Core No.	Parameter	Concentrations ($\mu g\,g^{-1}$)							
		Fe[a]	Mn	Pb	Cu	Cd	Ag	Hg	Organic Matter[a]
2	Mean	2.3	274	115	118	2.1	3.7	2.1	5.8
	SD	1.0	140	95	105	2.1	5.6	1.9	3.7
	Range	4.3–0.4	547–24	286–5	302–4	7–<0.2	27–<0.2	7–<0.2	14–2
3	Mean	2.4	244	161	197	1.9	2.9	1.9	6.0
	SD	1.5	134	288	419	1.6	2.7	1.5	4.3
	Range	3.6–0.3	605–54	1527–2	2197–2	6–<0.2	10–<0.2	5–<0.2	22–0.5
4	Mean	2.1	216	17	19	0.5	0.4	0.5	4.1
	SD	0.6	60	17	16	0.5	0.3	0.5	1.2
	Range	3.3–1.4	305–119	48–5	51–7	2–<0.2	1–<0.2	2–<0.2	4.6–3.0
5	Mean	2.5	280	79	82	1.7	2.9	1.5	5.8
	SD	1.0	120	70	74	1.9	2.4	1.2	2.6
	Range	3.7–0.4	511–5	245–2	268–2	7–<0.2	18–<0.2	4–<0.2	11–0.8
6	Mean	2.1	255	73	68	1.4	1.6	1.5	4.3
	SD	0.7	123	81	78	1.5	1.8	1.6	1.9
	Range	3.8–0.6	545–57	359–4	357–4	35–<0.2	6–<0.2	4–<0.2	8–1.2
8	Mean	2.8	276	153	130	2.4	3.6	2.8	7.9
	SD	0.9	121	59	74	2.1	2.5	1.5	3.7
	Range	4.0–1.3	554–100	240–96	283–23	7–<0.2	8–<0.2	5–0.6	13–2.4
9	Mean	2.7	300	136	132	9.0	2.4	2.3	7.0
	SD	0.7	98	50	81	34	1.4	1.1	2.0
	Range	4–1.5	557–143	225–29	421–30	151–<0.2	5–0.7	5–0.7	10–4

[a] $\times 10^4$

137

one core to another. Core 3 exhibited the greatest variations in the concentrations of Fe, Cu, and Pb. Within the core the concentrations of Cu and Pb varied by more than three orders of magnitude. Highest concentrations of Fe (7.71%), Cu (2330 $\mu g \, g^{-1}$), and Pb (1550 $\mu g \, g^{-1}$) were observed within the same subsection at a depth of 6.1–6.2 m. This core also exhibited the greatest range of organic matter, varying from 0.85% at the core top to 31.7% at a depth of 7 m.

The highly variable, sawtooth form of distributions of upslope cores 2, 3, and 6 are reflected by their relatively high standard deviation values. This can be attributed to the fact that the apex of the mound receives relatively undifferentiated dredged material derived from various sources, whereas the downslope areas of the deposit receive somewhat sorted secondary, fine-grained material (Fuhrmann, 1980).

6.3.3. Geochemical Correlations

The three important factors that are known to determine the distribution of trace metals in sediments are: (1) adsorption onto, or coprecipitation with, iron and manganese hydrous oxides; (2) formation of metal–organic complexes or adsorption on organic material; and (3) association with clays by processes such as adsorption or ion exchange. In order to determine the relative importance of each of these processes, covariance correlations between metal concentrations and selected sediment parameters were used. A least squares linear correlation was performed for each pair of relevant geochemical parameters for all cores collected within the dredged-material deposit. For this purpose cores 2–6, 8, and 9 were selected. Cores 1, 7, and 10 were not included in the geochemical correlations because they were composed predominantly of natural sediments and lie outside the perimeter of the dumpsite. Table 6.4 gives correlation coefficients among Fe, Mn, Cu, Pb, Cd,

Table 6.4. Correlation Coefficients Calculated Among the Metals and Organic Matter and Mud Content in Dredged-Material Dumpsite Sediments[c]

	OM[a]	MC[b]	Fe	Mn	Cu	Pb	Cd	Hg	Ag
OM	1.00								
MC	.65	1.00							
Fe	.84	.66	1.00						
Mn	.72	.61	.76	1.00					
Cu	.80	.49	.68	.53	1.00				
Pb	.86	.49	.70	.53	.90	1.00			
Cd	.65	.31	.56	.27	.80	.74	1.00		
Hg	.78	.41	.68	.38	.80	.86	.81	1.00	
Ag	.72	.32	.62	.33	.80	.77	.89	.74	1.00

[a]Organic matter.
[b]Mud content.
[c]The number of points considered in these calculations range from 187 for mud–organic matter to 132 for Cd–Ag correlation.

Hg, Ag, and organic matter and mud. Selected correlation plots are displayed in Figs. 6.8 through 6.10.

The Fe–metal plots indicate that Fe concentrations are strongly related to Mn but only moderately to the other metals determined in this study (Fig. 6.8; Table 6.4). Characteristic of the plots of Fe against the trace metals (Cu, Pb, Hg, Ag, and Cd) is scatter along the ordinate, for example a wide range of Fe concentrations at low metal levels. This scatter decreases in most of these plots at higher concentrations. Another interesting feature in these plots is a fairly large presence of Fe (1–2%) where other metals are nearly absent. This can be attributed to the presence of relatively uncontaminated sediment such as the natural sediment underlying the deposit.

Figure 6.9 presents trace metals plotted against each other. The correlations among these metals are strong, particularly for Cu versus Pb. Unlike the Fe and Mn versus trace metal plots, the scatter along the lower ends of axes is minimal but increases at higher concentrations.

As expected from their similar chemistries and the predominantly natural sources of these metals, Fe and Mn are strongly correlated in the dredged-material deposit. The wide spread in Fe and Mn concentrations at low trace metal levels indicate that the dredged materials originate in widely varied environments in terms of anthropogenic metal inputs and that the natural sediment underlying the deposit contains natural concentrations of Fe and Mn but is depleted in trace metals. Overall the trace metals exhibit correlation with Fe and Mn. It appears that iron hydrous oxides and, to a lesser extent, manganese hydrous oxides play a significant role in the adsorption of Cu, Pb, Cd, Hg, and Ag.

The strong interrelationships among some of the trace metals indicate that they behave similarly geochemically and probably are associated with the same phases in dredged-material sediments.

Correlations between metals and organic matter indicate strong association of Fe, Cu, Pb, and Hg with organic matter in dredged-material sediments. Correlation plots of Fe and Mn versus organic matter (Fig. 6.10) exhibit a similar relationship but the Mn covariance is weaker. The organic matter versus trace metal plots (Fig. 6.10) are fairly similar, all showing scatter at low metal concentrations, but the variation in the relationship differs. The Pb and Cu plots are strongly linear whereas those for Ag, Cd, and Hg are slightly more scattered.

The variation in organic matter content at low metal concentrations implies that plant debris from relatively pristine environments is intermixed with other waste such as sewage-derived organic matter. As previously mentioned, the dredged material is taken from areas that are exposed to widely varied degrees of pollutant loading. Mn and Cd appear to be less associated with the organic fraction than the other metals studied. The strong relationships of organic matter with the metals indicate that the organic matter may have a significant control over Fe, Mn, Pb, Cu, Hg, Ag, and Cd in dredged-material sediments. This agrees with previous studies in other locations for both natural and polluted sediments (Rashid and Leonard, 1973; Gross, 1976; Nissenbaum and Swaine, 1976; Marine Sciences Research Center, 1978).

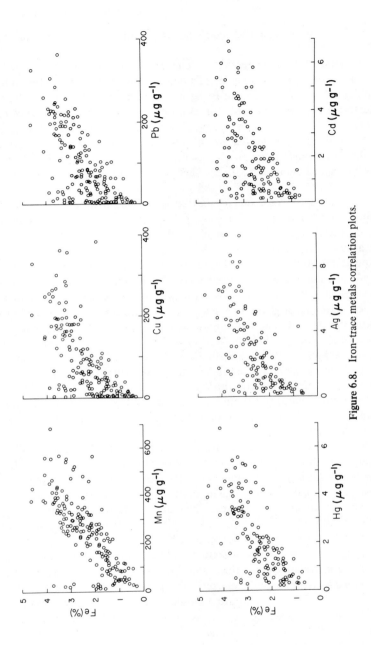

Figure 6.8. Iron–trace metals correlation plots.

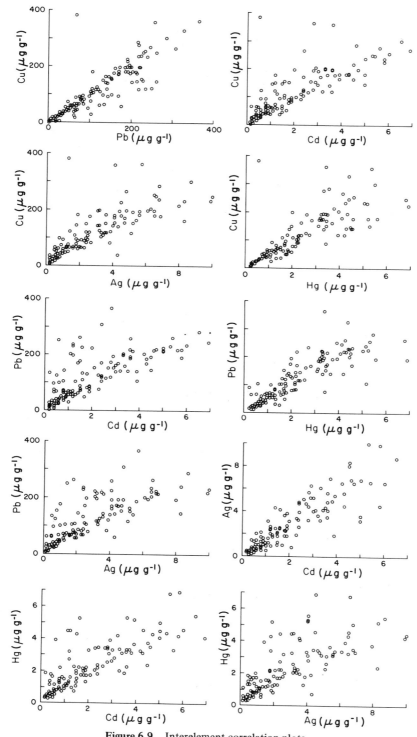

Figure 6.9. Interelement correlation plots.

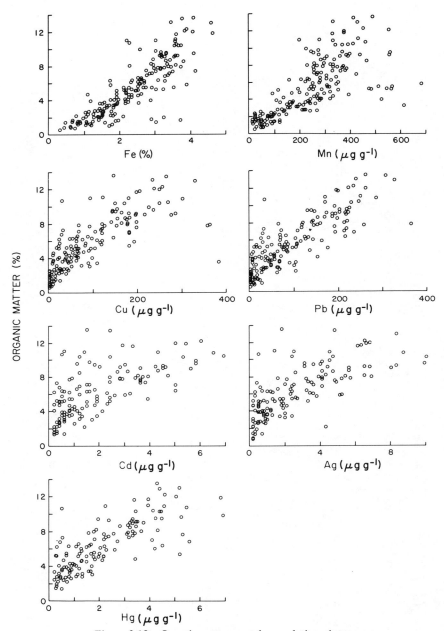

Figure 6.10. Organic matter–metals correlation plots.

Compared to metal–organic matter correlations, the metal versus mud content correlations are significantly weaker for each pair. Because of the highly organic rich nature of much of the dredged sediment, the mud fraction of the sediment does not appear to be the controlling factor with respect to the distribution of metals. Sewage-related materials may add large quantities of metals and organic matter without substantially altering the grain size of the samples.

From the results obtained, it is only possible to make certain generalizations. It appears that organic matter plays the most significant role in the distribution of metals in the dredged-material sediments. Iron, and to a lesser extent, manganese hydrous oxide phases may also control the trace metal distributions.

6.3.4. Inputs of Metals and Organic Matter

We calculated inputs of Fe, Mn, Pb, Cu, Cd, Ag, Hg, and organic matter from estimated sedimentation rates at each station for the periods of 1936–1973 and 1973–1978 (Dayal et al., 1981) and the observed depth distributions of metals in each core (Table 6.5). The arithmetical averages of metal concentrations in upper and lower units of each core, above the deposit basement, corresponding to 1973–1978 and 1936–1973 accumulations, respectively, were used for the calculations of pre- and post-1973 metal inputs. A value of 2.6 g cm^{-3} was assumed to be the density of the solid phases and a value of 31% as the average water content of deposited dredged material.

The wide distribution of coring stations in the study area provides information regarding inputs of metals and organic matter deposited in different parts of the dumpsite over a period of time. For example, the highest metal input values are obtained for the apex stations (cores 3 and 6) for the period 1936–1973. As expected, the lowest metal inputs are recorded in cores taken at the downslope stations (cores 4 and 8). Other stations, located on the top of middle of the slopes (cores 2, 5, and 9), exhibit intermediate input rates; the upslope cores showing higher values than the downslope cores.

For the period 1973–1978, however, highest input values for some trace metals are obtained for the upslope cores 2 and 5, lying on the southeast slope of the mound. The mound apex cores (3 and 6) exhibit relatively low inputs. This can be explained by the recent dumping that took place at a site to the southeast of the designated dumpsite used before 1973. Overall the southeast slope stations exhibit higher metal inputs than those located on the northwest slope.

For the period 1936–1973, the inputs of Pb and Cu at the apex and downslope stations (cores 3 and 4, respectively) vary by more th•n two orders of magnitude; Cd, Ag, and Hg by one to two orders of magnitude. The Pb and Cu inputs in each core are very similar as well are the inputs of Cd, Ag, and Hg. The organic matter and Fe inputs are also comparable. Mn input is slightly higher than those for Pb and Cu. For most cores, the order of the magnitude of the inputs decreases as follows: organic matter $>$ Fe $>$ Mn $>$ Pb $>$ Cu $>$ Ag $>$ Cd $\simeq$ Hg.

For the period 1973–1978, the input values for the trace metals vary over a smaller range, the maxima being relatively lower and the minima higher than the

Table 6.5. Anthropogenic Inputs of Metals and Organic Matter Associated with Dredged Materials Dumped in New York Bight During the Periods 1936–1973 and 1973–1978[a]

Anthropogenic Inputs (g m^{-2} y^{-1})

Core No.	Station Location	Period 1973–1978								Period 1936–1973							
		Fe[b]	Mn	Pb	Cu	Cd	Ag	Hg	Organic Matter[b]	Fe[b]	Mn	Pb	Cu	Cd	Ag	Hg	Organic Matter[b]
2	Top of southeast slope	13.9	185	64.9	73.1	1.48	1.84	1.12	14.6	6.0	67.7	30.3	29.9	0.52	1.03	0.55	18.2
3	Pile apex	12.4	146	47.5	66.7	0.89	1.28	0.67	35.1	18.3	196	150	181	1.70	2.50	1.77	48.6
4	Base of southeast slope	3.5	73.1	5.7	6.8	0.20	0.14	0.21	12.4	1.6	16.4	1.3	1.3	0.02	0.03	0.02	3.3
5	Middle of southeast slope	15.0	201	58.2	58.4	1.34	2.88	0.99	35.7	3.1	30.1	5.0	8.7	0.17	0.22	0.17	7.1
6	Pile apex	17.5	284	25.5	24.9	0.55	0.52	0.48	34.4	18.5	201	82.1	75.2	1.57	1.80	1.67	39.9
8	Base of northwest slope	3.9	47.7	24.9	25.4	0.65	0.81	0.55	13.5	2.8	26.4	14.9	11.9	0.17	0.29	0.26	7.5
9	Top of northwest slope	5.0	114	19.4	21.0	0.48	0.63	0.44	12.5	6.3	71.1	33.3	31.8	2.41	0.54	0.55	18.2

[a]In these estimates, a value of 2.6 g cm^{-3} was used for the density of the solid phases present in dredged materials and an average water content of 31% by weight.
[b]× 10^3.

corresponding values for the 1936–1973 period. The general order of the magnitude of the metal inputs is the same as above.

6.3.5. Records of Anthropogenic Metal Inputs to New York Bight and Other Coastal Areas

Comparison of metal enrichments calculated for the dredged-material deposit (Table 6.2) with other coastal deposits provides insight into the relative magnitude of metals deposited, via dredged-material dumping, in the Bight Apex. Table 6.6 gives enrichments of metals in naturally deposited sediments from several coastal areas, known to be heavily impacted by industrialization. The values reflect the extent of metal enrichment in the recently deposited surface sediments compared to those in deeper sediments accumulated earlier before the advent of the industrial period. The enrichments given for California Coastal Basins represent mean values based on the investigations of the deposits of the San Pedro, the Santa Monica, and the Santa Barbara basins off southern California, adjacent to highly industrialized Los Angeles area (Bruland et al., 1974). Erlenkeuser et al. (1974) attributed the enhanced levels of Cd, Pb, Zn, and Cu in the upper parts of the Baltic Sea sediments to the combustion of coal.

It is quite evident from the compilation in Table 6.6 that for the metals examined the extent of metal enrichment in the dredged-material deposit is greater than those reported for coastal deposits not impacted by dumping activities. Lead enrichment in the dredged-material deposit, for example, is four times higher than those reported for the California Coastal Basins, Baltic Sea, and Narragansett Bay sediments, whereas Cd is enriched by a factor of nine and two more than the California Basins and Baltic Sea sediments, respectively. Other metals such as Cu and Ag also exhibit enrichment in the dredged-material deposit. Even Fe and Mn, the elements that

Table 6.6. Metal Enrichments in Coastal Sediment Deposits

Element	California Coastal Basins[a]	Kieler Bucht, Baltic Sea[b]	Narragansett Bay[c]	New York Bight Dredged-Material Deposit[d]
Pb	4.2	4.1	4.0	16 ± 8
Cd	1.5	6.9	—	14 ± 14
Cu	1.8	1.9	6.7	22 ± 13
Mn	1.0	1.0	1.0	4.7 ± 0.5
Fe	1.0	1.0	1.0	1.7 ± 0.2
Zn	1.4	2.9	3.3	—
Ag	3.0	—	1.0	13 ± 6
Hg	—	—	—	9 ± 4

[a]Average values based on investigations of the deposits of the San Pedro, the Santa Monica, and the Santa Barbara basins off Southern California (Bruland et al., 1974).
[b]Erlenkeuser et al. (1974).
[c]Goldberg et al. (1977).
[d]Mean values based on 7 cores (Table 6.2; this study).

Table 6.7.   Anthropogenic Inputs of Metals in Coastal Sediment Deposits

Element	Metal Inputs (g m^{-2} y^{-1})			
	California Coastal Basins[a]	Kieler Bucht, Baltic Sea[b]	Narragansett Bay[c]	New York Bight Dredged-Material Deposit[d]
Pb	0.016	0.022	1.68	40 ± 39
Cu	0.013	0.012	2.60	44 ± 47
Cd	0.0007	0.0006	–	0.9 ± 0.7
Ag	0.0009	–	–	1.0 ± 0.9
Hg	–	–	–	0.7 ± 0.5
Mn	0.0[f]	0.0	0.0	119 ± 84
Fe[e]	0.0[f]	0.0	0.0	9 ± 6

[a]Average values based on investigations of the deposits of the San Pedro, the Santa Monica, and the Santa Barbara basins off southern California (Bruland et al., 1974).
[b]Erlenkeuser et al. (1974).
[c]Goldberg et al. (1977).
[d]Average values based on seven cores (Table 6.5; this study).
[e]× 10^3 g m^{-2} y^{-1}.
[f]Natural preindustrialization inputs of Mn and Fe to the California coastal basins are reported to be 0.15 and 18 g m^{-2} y^{-1}, respectively (Bruland et al., 1974).

normally show no record of anthropogenic input in coastal deposits, are considerably enriched in the dredged-material deposit.

To further evaluate the magnitude of metal inputs to the New York Bight via dredged-material dumping, we have compiled estimates of anthropogenic inputs of metals deposited in California Coastal Basins, the Baltic Sea, the Narragansett Bay, and the mean input values for the New York Bight for the dumping period 1936–1978. Sedimentation rates used for estimating metal inputs to the New York Bight are based on bathymetric surveys of the dumpsite conducted in 1936 and 1978 (Dayal et al., 1981). Erlenkeuser et al. (1974) determined the time scales for the Baltic Sea sediments with radiocarbon dates, and ^{210}Pb chronology was used for the California Coastal Basin sediments (Bruland et al., 1974) and for the Narragansett Bay sediments (Goldberg et al., 1977).

The compilation in Table 6.7 shows that Pb, Cu, Cd, and Ag inputs to the New York Bight, through dredged-material dumping, are generally much larger, up to three orders of magnitude higher than those reported for the Baltic Sea and the California Coastal Basins. Relative to the Pb and Cu inputs to the Narragansett Bay sediments, these metals are depositing at the dumpsite, as a result of dumping, at rates higher by factors of 20 and 16, respectively. Goldberg et al. (1977) reported that the Cu and Pb inputs to the Narragansett Bay sediments are two orders of magnitude higher than those from the Baltic Sea and the California Coastal Basins.

Anthropogenic inputs of Fe and Mn to the sediments of the California Coastal Basins, the Baltic Sea, and the Narragansett Bay are reported to be negligible (Bruland et al., 1974; Erlenkeuser et al., 1974; Goldberg et al., 1977). However, Table 6.6 shows large anthropogenic enrichments of Fe and Mn in New York Bight dredged material as compared to the underlying natural sediment. This leads to a strong anthropogenic input of these materials, via dredged-material dumping, to the New York Bight (Table 6.7). Bruland et al. (1974) reported average values of natural inputs of Fe and Mn for the California Coastal Basin deposits to be 18 g $m^{-2} y^{-1}$ and 0.15 g $m^{-2} y^{-1}$, respectively. The Mn and Fe inputs to the New York Bight through disposal of dredged material are more than two to three orders of magnitude higher than the natural weathering rates recorded in the California Coastal Basin sediments.

The large standard deviation values of metal input rates for New York Bight (Table 6.7) reflect the magnitude of lateral variability in dumping rates of dredged material at the dumpsite, the apex of the deposit being the area of heaviest dumping (Dayal et al., 1981).

6.4. CONCLUSION

The sediments of the dredged-material deposit are composed of a wide variety of sediment types, which can be classified as quartzose and glauconitic sands, muds, sandy muds, gravel intermixed with muds, and artifact material such as coal and fly ash, wood, slag, metal flakes, glass, and so on. Black sandy mud is characteristic of dredged material whereas glauconitic and gravelly quartzose sands are typical of the natural sediment underlying the deposit and in surrounding areas.

The spatial distributions of heavy metals such as Pb, Cu, Ag, Hg, Cd, Fe, and Mn in the dredged-material deposit exhibit highly variable and considerably elevated concentrations over those observed in sediment outside the deposit and in underlying natural sediment. Compared to metal enrichments reported for other coastal deposits, the metal enrichments observed in dredged-material sediments are significantly greater.

Organic matter appears to play a significant role in the distribution of metals in the dredged-material sediments. Iron, and to a lesser extent, manganese hydrous oxide phases also appear to control the trace metal distributions.

The estimated rates and magnitudes of anthropogenic metal inputs to the New York Bight, via dredged-material dumping, are found to be two to three orders of magnitude higher for Cd and Ag and more than an order of magnitude higher for Pb and Cu than those reported for naturally deposited coastal sediments from other regions. Even Fe and Mn were found to have significant anthropogenic inputs at the dumpsite.

ACKNOWLEDGMENTS

We gratefully acknowledge the assistance of the personnel on *RV Atlantic Twin* and *RV Kelez* during the sediment sampling and pore-water chemistry cruises. We also thank W. O'Brien, N. Moheban, B. Subramamian, and R. Wilke for their help in the laboratory. We are particularly indebted to L. Antonacci for typing the manuscript.

This work was supported by a grant from the National Oceanic and Atmospheric Administration, Marine EcoSystem Analysis (MESA) project and the New York District Office of the U.S. Army Corps of Engineers. We thank H. Stanford (MESA) for his help throughout the entire project. This chapter is Contribution No. 285 of the Marine Sciences Research Center.

REFERENCES

Bruland, K. W., K. Bertine, M. Koide, and E. D. Goldberg. 1974. History of metal pollution in southern California coastal zone. *Environmental Science and Technology*, 5, 425–432.

Carmody, D. J., J. B. Pearce, and W. E. Yasso. 1973. Trace metals in sediments of the New York Bight. *Marine Pollution Bulletin*, 4, 132–135.

Dayal, R., M. G. Heaton, M. Fuhrmann, and I. W. Duedall. 1981. A Geochemical and Sedimentological Investigation of the Dredged Material Deposit in the New York Bight. Technical Memorandum OMPA-3. National Oceanic and Atmospheric Administration, Stony Brook, New York, 265 pp.

Erlenkeuser, H., E. Seuss, and H. Willkomm. 1974. Industrialization affects heavy metal and carbon isotope concentrations in recent Baltic Sea sediments. *Geochimica et Cosmochimica Acta*, 38, 823–824.

Freeland, G. L. and G. F. Merrill. 1977. The 1973 Bathymetric Survey in the New York Bight Apex: Maps and Geological Implications. National Oceanic and Atmospheric Administration Technical Memorandum No. 19. Environmental Research Laboratories, Marine EcoSystems Analysis Program, National Oceanic and Atmospheric Administration, Boulder, Colorado, 20 pp.

Freeland, G. L. and D. J. P. Swift. 1978. Surficial Sediments. MESA New York Bight Atlas Monograph 10, New York Sea Grant Institute, Albany, New York, 93 pp.

Fuhrmann, M. 1980. Sedimentology of the New York Bight Dredged Material Dumpsite Deposit. M. S. Thesis, Adelphi University Garden City, New York, 160 pp.

Goldberg, E. D., E. Gamble, J. J. Griffin, and M. Koide. 1977. Pollution history of Narragansett Bay as recorded in its sediments. *Estuarine and Coastal Marine Science*, 5, 549–561.

Gross, M. G. 1976. Sources of urban waste. *In*: Middle Atlantic Continental Shelf and the New York Bight, M. G. Gross (Ed.). The American Society of Limnology and Oceanography, Inc. Lawrence, Kansas, pp. 150–162.

Gross, M. G. 1970. Preliminary Analysis of Urban Waste, New York Metropolitan Region. Technical Report No. 5. Marine Sciences Research Center, State University of New York, Stony Brook, New York, 35 pp.

Marine Sciences Research Center. 1978. Aquatic Disposal Field Investigations, Eatons Neck Disposal Sites, Long Island Sound. Appendix B: Water Quality Parameters and Physiochemical Sediment Parameters. Technical Report D-77-6. U.S. Army Engineer Waterways Experiment Station, Vicksburg, Mississippi, 322 pp.

Meade, R. H., 1972. Sources and sinks of suspended matter on continental shelves. *In*: Shelf Sediment Transport: Processes and Patterns, D. J. P. Swift, D. B. Duane, and O. H. Pilkey (Eds.). Dowden, Hutchinson and Ross, Inc., Stoudsburg, Pennsylvania, pp. 249–262.

Mueller, J. A., J. S. Jerris, A. R. Anderson, and C. F. Hughes. 1976. Contaminant inputs to the New York Bight. NOAA Technical Memorandum ERL MESA-6. Environmental Research Laboratory, Marine EcoSystems Analysis Office, National Oceanic and Atmospheric Administration, Boulder, Colorado, 347 pp.

Nissenbaum, A. and D. J. Swaine. 1976. Organic matter–metal interactions in recent sediments: the role of humic substances. *Geochimica et Cosmochimica Acta*, **40**, 809–816.

Panuzio, F. L. 1965. Lower Hudson River siltation. *In*: Proceedings of the Federal Inter-agency Sedimentation Conference, Jackson, Mississippi, 28 January–1 February 1963. Miscellaneous Publication Number 970, Agriculture Research Service, U.S. Department of Agriculture, Washington, D.C., pp. 512–550.

Rashid, M. A. and J. D. Leonard. 1973. Modifications in the solubility and precipitation behavior of various metals as result of their interaction with sedimentary humic acid. *Chemical Geology*, **11**, 89–97.

7

OCEAN DUMPING OF DREDGED MATERIAL IN THE NEW YORK BIGHT: ORGANIC CHEMISTRY STUDIES

P. D. Boehm and D. L. Fiest

Environmental Sciences Division
Energy Resources Co., Inc.
Cambridge, Massachusetts

ABSTRACT

Concentrations of polynuclear aromatic hydrocarbon (PAH) and polychlorinated biphenyl (PCB) were determined in a suite of samples from the waters of New York Bight prior to, during, and after a dredged-material disposal operation. The PAH profiles were compared with those of the source dredged material to evaluate short-term fractionation and weathering. Hydrocarbons associated with dredged material are rapidly altered in the water column by dissolution and microbial processes. The PAH and PCB measurements proved to be sensitive indicators of the movement and fate of dredged-material particulate plumes; 15 min after the dump the residual plume was found in near-bottom water and remained detectable for at least 2.5 h.

7.1. INTRODUCTION

Dredged material from heavily utilized harbors and waterways contains substantial quantities of inorganic and organic pollutants (Atwood et al., 1979). The disposal of dredged material in the coastal ocean may result in the release of large amounts of dissolved and particulate pollutants into the water column (Hatcher et al., 1978). The processes that must be examined to determine the flux and residence times of these compounds are summarized in Fig. 7.1. The impact on the disposal site of organic constituents contained in dredged material depends on their partitioning between solid and solution phases, their persistence in the marine environment, and their effects on organisms. Investigations of these processes provides an improved understanding of marine organic geochemistry.

Since the early part of this century, the New York Bight has been used extensively for the disposal of a variety of materials, including sewage sludge, dredged material, cellar dirt, and chemical wastes (Pararas-Carayannis, 1973). Sedimentation in the Bight is heavily influenced by anthropogenic inputs. The detailed organic composition of sewage sludge is poorly known (Pararas-Carayannis, 1973), but is better characterized than the variety of dredged materials disposed in the region. Dredged material ranges from 8 to 10% organic carbon and may contain substantial amounts of petrochemicals (Panuzio, 1965; Saila et al., 1972). As an example, fossil fuel hydrocarbons are present in high concentrations (500–3000 $\mu g\ g^{-1}$) in surface sediment from the entire New York Bight region and are transported offshore (Farrington and Tripp, 1977).

As part of a larger experimental effort designed to investigate the behavior of dredged-material plumes in the waters of New York Bight, we have undertaken a limited field sampling and analytical program to examine time-dependent changes in the organic chemical composition of water column particulates during and after disposal operations. The goals of this component of the Marine EcoSystem Analysis (MESA) New York Bight program were as follows:

1. To design and use a sampling and rapid filtration system to obtain suspended particulate material in the mixed layer, pycnocline, and bottom waters in the study region.

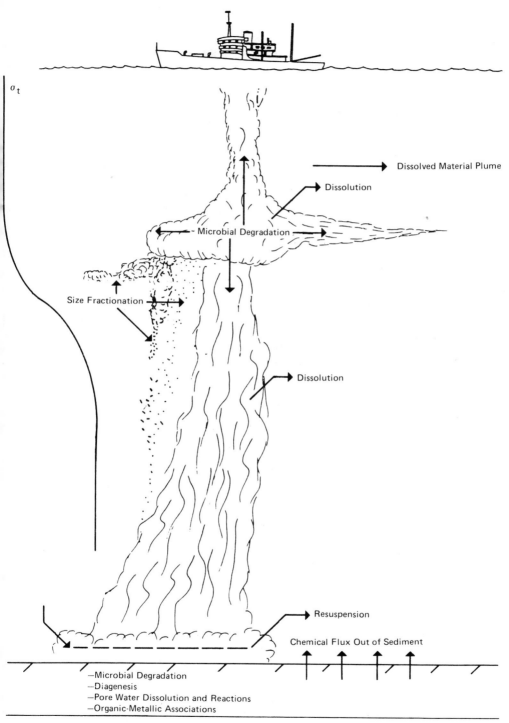

σ_t

Dissolved Material Plume

Dissolution

Microbial Degradation

Size Fractionation

Dissolution

Resuspension

Chemical Flux Out of Sediment

—Microbial Degradation
—Diagenesis
—Pore Water Dissolution and Reactions
—Organic-Metallic Associations

Figure 7.1. Schematic representation of processes influencing the distribution and fate of dredged-material–associated organic compounds. (Adapted from Dredged Material Research Program, U.S. Army Corps of Engineers, Vicksburg, Mississippi.)

153

2. To determine the levels of polynuclear aromatic hydrocarbons (PAHs) and polychlorinated biphenyls (PCBs) in source dredged material, background water (predump), and receiving water (postdump) samples.
3. To use these organic tracers to determine the residence time of the dredged-material plume in the water column.

7.2. METHODS AND MATERIALS

7.2.1. Sampling

Samples of suspended particulates were collected aboard the *RV Kelez* on 21 June 1979. The water was sampled using 10-liter Teflon-lined GO-FLO® bottles (General Oceanics Inc., Miami, Florida) on a 12-bottle rosette array. Sample bottles were closed at depths dependent on water column structure as well as on the depth of the dredged-material plume that was detected by an acoustical profiler (Proni and Hansen, 1981). The 10-liter water samples were brought onboard, inverted, and placed on a bottle rack. The inverted bottles minimized the settling of particulates within the bottle prior to filtration. The bottles were pressurized with water-pumped purified nitrogen (99.9%) to 10 mm Hg and the contents were transferred to a 142-mm diameter stainless steel filter holder containing a precombusted Gelman AE glass fiber filter (Gelman Instruments Co., Ann Arbor, Michigan), through a 1.3-cm stainless steel transfer line.

A complete listing of the samples is presented in Table 7.1. Samples were obtained at three depths: surface, thermocline, and bottom. Sampling occurred prior

Table 7.1. Summary of Suspended Particulate Samples Obtained on 21 June 1979 [a]

Station	Sample Number (Station-Depth)	Depth (m)
6 (control)	6-2	2.0
	6-14	14.2
	6-22	22.4
7 (0.25 h[b])	7-5	5.1
	7-12	11.8
	7-15	14.5
	7-21	20.5
8 (2.5 h[b])	8-4	4
	8-10 (1)	10
	8-10 (2)	10
	8-10 (3)	10
	8-21	21

[a]Three replicate samples were taken at station 8, 10m.
[b]Time after dump.

to the dredged-material dump (station 6), 15 min after the dump (station 7), and 2.5 h after the dump (station 8). Replicate samples were obtained at station 8 at 10-m depth.

A 30-cm dredged-material core was taken on the barge prior to the dump with a polycarbonate core liner. Two samples of this source material were taken for subsequent analyses for PAH and PCB compounds.

All samples were frozen onboard soon after collection and transported frozen to our laboratory.

7.2.2. Analytical Procedures

7.2.2a. Filters

Filter samples were thawed in the laboratory and cut into small strips using precleaned stainless steel utensils. The strips were placed in a round-bottom flask for extraction. The analytical procedure involving extraction, fractionation, and analysis is shown in Fig. 7.2.

7.2.2b. Dredged-Material Samples

Two samples of the source material were analyzed by a methanol and methylene chloride/methanol shaking–extraction procedure (Boehm et al., 1981). This procedure (Fig. 7.3) is a modified version of that of Brown et al. (1979, 1980).

7.2.2c. Gas Chromatography

Glass capillary gas chromatography (GC) analyses were performed on selected f_1 and f_2 hydrocarbon fractions (see Figure 7.2). Hewlett Packard Model 5840 (Hewlett Packard, Palo Alto, California) reporting gas chromatographs equipped with splitless injection systems were used for all analyses. Thirty-m SE-30 glass capillary columns (J&W Scientific, Rancho Cordova, California) were used. The GC analytical conditions were as follows:

Temperature program	60–275°C @ 3° min^{-1}
Carrier gas	Helium
Carrier flow	1 cm^3 min^{-1}
Injection temperature	275°C
Detector temperature	300°C

Retention indices were obtained through a digital communications interfacing system with a PDP-10 computer.

PCB concentrations were determined on a Hewlett Packard Model 5840 GC equipped with a ^{63}Ni electron capture detector (ECD) and a 2-m long, 2-mm internal diameter glass column packed with 1.5% SP2750/1.95% SP2401. Runs were made in the isothermal mode (180°C). Quantification was accomplished through

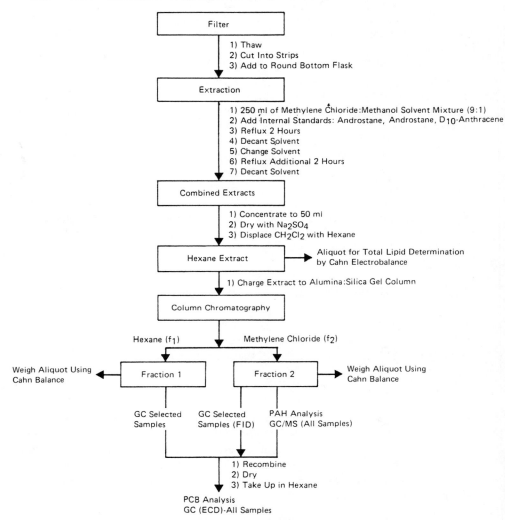

Figure 7.2. Analytical scheme for suspended particulate samples.

matching PCB peaks of authentic Arochlor standards and comparing peak areas with those of a known Arochlor calibration GC injection series.

7.2.2d. Gas Chromatography–Mass Spectrometry

The aromatic hydrocarbons in all samples were determined by quantitative gas chromatography–mass spectrometry (GCMS) using the technique of mass fragmentography (Albaiges and Albrecht, 1979). Once the total ion chromatogram was obtained and stored in the computer, the data were searched for aromatic parent

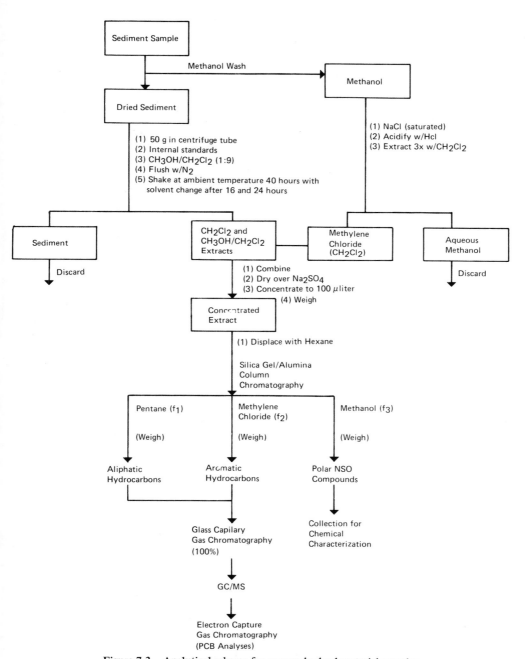

Figure 7.3. Analytical scheme for source dredged-material samples.

ions. Retention times of the parent ion mass fragmentograms obtained through the selected mass searches were compared with authentic PAH standards. The total ion current for each parent ion (e.g., phenanthrene: $M^+ = 278$) was measured and compared with that for the internal standard (D_{10} anthracene: $M^+ = 188$).

Relative instrumental response factors were applied to correct for the differences in sensitivity to equal quantities of each PAH and the internal standard. Response factors for those PAH compounds that were not available as pure standards were obtained by extrapolation.

A Hewlett Packard Model 5895 GCMS computer system (GC: 5840; Data System 5934A) equipped with a 30-m SE-30 glass capillary column was used for all PAH analyses. The quadrupole mass spectrometer conditions were set as follows: ionization voltage, 70 eV; electron multiplier voltage, 2200 volts; and scan conditions 40–500 atomic mass units (amu) at 225 amu s^{-1} (one scan every 2.1 s).

7.3. RESULTS AND DISCUSSION

7.3.1. Chemical Characterization of Dredged Material

The results of the organic chemical analyses of the dredged material dumped during the tracking experiment are presented in Table 7.2. The samples represent composites of cores taken on the barges prior to the dump. The similarity between the two samples is striking. Of the total extractable organic matter, approximately 15% is nonelutable residue on the silica gel column. The total PCB concentrations range from 3.7 to 6.9 $\mu g\ g^{-1}$ and appear to be comprised of a mixture of 67% Arochlor 1254 and 33% Arochlor 1016.

Individual polynuclear aromatic hydrocarbon (PAH) concentrations ranged from 800 to 7,000 ng g^{-1} with the unsubstituted parent compounds phenanthrene, fluoranthene, pyrene, benzanthracene, chrysene, and the benzopyrenes present at $\mu g\ g^{-1}$ levels. Again, the agreement between the two samples is excellent.

The glass capillary gas chromatograms of the f_1 (saturated) and f_2 (aromatic) hydrocarbon profiles are presented in Fig. 7.4. The saturated distribution appears to be a composite of a light petroleum with a prominent n-alkane distribution from n-C_{11} to n-C_{22}, and a residual, highly degraded anthropogenic input consisting largely of an unresolved complex mixture (UCM) with small n-alkane peaks (n-C_{23} to n-C_{27}). Some of the resolved features in the GC trace between n-C_{27} and n-C_{31} are pentacyclic triterpanes (hopanes) which are saturated cyclic structures of great stability attributable to petroleum inputs (Dastillung and Albrecht, 1976). The isoprenoids (branched alkanes), farnesane, pristane, and phytane, are more prominent than the adjacent n-alkanes, indicating that even the light petroleum-related segment is biodegraded to some extent.

The aromatic hydrocarbon GC trace exhibits many hydrocarbon component peaks (the two largest peaks are phthalates), in addition to a considerable UCM. The best explanation for this distribution is that the dredged-material organic compounds are a composite of petrogenic hydrocarbons and other anthropogenic

Table 7.2. Chemical Composition of Dredged-Material Sample from 21 June 1979 New York Bight Disposal Operation

Parameter	Sample 1	Sample 2
Moisture (%)	58	63
Total extractable organic compounds (μg g^{-1})	9600	8900
Aliphatic hydrocarbons (f_1) (μg g^{-1})	1300	1300
Aromatic hydrocarbons (f_2) (μg g^{-1})	370	650
Polar organic compounds (f_3) (μg g^{-1})	930	1100
Polychlorinated biphenyl compounds (PCB) (μg g^{-1})		
Aroclor 1016	1.3	2.3
Aroclor 1254	2.4	4.6
Individual PAH compounds (ng g^{-1})		
naphthalene (N)	2300	2000
2-methylnaphthalene (2MN)	1600	1400
1-methylnaphthalene (1MN)	1200	890
biphenyl (BP)	1300	1200
dibenzothiophene (DBT)	630	600
phenanthrene (P)	4200	4000
anthracene (A)	1800	1700
1-methylphenanthrene (1MP)	2100	2300
fluoranthene (F)	6900	5800
pyrene (PY)	6300	6400
benzo(a)anthracene (BA)	3400	3400
chrysene (C)	3900	3800
benzo(e)pyrene (BEP)	930	930
benzo(a)pyrene (BAP)	1800	2100
perylene (PE)	1100	1200

compounds probably from urban air fallout and runoff. Indeed, the prominence of phenanthrene, anthracene, and the fluoranthene/pyrene couple indicates that fossil fuel combustion products are strong contributors to the PAH fraction (Lee et al., 1977).

7.3.2. Hydrocarbon-Bearing Particulates in the Water Column

The analytical results for the particulate hydrocarbons are presented in Table 7.3. Hydrocarbon levels in the control (predump) samples (station 6) indicate that background levels of hydrocarbons (aliphatic plus aromatic) range from 5.1 to 16.4 μg liter^{-1}. Total extractable organics are highest at the surface (sample 6-2; 206 μg liter^{-1}) as are the PCB levels (9.6 ng liter^{-1}). This surface sample also illustrates significant PAH concentrations, with 2- 3- and 4-ringed PAH compounds present at detectable levels ($>$0.5 ng liter^{-1}).

At station 7 (15 min after the dump), mixed surface layer (0–12 m) and thermo-

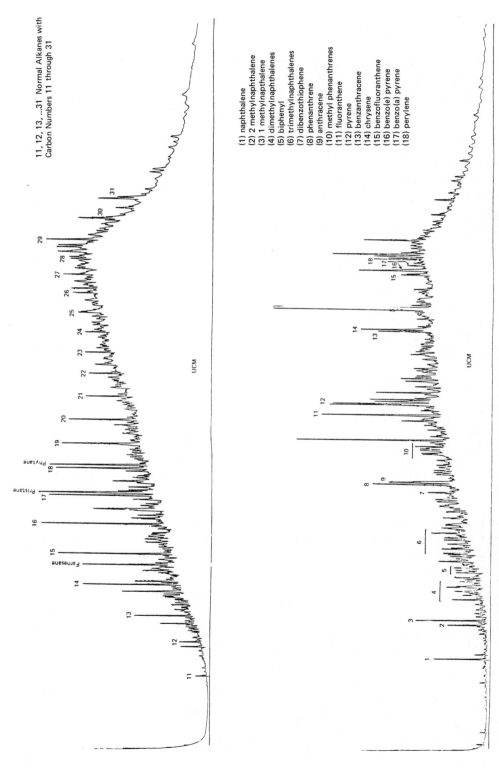

11, 12, 13,...31 Normal Alkanes with Carbon Numbers 11 through 31

UCM

(1) naphthalene
(2) 2 methylnaphthalene
(3) 1 methylnapthalene
(4) dimethylnaphthalenes
(5) biphenyl
(6) trimethylnaphthalenes
(7) dibenzothiophene
(8) phenanthrene
(9) anthracene
(10) methyl phenanthrenes
(11) fluoranthene
(12) pyrene
(13) benzanthracene
(14) chrysene
(15) benzofluoranthene
(16) benzo(e) pyrene
(17) benzo(a) pyrene
(18) perylene

UCM

Figure 7.4. Gas chromatographic traces of dredged-material; saturated (*a*) and aromatic (*b*) hydrocarbons; UCM = unresolved complex mixture.

cline (~12 m) hydrocarbon and PCB levels appear similar to the control site with several PAH compounds being detected (phenanthrene, fluoranthene, pyrene) in the 1-10 ng liter^{-1} range. However, the main dredged-material particulate plume apparently is located in the well-mixed bottom layer below the thermocline, at approximately 21 m as evidenced by the results for the 7-21 sample. Extremely high levels of aliphatic hydrocarbons (71.6 μg liter^{-1}), aromatic hydrocarbons (21.8 μg liter^{-1}), PCB (58.0 ng liter^{-1}), and individual PAH compounds are observed.

At 2.5 h after the dump, we again found elevated hydrocarbon, PCB, and PAH levels in the bottom samples (8-21) and no indication of dredged-material particulate organics above or at the thermocline. After 2.5 h, PCB levels in the particulate samples were 38.1 ng liter^{-1} and individual PAH levels ranged from nondetectable to 60 ng liter^{-1}. An expanded PAH search was performed for both the 7-21 and 8-21 samples as shown in Table 7.3. High levels of *substituted* (alkylated) phenanthrenes, dibenzothiophenes, and fluorenes were found in the 7-21 samples but were nondetectable in the 8-21 samples. An abundance of alkylated PAH compounds relative to the parent (unsubstituted) compound is probably directly related to the presence of petroleum-related material. In contrast, the parent compounds of each homologous series are more abundant than the alkylated constituents where pyrolytic sources (fossil fuel combustion) dominate the assemblage (Youngblood and Blumer, 1975). Thus, the difference in 7-21 and 8-21 may indicate inhomogeneity of the dredged material or a mixture of pyrogenic and petroleum-related compounds in the 7-21 sample. In any event, these two samples (7-21 and 8-21) are the only ones obtained that contain elevated PCB, PAH, and saturated hydrocarbon levels.

Total suspended matter (TSM) values (P. Mukherji, personal communication) roughly corresponding to the sample locations are presented in Table 7.3 as well. Two important points are: (1) while elevated TSM values for bottom water seem to be prevalent in the area even prior to dumping, dredged-material related PCB and PAH were detected only after the dump; (2) organic concentrations when placed on a weight basis using sample 7-5 values are excessively high compared with Table 7.2 values. We therefore believe the TSM values not to be representative of the plume material that was sampled by the organic chemistry component of the experiment. Differences may be attributable to lack of synopticity of the two sets of samples and to different sampling devices [1-liter Niskin bottles (General Oceanics Inc., Miami, Florida) for TSM; 10-liter GO-FLO® bottles for organics.]

Gas chromatograms of the source dredged material and the 8-21 sample, compared with the control bottom sample (6-21), are presented in Fig. 7.5 and 7.6. The saturated hydrocarbon distribution of the 8-21 sample reveals a pattern depleted in the low end of the hydrocarbon distribution relative to the source material. A large UCM with prominent isoprenoid hydrocarbons and lesser amounts of *n*-alkanes characterize the 8-21 sample. Presumably, depletion of the low-boiling *n*-alkanes (n-C_{11} to n-C_{20}) occurs due to solubilization. The depletion of the *n*-alkanes relative to the isoprenoids results from rapid microbial degradation on the fine-grained waterborne particulates (Atlas et al., 1981). The control sample

Table 7.3. Chemical Composition of Suspended Particulate Samples

Parameter	Sample Number (Station-Depth)												
	6-2	6-14	6-22	7-5	7-12	7-15	7-21	8-4	8-10(1)	8-10(2)	8-10(3)	8-21	Blank
Total extractable organic matter (μg liter^{-1})	206.0	48.0	54.6	122.5	36.0	56.2	224.3	64.8	85.3	42.8	31.8	113.5	3.0
Aliphatic hydrocarbons (f_1) (μg liter^{-1})	7.3	1.4	3.2	4.4	2.5	0.6	71.6	10.9	3.1	5.1	1.0	35.1	0.4
Aromatic hydrocarbons (f_2) (μg liter^{-1})	7.5	3.7	13.2	6.3	3.2	6.9	21.8	6.3	15.1	3.9	1.1	14.3	0.5
PCB (ng liter^{-1}) (Arochlor 1254)	trace[a]	ND	ND	trace	6.9	ND	58.0	ND	trace	trace	trace	38.1	ND
Total suspended material (μg kg^{-1})[b]	—	289[c]	1497[c]	675	171	235	1045	289	288	288	288	~1000	—
Individual PAH (ng liter^{-1})													
naphthalene	7.5	9.9	16.0	3.3	6.0	4.5	4.2	2.1	6.0	5.1	7.5	9.0	1.5
2-methylnaphthalene	5.1	ND	4.2	ND	ND	ND	ND	ND	ND	ND	1.8	8.1	ND
1-methylnaphthalene	3.0	ND	ND	ND	ND	ND	ND	ND	ND	ND	ND	3.9	ND
biphenyl	<1.5	ND	ND	ND	ND	ND	ND	ND	ND	ND	ND	ND	ND
dibenzothiophene	ND	ND	ND	ND	ND	ND	13.2	ND	ND	ND	ND	3.6	ND
phenanthrene	5.7	ND	ND	6.0	3.3	3.0	58.5	3.6	ND	7.2	1.5	31.5	ND
anthracene	ND	ND	ND	ND	ND	ND	23.1	ND	ND	ND	ND	18.9	0.5
1-methylphenanthrene	2.7	ND	ND	6.6	ND	ND	47.7	ND	ND	ND	ND	23.1	ND

fluoranthene	3.3	1.5	8.4	1.5	1.5	101.1	ND	ND	ND	44.1	ND
pyrene	1.0	ND	11.4	4.2	3.0	117.0	ND	3.0	ND	60.3	ND
benzo(a)anthracene	ND	ND	ND	ND	ND	101.4	ND	6.3	ND	30.0	ND
chrysene	ND	ND	ND	ND	ND	219.6	ND	ND	ND	42.9	ND
benzofluoranthene	ND	ND	ND	ND	ND	127.2	ND	ND	ND	24.0	ND
benzo(e)pyrene	ND	ND	ND	ND	ND	43.8	ND	ND	ND	7.8	ND
benzo(a)pyrene	ND	ND	ND	ND	ND	24.4	ND	ND	ND	15.6	ND
perylene	ND	ND	ND	ND	ND	22.6	ND	ND	ND	ND	ND
C2 naphthalenes	ND	ND	ND	ND	ND	ND	ND	ND	ND	ND	ND
C3 naphthalenes	ND	ND	ND	ND	ND	14.1	ND	ND	ND	ND	ND
C4 naphthalenes	ND	ND	ND	ND	ND	ND	ND	ND	ND	ND	ND
fluorene	ND	ND	ND	ND	ND	6.3	ND	ND	ND	ND	ND
C1 fluorene	ND	ND	ND	ND	ND	10.5	ND	ND	ND	ND	ND
C2 fluorene	ND	ND	ND	ND	ND	63.3	ND	ND	ND	ND	ND
C1 dibenzothiophene	ND	ND	ND	ND	ND	34.8	ND	ND	ND	ND	ND
C2 dibenzothiophene	ND	ND	ND	ND	ND	81.0	ND	ND	ND	ND	ND
C3 dibenzothiophene	ND	ND	ND	ND	ND	113.7	ND	ND	ND	ND	ND
C2 phenanthrene	ND	ND	ND	ND	ND	149.1	ND	ND	ND	54.2	ND
C3 phenanthrene	ND	ND	ND	ND	ND	181.2	ND	ND	ND	60.0	ND
C4 phenanthrene	ND	ND	ND	ND	ND	217.8	ND	ND	ND	10.1	ND

[a] Trace = <10; ND = not detected.
[b] P. Mukherji, personal communication.
[c] Background TSM values not synoptic with organic parameters.

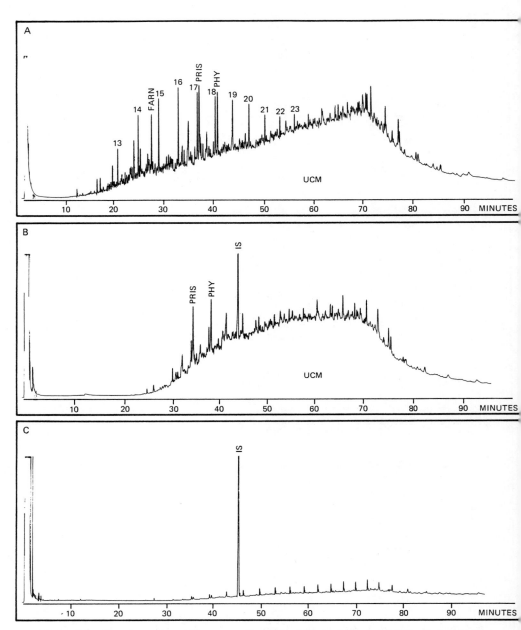

Figure 7.5. Gas chromatographic traces of saturated hydrocarbons. (*a*) dredged-material; (*b*) particulate matter from sample 8-21; and (*c*) particulates from sample 6-22. UCM = unresolved complex mixture, PRIS = pristane, PHY = phytane, IS = internal standard.

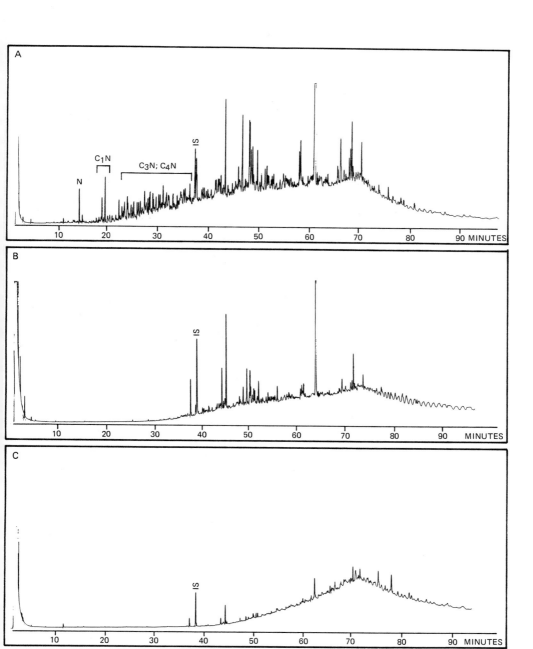

Figure 7.6. Gas chromatographic traces of aromatic hydrocarbons. (*a*) dredged-material; (*b*) particulates from sample 8-21; and (*c*) particulates from sample 6-22 (C).

(6–21) shows only trace levels of resolved hydrocarbons relative to the internal standard.

Comparison of the aromatic hydrocarbon GC traces (Fig. 7.6) shows that the 8–21 sample is also depleted in the low-boiling, presumably more soluble, aromatic compounds. The 6–21 control consists of a different GC pattern, one illustrating a heavily degraded distribution consisting primarily of UCM material. Figure 7.7 shows aromatic hydrocarbon profiles on a comparative basis for the two dredged-material samples, and the 7–21 and 8–21 particulate samples; the concentrations of aromatic hydrocarbons were normalized to chrysene. Such a presentation assumes that chrysene undergoes minimal relative change between the samples due to dissolution or degradation. Thus, it can be seen that: (1) the two dredged-material samples were similar; (2) the 8–21 sample was similar to the source material in its 3- and 4-ringed aromatic composition, the 2-ringed compounds being depleted presumably by dissolution (Zurcher and Thuer, 1978); and (3) the 7–21 sample is also similar to the dredged material, although almost totally depleted in 2-ringed aromatics.

Sampling replication was examined at station 8 with the 10-m samples collected in triplicate. Some variation was noted in total extractable organics (Table 7.3) and in the hydrocarbon levels in 8–10(3). PCB levels are quite similar in all replicates. Naphthalene was detected in similar concentrations in all three samples. Fluoranthene and pyrene were detected in one of the samples. The variation in these replicates illustrates the heterogeneous nature of the water column particulate distributions and the resultant patchiness in the distribution of some of the PAH compounds.

PCB levels in the water column observed during the disposal operations ($\sim$40–60 μg liter^{-1}) are similar to those observed by Hatcher et al. (1978) during sewage sludge spot-dump disposal operations. In the sewage disposal study PCB-bearing particulates quickly penetrated the thermocline and were observed in bottom waters to a much greater extent than above the thermocline. This is also the case with the dredged-material spot-dump investigated in this study.

7.4. CONCLUSIONS

The dredged material contained a complex mixture of anthropogenic organic compounds including large concentrations of PAH and PCB compounds. This complexity was reflected in the two near-bottom samples collected after the dump, which had a PAH distribution and PCB levels indicative of dredged material, albeit a somewhat "weathered" distribution. No indication of dredged-material particulate matter in the water column was observed at or above the thermocline. The sample taken at 2.5 h (8–21) appeared to contain a PAH distribution more similar to the dredged material than that shown in the sample taken at 15 min (7–21).

The method of sampling and onboard processing of samples for organic analysis was successful in determining both the location and composition of the dredged-material plume in the water column; the analytical results indicated qualitative and quantitative differences between pre- and postdump sample sets.

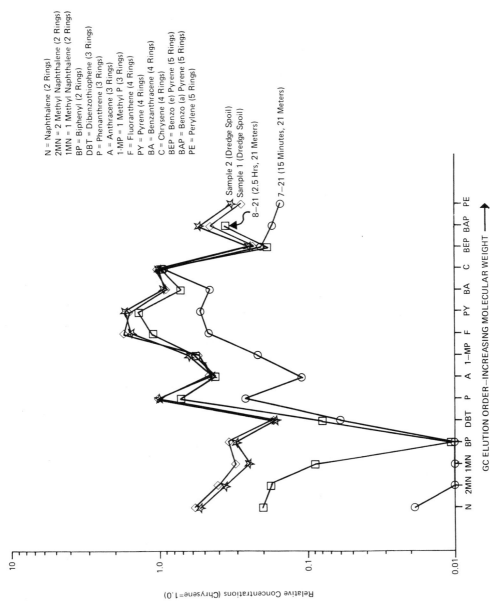

Figure 7.7. Comparative aromatic hydrocarbon composition plot of source dredged material and suspended particulate samples.

167

Due to relatively lower levels of PAH and PCB compounds in background coastal seawater in New York Bight, quantitative and qualitative determination of these compounds in the water column after dredged-material disposal can serve as extremely sensitive (parts per trillion) chemical indicators of the movement and persistence of dredged-material organic compounds on suspended particles.

ACKNOWLEDGMENTS

We thank Scott Drew, Neil Mosesman, and Ann Jefferies of Energy Resources Co., Inc. for their assistance with GC and GCMS analytical determinations. This research was supported by funding from the U.S. Department of Commerce, NOAA-MESA New York Bight Program, Contract No. NA-79-RAA-03401.

REFERENCES

Albaiges, J. and P. Albrecht. 1979. Fingerprinting marine pollutant hydrocarbons by computerized gas chromatography–mass spectrometry. *International Journal of Environmental and Analytical Chemistry*, **6**, 171–190.

Atlas, R. M., P. D. Boehm, and J. A. Calder. 1981. Chemical and biological weathering of oil from the *Amoco Cadiz* oil spillage, within the littoral zone. *Estuarine and Coastal Marine Science*, **12**, 589–608.

Atwood, D., D. W. Brown, V. Cabelli, J. Farrington, C. Garside, G. Han, D. V. Hansen, G. Harvey, K. S. Kamlet, J. O'Connor, L. Swanson, D. Swift, J. Thomas, J. Walsh, and T. Whitledge. 1979. The New York Bight, *In*: Proceedings of a Workshop on Assimilative Capacity of U.S. Coastal Waters for Pollutants, Crystal Mountain, Washington, E. D. Goldberg (Ed.). Special Report, National Oceanic and Atmospheric Administration, Environmental Research Laboratories, Boulder, Colorado, pp. 148–178.

Boehm, P. D., D. L. Fiest, and A. Elskus. 1981. Comparative weathering patterns of hydrocarbons from the *Amoco Cadiz* oil spill observed at a variety of coastal environments. Proceedings, International Symposium on the Amoco Cadiz: Fates and Effects of the Oil Spill. Brest, France, November 19–22, 1979.

Brown, D. W., L. S. Ramos, A. J. Friedman, and W. D. MacLeod. 1979. Analysis of trace levels of petroleum hydrocarbons in marine sediments using a solvent/ slurry extraction procedure. *In*: Trace Organic Analysis: A New Frontier in Analytical Chemistry. National Bureau of Standards Special Publication 519. U.S. Department of Commerce, Washington, D.C., pp. 161–167.

Brown, D. W., L. S. Ramos, M. Y. Uyeda, A. J. Friedman, and W. D. MacLeod, Jr. 1980. Ambient temperature contamination of hydrocarbons from marine sediment—comparison with boiling solvent extractions. *In*: Petroleum in the Marine Environment. Advances in Chemistry Series No. 185, L. Petrakis, and F. T. Weiss (Eds.). American Chemical Society, Washington, D.C., pp. 313–326.

Dastillung, M. and P. Albrecht. 1976. Molecular test for oil pollution in surface sediments. *Marine Pollution Bulletin*, **7**, 13–15.

Farrington, J. W. and B. W. Tripp. 1977. Hydrocarbons in western North Atlantic surface sediments. *Geochimica et Cosmochimica Acta*, **41**, 1627–1641.

Hatcher, P. G., G. A. Berberian, A. Y. Cantillo, P. A. McGillivery, P. Hanson, and R. H. West. 1981. Chemical and physical processes in a dispersing sewage sludge plume. *In*: Ocean Dumping of Industrial Wastes, B. H. Ketchum, D. R. Kester, and P. K. Park (Eds.). Plenum Press, New York, pp. 347–378.

Lee, M. L., G. P. Prado, J. B. Howard, and R. A. Hites. 1977. Source identification of urban airborne polycyclic aromatic hydrocarbons by gas chromatographic mass spectrometry and high resolution mass spectrometry. *Biomedical Mass Spectrometry*, **4**, 182–186.

Proni, J. R. and D. V. Hansen. 1981. Dispersion of particulates in the ocean studied acoustically: the importance of gradient surfaces in the ocean. *In*: Ocean Dumping of Industrial Wastes, B. H. Ketchum, D. R. Kester, P. K. Park (Eds.). Plenum Press, New York, pp. 161–173.

Pararas-Carayannis, G. 1973. Ocean dumping in the New York Bight: an assessment of environmental studies. U.S. Army Corps of Engineers Technical Memorandum 39. Coastal Engineering Research Center, Springfield, Virginia, 159 pp.

Panuzio, F. L. 1965. Lower Hudson River Siltation. Proceedings of the Federal Inter-Agency Sedimentation Conference, Jackson, Mississippi, 28 January–1 February 1963. *In*: Miscellaneous Publication Number 970, Agriculture Research Service, U.S. Department of Agriculture, Washington, D.C., pp. 512–550.

Saila, S. B., S. D. Pratt, and T. T. Polgar. 1972. Dredge spoil disposal in Rhode Island Sound. Marine Technical Report No. 2, University of Rhode Island, Kingston, 48 pp.

Youngblood, W. W. and M. Blumer. 1975. Polycyclic aromatic hydrocarbons in the environment: homologous series in soils and recent marine sediments. *Geochimica et Cosmochimica Acta*, **39**, 1303–1314.

Zurcher, F. and M. Thuer. 1978. Rapid weathering processes of fuel oil in natural waters: analyses and interpretations. *Environmental Science and Technology*, **12**, 838–843.

PART III: BIOLOGICAL FACTORS RELATED TO DREDGED-MATERIAL DISPOSAL IN THE OCEAN

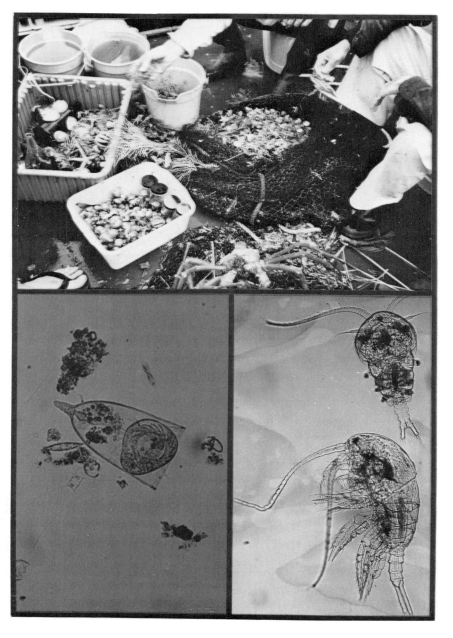

8

SEDIMENT-COPPER RESERVOIR FORMATION BY THE BURROWING POLYCHAETE *NEPHTYS INCISA*

Wayne R. Davis

U.S. Environmental Protection Agency
Environmental Research Laboratory
Narragansett, Rhode Island

ABSTRACT

The activities of benthic infauna may be a major mechanism for exchange of contaminants between seawater and fine-grained sediments. For example, enhanced sediment uptake of copper can result from the burrowing and irrigation activities of the deposit-feeding polychaete, *Nephtys incisa*. The burrow walls provide additional surface for sorption of waterborne copper similar to that occurring at the sediment surface. Both of these surfaces concentrate copper to depths not exceeding 4 mm, suggesting a simple diffusion process. The burrow wall uptake of copper is of greater importance than surface sediment exchange for two reasons. First, the burrow penetrates the sediment to a depth of between 5 and 20 cm, depending on worm size; this may result in an approximately 10–40 times increase in potential copper uptake by the sediment. Secondly, *N. incisa* periodically extends its U-shaped burrow, leading to formation of a new burrow. This new burrow enhances sediment uptake of copper by exposing clean sediment to burrow irrigation water.

Major variables affecting this biologically mediated uptake of copper include: abundance of *N. incisa*; worm size, which influences burrow depth and length; organic content of the sediment surrounding the burrow, which directly influences copper uptake; and the presence of particulate material in the overlying seawater, which acts to scavenge copper from the water. *N. incisa* burrow irrigation transports these suspended particles, with their sorbed copper, into the burrow for accumulation in the benthos.

8.1. INTRODUCTION

Many contaminants entering marine water have a high affinity for suspended particulate matter and fine-grained sediments (Jungclaus et al., 1978). Knowledge of the factors that influence the flux of contaminants to the benthos is important to predict transport and fate of contaminants in marine ecosystems. Additionally, such information is crucial to evaluate potential contaminant effects of aquatic life or their potential for entering human food chains.

There is some evidence that benthic infauna, particularly the so-called bioturbators, are important in the chemical exchange between sediment and water. For example, tube irrigation by the polychaete *Amphitrite ornata* enhances the ammonia flux to overlying water (Aller and Yingst, 1978). Burrow irrigation has also been shown to influence the benthic flux of methane (Martens, 1976), dissolved oxygen (Davis and Miller, 1979), sulfate (Goldhaber et al., 1977), and manganese (McCaffrey et al., 1980). The direction of the flux of each of the above dissolved substances was from an area of high concentration to an area of low concentration, consistent with the diffusion process, but enhanced by bioturbation. The benthic fauna may enhance the development of contaminant reservoirs in the sediment or conversely contribute to the release of contaminants from sediments, depending on the direction of pollutant concentration gradients.

This chapter focuses on the question: *How do the activities of a burrowing animal influence the formation of contaminant reservoirs in sediment?* Experiments were conducted to evaluate the influence of several variables on the flux of copper to sediment by *Nephtys incisa*. Geochemical variables considered included seawater copper concentration, the organic content of the sediment, and the presence of particulate matter in overlying seawater. Biological variables considered include the burrowing habits of *N. incisa*, the size of burrowing worms, and the population density.

My hypothesis is that *N. incisa* is important to sediment–water exchange of contaminants because it burrows continuously in anoxic sediments, it irrigates an open burrow, and hence it aerates the sediment adjacent to each burrow lumen. Such habits, not uncommon to infaunal polychaetes, serve to increase substantially the sediment–water interface, and hence to increase the surface area available for the diffusion of contaminants into or out of the sediment. The action of *N. incisa* as a bioturbator affecting a flux of contaminants from sediment is of special interest when considering the effects of dredged-material disposal, because this species is one of few which persists in both polluted estuaries such as upper Narragansett Bay (Farrington et al., 1973), and which also colonizes offshore dredged-material dumpsites (Donald Rhoads, personal communication).

8.2. MATERIALS AND METHODS

8.2.1. Experimental Design

The experimental unit for this study was a thin, glass-walled aquarium filled with sediment (Fig. 8.1a). Single preweighed 1- to 2-year-old *N. incisa* were placed in each of several aquaria. The extent of burrowing activity against the glass walls could be observed directly, photographed, and quantified by electronic planimetry. The sliding glass walls were removed at the completion of an experiment and sediment samples were taken at selected points along the burrow walls. Groups of ten thin aquaria were placed in a larger aquarium for exposure to copper (Fig. 8.1b). The flow rates of seawater, the concentration of waterborne copper and suspended particles were controlled in the large aquarium. Seawater was delivered at 100 ml min^{-1} at 18°C. An ionic copper solution was delivered with a peristaltic pump at 1 ml min^{-1} and mixed with the flowing seawater before it entered the tank. Particulate matter suspended in seawater was pulsed into the tank using an air-lift siphon connected to an aerator which was energized for 5 s every 6 h.

The collection site of both *N. incisa* and experimental sediment was from mid-Narragansett Bay, Rhode Island (Davis and Miller, 1979). The collection site was dominated by fine-grained sediment with a high silt-clay content. The surface layer (≤ 1 cm) was flocculant, watery, and contained 10–11% ignitable organic matter. The remainder of the bioturbation zone, which may extend down 20–30 cm, possessed only half as much ignitable organic matter and the sediment was more compact. *Nephtys incisa* is prevalent in this type of sediment, along with the deposit-feeding bivalves *Nucula annulata* and *Yoldia limatula*. The surface sediment of this type of bottom is subjected to resuspension followed by resedimentation within a single tidal period (Oviatt and Nixon, 1975; Roman and Tenore, 1978). This resuspension-resedimentation cycle was simulated over 6-h tidal cycles by recycling seawater in the large aquarium. During the recycling periods, the maximum tidal currents, the quantity of suspended sediment and the rate of sedimentation were simulated to the approximate levels reported for Narragansett Bay (Oviatt and Nixon, 1975).

8.2.2. Analytical Methods

All seawater copper measurements were made by direct injection of the samples into a Perkin-Elmer (Perkin-Elmer, Inc., Norwalk, Connecticut) atomic absorption

(a)

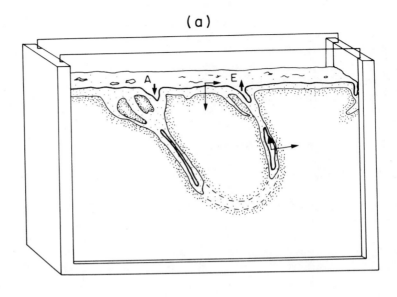

(b)

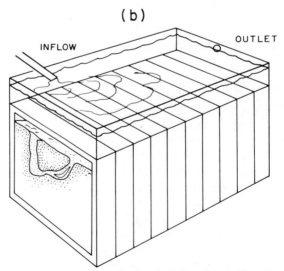

Figure 8.1. (*a*) Thin, sediment-filled aquarium with sliding glass walls. A–afferent burrow opening; E-efferent burrow opening. (*b*) Ten thin aquaria in larger flow-through aquarium.

spectrophotometer (AAS) equipped with a heated graphite atomizer after acidification with 10% HNO_3.

Sediment and tissue copper levels were analyzed with a Perkin-Elmer conventional flame AAS. All tissue and sediment samples were prepared for analysis using a dilute acid elution technique (5% HNO_3) to extract the copper quantitatively from these matrices (Hoffman and Zanni, 1979). Storing the dried worms or sediment in HNO_3 for approximately 1 week at room temperature produced copper concentrations in the dilute acid solution equivalent to heating the worm tissue or sediment with a combination of concentrated HNO_3 and 30% H_2O_2 over several days. Comparison between the two techniques for worm tissue and three distinct sediment types resulted in 13 ± 4% higher values for copper occurring with the dilute acid elution method. Hence, this method was adopted for this study.

Seawater particle loads and particle sizes were monitored using a Coulter Counter Model TAII (Hialeah, Florida), modified to use both 100- and 200-μm orifices. Particle counts and size fractionation were measured over the 6-h cycle periods of the simulated tide cycle. Suspended matter was independently measured as mg dry weight per liter following filtration on 0.45-μm cellulose acetate filter pads.

8.3. RESULTS

The amount of copper taken up by the surface sediment and the sediment along the burrow walls of *N. incisa* is proportional to the copper concentration of the overlying seawater (Fig. 8.2) and the duration of the copper exposure period. The results summarized in Fig. 8.2 also suggest that sediment uptake of copper was largely a diffusion process, because uptake was greatest within the initial 2 mm and it was reduced sharply at the 3 and 6 mm sampling points. Sediment samples taken from the burrow walls (Fig. 8.2b) demonstrate that *N. incisa* burrow building enhances copper uptake by the sediment as the worm penetrates the sediment and greatly extends the water–sediment interface below the sediment surface. However, in the experiment summarized in Fig. 8.2, surface sediment accumulated 3-fold more copper than did the burrow walls. This difference reflects the contrasting exposure periods of these two sediments. The surface sediment was exposed to the copper-treated seawater for 30 d, whereas the burrows sampled were only 2–14 days old because the worm continued to burrow.

The quantity of copper adsorbed by interface sediment was increased by higher organic levels in the sediment (Table 8.1). The lower organic load of 5.2% ignitable loss is typical of deep, consolidated sediment, while the higher value of 10.6% is typical for the surface flocculant layer of fine sediments. When these two sediments were exposed for 30 d to seawater with a background copper concentration ($>$1-3 μg Cu liter^{-1}), resulting copper levels were 38 and 59 μg Cu g^{-1} sediment respectively for the low and high organic sediment. Uptake at the two elevated copper exposure levels continued to reflect this relationship, averaging a 158 and 160% increase in copper uptake above that of low organic sediment. Uptake, expressed as a concentration factor, averaged a 980-fold increase for the low organic matter sediments over seawater concentrations, whereas high organic sediment averaged a 1960-fold increase. Thus, a doubling of the organic content resulted in a doubling in the concentration factor.

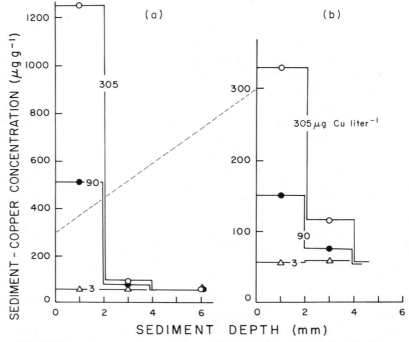

Figure 8.2. Relation between copper content of water and copper content of sediment at the water–sediment interface (30-d exposure). Waterborne copper treatment levels are indicated as 3 (background), 90, or 305 μg Cu liter^{-1}. (*a*) Interface at upper sediment surface. (*b*) Interface across burrow wall of *N. incisa*. The dashed line indicates the vertical scale expansion of part *b* relative to part *a*.

The copper flux to the sediment was greatly increased when suspended sediment was present. Suspended particulate matter, which was introduced into the flow-through system every 6 h, gradually settles out over a 3- to 4-h period. Most particles settled out on the sediment surface or were pumped into the deeper sediment by irrigation of *N. incisa*. Fig. 8.3a shows the quantitiy of suspended particles by size class over a 6-h cycle; the dry weight of this suspension is shown in Fig.

Table 8.1. Relationship of Sediment Copper Content (μg g^{-1}) to Ignitable Organic Content

Ignitable Organic Content (%)	Waterborne Copper Concentration (μg liter^{-1})		
	3 (Control)	95	300
5.6	26	65	125
10.6	60	155	325

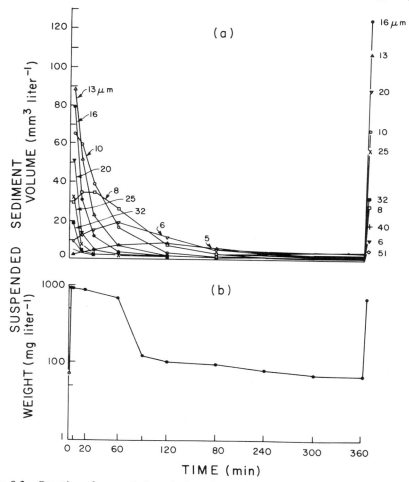

Figure 8.3. Quantity of suspended particulates in overlying seawater in relation to 6-h time cycle. (*a*) Computed volume for 16 size fractions (Coulter Counter TAII; 200 μm orifice). (*b*) Weight of suspended particulates (Millipore filtered; 0.4 μm).

8.3b. Eventually, all abandoned burrows of *N. incisa* became filled with suspended particulates. This material contained the highest level of copper at the 95 μg Cu liter^{-1} exposure level (Fig. 8.4). Thus, suspended sediment (high organic content) scavenged more copper than the sediment on the bottom (260 versus 155 μg g^{-1} (Table 8.1).

These results (Figs. 8.2 and 8.4) demonstrate that the burrow wall of *Nephtys* sorbs waterborne copper as a function of the copper concentration and the organic content of the sediment wall. Further, if there are suspended particles present, they scavenge copper and gradually fill the burrow. Thus the resulting worm-mediated copper reservoir is a function of both the surface area of the burrow wall

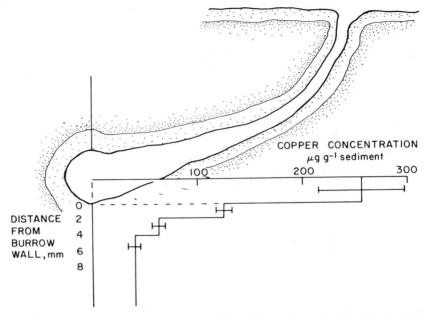

Figure 8.4. Diagrammatic cutaway of a burrow indicating measured copper levels present in the particles filling a burrow lumen and in the sediment adjacent to lumen.

and the volume of the burrow lumen; both of these variables are a function of the size of the worm.

An unusual burrowing habit by *N. incisa* further expands the potential copper reservoir: *Nephtys* burrows in fine sediment to form an open burrow which it irrigates constantly in a flow-through manner. However, *N. incisa* will abandon its burrow or portions of it at a temperature-dependent rate to form another burrow, often continuous with the older one (Fig. 8.5). This habit results in continual

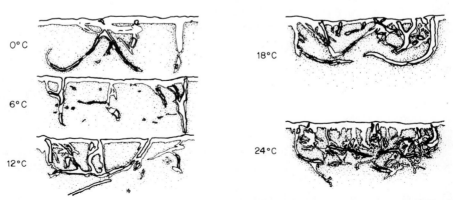

Figure 8.5. Representative burrowing patterns of single *N. incisa* visible against glass walls of sediment-filled aquaria (56-d record at 0, 6, 12, 18, and 24°C).

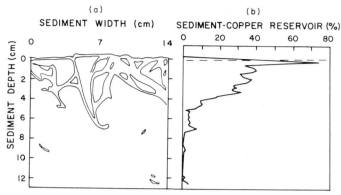

Figure 8.6. Diagram of the visible bioturbation record and the distribution of sampling the copper reservoir of the sediment against wall of a thin aquarium. (*a*) Tracing of photograph of aquarium wall after 30-d exposure conditions. (*b*) Computed volume of copper-enhanced sediment (%) in relation to sediment depth.

exposure of clean sediment which serves to maintain a gradient between metal-polluted seawater and the sediment. Eventually a characteristic bioturbation record emerges, consisting of burrow lumens and halos of aerobic sediment surrounding each burrow (Fig. 8.5). Each visible record is virtually a record of the site of copper-enhanced sediment. For instance, Fig. 8.6a is an illustration of the burrowing activity of *N. incisa* and as determined from small scale sampling the copper

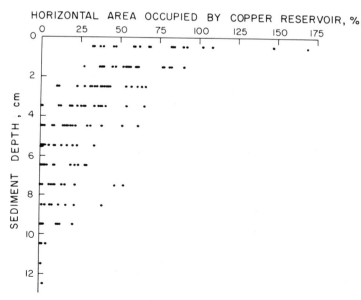

Figure 8.7. The computed surface area of visible bioturbation and the copper reservoir (%) of the sediment for 20 experimental aquaria shown in Fig. 8.6.

reservoir for a single worm after 30 d. The surface area of visibly disturbed sediment was electronically digitized, permitting computation of related copper reservoir with respect to depth in sediment. Fig. 8.6b shows this computation of copper-enhanced sediment with depth for a single worm. The large spike at the surface represents copper enhancement at the sediment–water interface which occurs regardless of the presence of *N. incisa*. Copper uptake exponentially declined with depth. The exponential decline in burrowing with depth accounts for the drop in the vertical copper reservoir with depth. As a consequence, an apparent large scale (6–12 cm) sediment-copper profile, the kind of data derived from coring, was found to be the integrative result of microscale uptake (~2 mm). This is illustrated by Fig. 8.7 which summarizes the vertical distribution of 20 separate bioturbation records.

Much of the variation between copper uptake and depth is due to worm size, and is apparent when the depth of individual copper reservoirs are plotted against that worm's weight (Fig. 8.8). Also shown in Fig. 8.8 is the measured depth of 50% of the reservoir. An increase in worm size produces a corresponding increase in burrow length and depth, which results in a corresponding increase in the volume and depth of sediment exposed to water-borne copper. Larger worms produce wider and longer burrows. Their burrows extend to a greater depth and the larger *Nephtys* pump more irrigation water (Davis and Miller, 1979). Since copper uptake is a result of individual worms irrigating their burrows, population density would directly affect the quantity of copper uptake per unit time. Thus, greater worm densities lead to a greater rate of sediment loading.

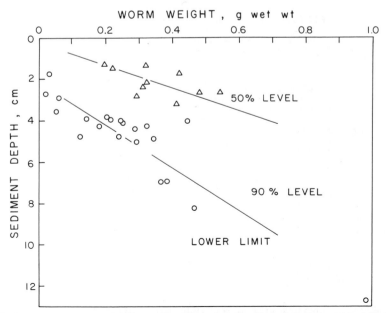

Figure 8.8. The depth of copper enhancement in relation to the wet body weight of *N. incisa*. Best fit linear regression lines indicate the depth at which 50 and 100% of the copper reservoir is located in relation to body weight.

8.4. DISCUSSION

Burrowing by *Nephtys incisa*, typical of vermiforms, effectively expands the sediment–water interface surface area. The amount of this surface area is increased by animal density and size because larger worms possess wider, longer, and deeper burrows. Because occupied burrows are irrigated, the worm-mediated sediment–water interface can increase sediment–water exchange, assuming that concentration gradients exist.

The relationships between worm burrow, copper exposure levels, and sediment uptake observed in this study support a sorption process. It is thus concluded that the irrigated burrow of *Nephtys* influences copper uptake by acting as an invagination of the surface sediment–water interface. The effective copper uptake depth then becomes the burrowing depth of 10–20 cm, a marked contrast to 2–4 mm in undisturbed sediment. Besides explaining one means of copper reservoir formation in sediment, the copper sorption of burrow walls can serve to detoxify copper-contaminated seawater. Pesch (1979) demonstrated a marked drop in copper mortality of *Neanthes arenaceodentata* when fine-grained sediment was placed in the worm exposure system.

Copper uptake in sediment is mediated by *Nephtys* as a result of the worm providing additional sediment–water interface area. The direction of copper movement is probably a function of the concentration gradient between these two matrices. Thus, it is entirely possible that infaunal burrow irrigation in contaminated sediment could produce a flux from the sediment to the overlying seawater. Conditions that produce such a reversal in sediment–water concentration gradients would exist at offshore disposal sites where contaminated material has been dumped, or in previously polluted areas where water column concentrations have been reduced by pollution control.

ACKNOWLEDGMENTS

I am indebted to Dr. Gerry Hoffman whose patient schooling in H.G.A. atomic absorption spectrophotometry, sample preparation, and peak analyses was crucial to this study. I am very grateful to Robert Ballek for the careful sampling and data reduction. I owe much to my supervisor, Dr. Don C. Miller, for support and encouragement during this study.

REFERENCES

Aller, R. C. and J. Y. Yingst. 1978. Biogeochemistry of tube-dwellings: A study of the sedentary polychaete *Amphitrite ornata* (Feidy). *Journal of Marine Research*, 35, 201–254.

Davis, W. R. and D. C. Miller. 1979. Burrowing activities and sediment impact of *Nephtys incisa*. *In*: Advances in Marine Environmental Research, Proceedings of a Symposium. EPA-600/9-79-035. F. S. Jacoff (Ed.). U.S. Government Printing Office, Washington, D.C., pp. 302–319.

Farrington, J. W., J. G. Quinn and W. R. Davis. 1973. Fatty acid composition of *Nephtys incisa* and *Yoldia limatula*. *Journal of the Fisheries Research Board of Canada*, **30**, 181–185.

Goldhaber, M. B., R. C. Aller, J. K. Cochran, J. K. Rosenfeld, C. S. Martens, and R. A. Berner. 1977. Sulfate reduction, diffusion, and bioturbation in Long Island Sound sediments: Report of the FOAM Group. *American Journal of Science*, **277**, 193–237.

Hoffman, G. L. and R. M. Zanni. 1979. A simple elution technique for the analysis of copper in *Neanthes arenaceodentata*. *In*: Advances in Marine Environmental Research, Proceedings of a Symposium. EPA-600/9-79-035. F. S. Jacoff (Ed.). U.S. Government Printing Office, Washington, D.C., pp. 62–67.

Jungclaus, G. A., V. Lopez-Avila and R. A. Hites. 1978. Organic compounds in an industrial wastewater: A case study of the environmental impact. *Environmental Science and Technology*, **12**, 88–96.

Martens, C. S. 1976. Control of methane sediment–water transport by macro-infaunal irrigation in Cape Lookout Bight, North Carolina. *Science*, **192**, 998–1000.

McCaffrey, R. J., A. C. Myers, E. Davey, G. Morrison, M. Bender, N. Luedtke, D. Cullen, P. Froelich, and G. Klinkhammer. 1980. The relation between pore water chemistry and benthic fluxes of nutrients and manganese in Narragansett Bay. *Limnology and Oceanography*, **25**, 31–44.

Oviatt, C. A. and S. W. Nixon. 1975. Sediment resuspension and deposition in Narragansett Bay. *Estuarine and Coastal Marine Science*, **3**, 201–217.

Pesch, C. E. 1979. Influence of three sediment types on copper toxicity to the polychaete *Neanthes arenaceodentata*. *Marine Biology*, **52**, 237–245.

Roman, M. R. and K. R. Tenore. 1978. Tidal resuspension in Buzzards Bay, Massachusetts. *Estuarine and Coastal Marine Science*, **6**, 37–46.

9

FACTORS AFFECTING UPTAKE OF CADMIUM AND OTHER TRACE METALS FROM MARINE SEDIMENTS BY SOME BOTTOM-DWELLING MARINE INVERTEBRATES

S. Ray and D. W. McLeese

Fisheries and Environmental Sciences
Fisheries and Oceans Canada
Biological Station
St. Andrews, New Brunswick, Canada

ABSTRACT

A natural bioassay was conducted to determine the relationship, if any, between tissue contents of Cu, Zn, Cd, and Pb in bottom-dwelling marine invertebrates (crustaceans, polychaetes, and bivalves) and metal contents of the sediments. Bioaccumulation of these metals in the animals was low under natural circumstances. Metal contents of tissues remained fairly constant regardless of the metal contents of the sediments except for *Macoma*, a deposit-feeding bivalve. In laboratory studies, invertebrates were exposed to two naturally contaminated sediments for 30 d to simulate field conditions. Only *Macoma* showed increases in all four metals from one sediment, and in Cu and Pb from the other. The polychaete *Nereis* and the crustacean *Crangon* showed regulation of Cu and Zn from both sediments. *Nereis* showed increase in Cd and Pb contents of the animals exposed to only one of the two sediments, whereas *Crangon* showed increase in only Pb content of the animals exposed to both sediments.

The bottom-dwelling polychaete *Nereis virens*, when exposed to Cd-spiked sediment in the laboratory, showed a linear increase of Cd in the animal tissue with time. Smaller worms accumulated higher amounts of Cd (per unit weight) than bigger ones. Cd excretion was not observed during the depuration phase. The Cd concentration within *Nereis* was related to the Cd concentration in the sediment, which in turn was related to the concentration of the element leached into the water.

A study of the adsorption-desorption process of Cd in sediment–seawater systems indicated that the process is controlled by cation exchange capacity and organic carbon content of the sediments.

9.1. INTRODUCTION

One of the most pressing estuarine management problems is related to the disposal of dredged sediment. The physical effects of dumping dredged material in coastal areas have long been recognized and steps have been taken to select dumpsites where such effects are minimized. The chemical contamination of certain dredged material has also received considerable attention.

Marine sediments are the ultimate recipients of nearly all metals introduced by man to the aquatic ecosystem, and only a small percentage of the metals remains in true solution. As a result, the concentration of the metals in the sediments is several orders of magnitude higher than in the waters. Dumping of dredged material containing several contaminants (viz., Cd, Hg, PCBs) in Canadian ocean waters is regulated strictly (Canada Gazette, 1975). Sediment containing trace elements may become a source of contamination due to biogeochemical interactions (Wolfe and Rice, 1972; Holmes et al., 1974; Lu and Chen, 1977). The aspects that have received considerable attention are impact on water quality and biological availability of the metals. High concentrations of heavy metals in marine organisms, due to bioaccumulation processes, have been correlated, in some cases, with high concentrations in the sediment and water (Ratkowski et al., 1974; Bryan and Uysal, 1978; Goldberg et al., 1978); bioaccumulation is the process where by a marine organism stores substances in various tissues or organs of the body.

The availability of sediment-bound metals to bottom-dwelling animals has been the subject of several studies (Jenne and Luoma, 1977; Neff et al., 1978). We have examined factors affecting uptake of Cd and other trace metals (Cu, Zn, and Pb) from marine sediments by bottom-dwelling invertebrates, under field and laboratory conditions.

9.2. EXPERIMENTAL

9.2.1. Exposure Studies

For the field study, the invertebrates (*Nereis virens*, *Crangon septemspinosa*, and *Macoma balthica*) and the sediments were collected at the same sites from coastal areas of New Brunswick, Canada. Individual animal weights were selected to be within a narrow range because metal contents in tissues of several invertebrates have been shown to be dependent on size (Boyden, 1977). The naturally contaminated sediments for the exposure studies in the laboratory were frozen immediately upon collection. Only the fraction <0.5 mm was used for animal exposure. Laboratory analogs of contaminated field sediments were prepared by spiking local beach sediments (500–1000 μm) in seawater with $CdCl_2$ solution, with vigorous stirring. The mixture was allowed to settle overnight, decanted, and washed repeatedly with seawater until an equilibrium level was reached in the overlying water.

The test animals were collected from uncontaminated areas near St. Andrews, New Brunswick and acclimated to the test conditions ($10 \pm 1°C$ and photoperiod 12 h light : 12 h dark) for a week before testing. The sizes of the animals selected for the study were: *Nereis*, 1–2 and 5–7 g; *Crangon*, 2–4 g; and *Macoma*, 1 cm length. Four to eight animals were exposed in a 2-liter beaker to about 300 ml sediment and fresh seawater (total volume 1.8 liters). The overlying water was not changed but was aerated gently during the test (30 d). Samples of water, animal, and sediments were taken periodically for metal analysis. Only *Nereis* was exposed to the spiked sediment and the overlying water was changed at 48-h intervals during the test. After sampling, the animals were transferred to uncontaminated sediment for 24 h to allow clearance of contaminated sediment from the gut. For excretion experiments following exposure, the animals were kept in uncontaminated sediments. The animals were not fed during exposure or excretion, though the *Nereis* and *Macoma* would get some food from the sediments.

9.2.2. Chemical Analysis

Individual whole *Nereis* and *Crangon* and pooled soft tissues of 5–7 *Macoma* were analysed for trace metals. The animals were freeze-dried, ashed for 12 h at 450°C, taken up in concentrated HNO_3 and made to volume for metal analysis. The sediments were digested with $HCl : HNO_3$ (1 : 3), filtered, and made to volume for analysis. The HCl and HNO_3 were Aristar grade® (B.D.H. Chemicals Ltd., Poole,

England).   All glassware was acid-washed; distilled-deionized water (Milli-Q®, Millipore Corp, Bedford, Massachusetts) was used for analytical work. Cd, Pb, and Cu at low concentrations were measured by graphite furnace atomic absorption spectrophotometry using a Perkin-Elmer model 503 spectrophotometer (Perkin-Elmer Corp., Norwalk, Connecticut) equipped with model HGA-2100 graphite furnace and a ramp accessory.   Zn and Cu at high concentrations were measured by flame technique.   Organic carbon in the sediments was determined by modified Walkley-Black oxidation of dried samples (Akagi and Wildish, 1975).   Cation exchange capacity of the sediments was determined following the procedure of Hesse (1971).

Accuracy and precision of the method for trace metal analysis were checked against U.S. National Bureau of Standards reference materials No. 1577 (bovine liver) and No. 1566 (oyster tissue).   The analytical results reported here are on a dry-weight basis.

9.2.3. Sorption Isotherm

A static batch method was used to determine the sorption isotherm on four different size fractions of local estuarine sediment.

For adsorption, about 1 g of untreated sediment was weighed and then added to 35 ml of seawater containing Cd (10–250 ng Cd ml^{-1}); the mixture was gently agitated for 24 h.   Water samples were withdrawn at regular intervals, centrifuged, and Cd remaining in the solution was determined.   For desorption, the sediment used for the adsorption study was washed quickly with seawater, centrifuged, and drained.   The preceding process was repeated except that 35 ml of clean seawater was added to the sediment.

9.2.4. Data analysis

A *student's t-test* was used to determine if the differences between the initial metal concentrations and the concentration at the end of respective study periods were significant.

Concentration factors are defined as concentration of metal in the animal divided by the concentration in water or sediment.   Uptake rates of the metals were obtained by linear regression analysis of the metal content in the tissues from 0 to 14 d.

9.3. RESULTS AND DISCUSSION

9.3.1. Natural Bioassay

Cu, Zn, Cd, and Pb levels in the animals *Nereis virens*, *Crangon septemspinosa*, *Macoma balthica* and their host sediments (Table 9.1) indicate that the bioaccumulation of the metals by the animals was low under natural circumstances. Only *Macoma* and *Crangon* were present at the majority of the sites.   The logarithmic relationships between the metal concentration factor of the tissue and the metal content of sediment are shown in Table 9.2.

Table 9.1. Range of Cu, Zn, Pb, and Cd Contents (μg g^{-1}, dry weight) in *Crangon*, *Macoma*, and *Nereis* and for the Host Sediments, Collected from Coastal Areas of New Brunswick

Sample	Cu	Zn	Pb	Cd
Sediments	2.6–37	21–640	2.0–195	0.06–6.9
Crangon	7.5–12	17–45	1.5–8.0	0.40–1.4
Macoma	3.5–7.0	27–190	0.3–22	0.10–0.45
Nereis	6.0–13	50–100	3.5–12	0.15–0.20

The negative slopes approaching unity and the high correlation coefficients, except for Pb in *Macoma*, indicate that metal content in these animals is in constant proportion to the metal concentration in the surrounding media. The regulation of essential trace elements Cu and Zn, by crustaceans has been reported (Bryan, 1968). Excretion of Cd by *Crangon* (Dethlefson, 1977/1978) has been observed; however, regulation of Cd by *Nereis*, as suggested in Table 9.1, is in contrast to field observations of Bryan and Hummerstone (1973) and the laboratory study of Ray et al. (1980). In view of insufficient data, this finding should be treated with caution and needs further confirmation.

The negative slope of 0.54 for Pb (Table 9.2) and a poor correlation coefficient indicated lack of equilibrium for Pb in *Macoma*. A comparison with the bioaccumulation data of other elements in the *Crangon* and *Macoma* seems to indicate that *Macoma* may be a suitable bioindicator for the presence of Pb in the field. The hypothesis is further supported if the maximum : minimum ratios of the metal content in the sediments and the animals are compared (Table 9.3). Though the maximum : minimum ratios of metal contents in the sediments were 14, 30, 115, and 98 for Cu, Zn, Cd, and Pb, respectively, the corresponding ratios in all animals

Table 9.2. Relationships Between Logarithm of the Concentration Factors of Metal in Animals (log Y) and the Logarithm of the Metal Concentration in Sediment (log X) for *Grangon* and *Macoma*[a]

Copper		
Crangon:	log Y = 0.91 − 1.00 log X	(r = −0.99)
Macoma:	log Y = 0.65 − 1.02 log X	(r = −0.98)
Zinc		
Crangon:	log Y = 1.30 − 0.87 log X	(r = −0.77)
Macoma:	log Y = 1.64 − 0.88 log X	(r = −0.88)
Lead		
Crangon:	log Y = 0.60 − 1.02 log X	(r = −0.97)
Macoma:	log Y = 0.34 − 0.54 log X	(r = −0.30)
Cadmium		
Crangon:	log Y = −0.28 − 1.00 log X	(r = −0.99)
Macoma:	log Y = −0.60 − 0.99 log X	(r = −0.96)

[a]Number of samples = 5.

Table 9.3.   Ratios of Maximum:Minimum Concentration of Metal in the Sediments and in the Animals Collected from Coastal Areas of New Brunswick, Canada

Sample	Cu	Zn	Pb	Cd
Sediments	14	30	98	115
Crangon	1.5	2.6	5.3	3.2
Macoma	2.0	7.0	73	4.5
Nereis	2.2	2.0	3.4	1.3

were only 1.5–2.2 for Cu, 2.0–7.0 for Zn, 1.3–4.5 for Cd, and 3.4–5.3 for Pb except that the ratio for *Macoma* was 73. These observations indicate that the concentrations of the elements within the animals do not reflect the sediment metal concentrations, except in the case of *Macoma* for Pb; the metal levels are almost constant within the animals under field conditions and probably only *Macoma* is suitable as a bioindicator for Pb.

Our field observations (Ray et al., 1979) indicate that *Crangon septemspinosa* can regulate the essential trace elements Cu and Zn as well as the nonessential metals Cd and Pb (Fig. 9.1). *Macoma* can regulate Cu, Zn, Cd, but not Pb.

9.3.2.   Laboratory Study with Naturally Contaminated Sediment

Two naturally contaminated sediments (designated *A* and *B*) were chosen to determine bioaccumulation of Cu, Zn, Cd, and Pb by the bottom-feeding animals, *Crangon*, *Macoma*, and *Nereis* under laboratory exposure conditions. The animals were exposed to the two sediments in static conditions for 30 d. The sediment characteristics are given in Table 9.4. Concentrations of Cu, Zn, and Pb in the over-

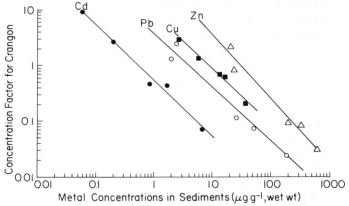

Figure 9.1. Concentration factors for heavy metals in *Crangon* in relation to heavy-metal concentrations in sediments where the animals were collected.

Table 9.4. Particle Size Distribution and Heavy Metal Content of Sediments Used for Uptake Studies

Sediment	Organic Carbon (%)	Size Distribution		Heavy Metal Concentration (μg g^{-1} air dry)			
		% Sand	% Silt	Cu	Zn	Pb	Cd
A	5.2	48	52	37.4	926	96	2.2
B	4.6	33	67	55.5	4030	243	6.7

lying waters at the end of the experiment were 0.06, 0.02 and 0.0002 μg ml^{-1}, respectively, for sediment A; and 0.06, 0.02 and 0.0008 μg ml^{-1}, respectively, for sediment B. Cd was not detectable in the water overlying sediment A but was present in trace amounts in the water overlying sediment B. Bioaccumulation characteristics of the animals exposed to the sediments are given in Table 9.5.

We found that the water overlying sediment A had no detectable amount of Cd and none of the animals exposed to the sediment showed any increase in the metal concentration. However, the increase in the Cd levels of the animals exposed to sediment B coincided with the presence of trace amounts of Cd in the water overlying the sediment. The absence of any increase of Cd in *Crangon* is in agreement with our earlier findings from the field study (Fig. 9.1, Table 9.2) and with Dethlefsen's (1977/78) study.

9.3.3. Laboratory Study with Spiked Sediment

In a laboratory study, *N. virens* was exposed to sediment spiked with Cd for a period of up to 24 d in semistatic conditions to determine the rate of accumulation of cadmium (Ray et al., 1980). We found that Cd concentration in the worms increased linearly with time without attaining equilibrium during the exposure phase (Fig. 9.2). The concentration of Cd in the worms increased with increasing concentration of Cd in the sediment; smaller worms accumulated higher amounts of Cd per unit weight and at a greater rate than larger worms (Table 9.6).

Table 9.5. Bioaccumulation Response, Expressed Qualitatively, of the Invertebrates to the Metal Content of the Two Sediments, A and B[a]

Sediment	Copper		Zinc		Lead		Cadmium	
	A	B	A	B	A	B	A	B
Crangon	–	–	–	–	+	+	–	–
Macoma	+	+	–	+	+	+	–	+
Nereis	–	–	–	–	–	+	–	+

[a]+ indicates bioaccumulation; – indicates no bioaccumulation.

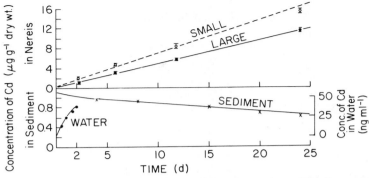

Figure 9.2. Cadmium concentration in *Nereis virens* from southwest New Brunswick exposed to sediment containing 1 μg g^{-1} Cd for 24 d and concentration in sediment and water.

Nereis virens, with an initial concentration of 4-21 μg Cd g^{-1} (dry wt), when transferred to clean conditions for a period up to 75 d did not show any excretion of Cd (Ray et al., 1980). During the exposure studies with the spiked sediment, we observed that the overlying water contained significant amounts of Cd (Fig. 9.2); the amounts were related to the Cd levels in the sediment. The maximum concentrations of Cd in the water were 0.04, 0.06, and 0.1 μg g^{-1} in the 1-, 2- and 4-μg g^{-1} sediment tests, respectively. *Nereis virens* was also exposed to seawater spiked with Cd corresponding to the amount found in the overlying waters of the sediment tests to determine uptake rates of Cd directly from water. Comparison of the data shows that the accumulation rates obtained from sediment tests [0.014–0.037 μg Cd g^{-1} (dry wt) h^{-1}] (Table 9.6) are almost identical to the rates obtained from the water tests [0.013–0.037 μg Cd g^{-1} (dry wt) h^{-1}] at 0.03 to 0.1 μg g^{-1} Cd (Ray et al., 1980). It thus appears that uptake rate of Cd by the worms is related to the concentration of Cd in the water which, in turn, is related to the concentration of Cd in the sediment. The Cd uptake by *N. virens* is primarily from the aqueous phase.

Table 9.6.   Regression Equations for Concentration of Cd in Worms (μg g^{-1}, dry wt) Exposed to Sediment Containing 1 to 4 μg g^{-1} Cd for 24 d, versus time (X) in h (from Ray et al., 1980)

Sediment Cd Concentration (μg g^{-1})	Worm Size (g, wet wt)	Regression Equations
1.0	1–2	$Y = 1.84 + 0.018X$ ($r = 0.97, n = 21$)
	5–7	$Y = 1.15 + 0.014X$ ($r = 0.96, n = 18$)
2.0	1–2	$Y = 2.71 + 0.024X$ ($r = 0.83, n = 19$)
	5–7	$Y = 1.73 + 0.017X$ ($r = 0.94, n = 20$)
4.0	1–2	$Y = -0.39 + 0.037X$ ($r = 0.99, n = 23$)
	5–7	$Y = -0.13 + 0.024X$ ($r = 0.97, n = 24$)

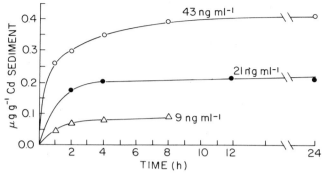

Figure 9.3. Time for sediment (particle size 63–125 μm) to attain equilibrium adsorption from three Cd concentrations in seawater.

9.3.4. Flux of Cadmium in Sediment–Water System

Animals exposed to naturally contaminated and spiked sediments in the laboratory showed that, for Cd to be bioavailable, the metal has to be released into the seawater from the sediment. However, prediction of bioavailability of trace metals in sediments to marine invertebrates is difficult (Ray and McLeese, 1980) since the factors controlling the sorption process are not well understood.

Sorption characteristics of Cd in a sediment–seawater system were investigated with local estuarine sediment separated into four size fractions.

Figure 9.3 shows the time required to attain equilibrium for sediment (63–125 μm) at three Cd concentrations ranging from 9 to 43 ng Cd ml^{-1}. The other sediment size ranges give similar plots. All isotherm experiments were performed for 24 h at room temperature.

The sorption data were fited to the Freundlich isotherm

$$q = KC^n$$

where: q = equilibrium concentration of adsorbate in sediment $(\mu g\ g^{-1})$; C = equilibrium concentration of adsorbate in water $(\mu g\ ml^{-1})$; K = equilibrium of partition coefficient; and n = exponent.

Table 9.7. Exponents and Adsorption Coefficients of Freundlich Isotherm, $q = KC^n$, for Adsorption and Desorption Experiments with Sediments of Different Particle Size

Sediment Size (μm)	TOC (%)	CEC [meq $(100\ g)^{-1}$]	Adsorption		Desorption	
			n	K	n	K
<63	2.0	17	0.9	23	1.2	42
63–125	0.3	3.5	1.1	9.7	1.1	14
125–250	0.2	4.2	1.2	6.1	1.1	38
250–500	2.9	9.4	0.9	31	1.9	74

Table 9.8. Percent Cd Adsorbed by Sediment Fractions of Different Sizes at Several Concentrations of Cd

Concentration of Cd (μg liter^{-1})	% Cd Adsorbed by Different Particle Size (μm)			
	<63	63–125	125–250	250–500
9.3	41	39	32	59
47	47	45	41	50
116	50	45	45	61
216	53	41	40	50
Average	48	42	40	55

Particle size distribution, total organic carbon (TOC), and cation exchange capacity (CEC) of the sediments, and the K and n values of the isotherm for the inidividual fractions are given in Table 9.7. These results show close relationship among the K values and the total organic carbon (TOC) and cation exchange capacity (CEC) of the four size fractions of the sediment. Higher K values indicate stronger adsorption of Cd from the seawater. The ease of release of Cd from the adsorbed state as measured by extraction with seawater was considerably lower at higher desorption K values (Table 9.7) and suggests that Cd is strongly bound by sediment particles having high TOC and CEC.

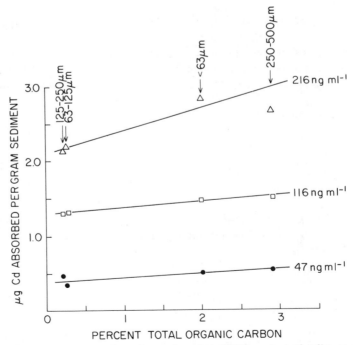

Figure 9.4. Relationship between total organic carbon (TOC) content of sediment and adsorption of Cd from seawater.

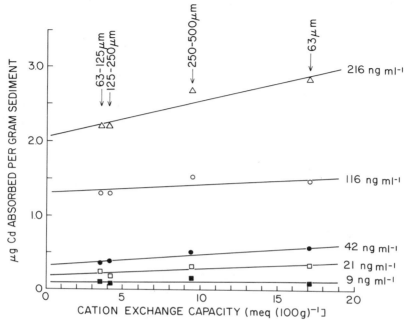

Figure 9.5. Relationship between cation exchange capacity (CEC) of sediments and adsorption of Cd from seawater.

Table 9.8 shows the amount of Cd adsorbed at different concentrations by sediments of different size fractions. The average values of percent Cd adsorbed by the fractions correspond to the organic carbon content of the sediments, that is, the fraction with higher carbon content adsorbed more cadmium.

Effects of TOC and size on sorption equilibrium are shown in Fig. 9.4. It is apparent that the process is predominantly controlled by the organic carbon content. The sediment size fractions 63-125 and 125-250 μm are very similar in their TOC, and the equilibria attained are of the same order of magnitude. The relationship is linear with TOC for all concentrations of Cd studied.

Similarly, the effect of CEC on the adsorption isotherm for sediments of different particle size is given in Fig. 9.5. Again, we find that the isotherm equilibria are highly dependent on CEC and not on particle size.

9.4.   CONCLUSIONS

The laboratory and field data show that bioaccumulation of Cd and other trace metals (Cu, Zn, and Pb) by bottom-dwelling invertebrates, *Nereis*, *Macoma*, and *Crangon*, exposed to naturally contaminated sediments is low and controlled by factors other than the total extractable metal content. In natural bioassay studies, the metal content of the animal tissues remained fairly constant regardless of the metal content of the sediments, except for *Macoma*, which had an elevated Pb level in the tissue. In laboratory exposure studies with naturally contaminated sediments, the metal concentration in the animal tissues did not parallel those obtained in field observations. The discrepancy may be due to the short (30 d) exposure time that may not have allowed attainment of equilibrium conditions as observed in the natural condition. Elevated levels of Cd were observed in the animal tissues only when Cd was present in the overlying water during the exposure studies.

Cd concentration in *Nereis* exposed to sediment spiked with Cd increased linearly with time and was found dependent on length of exposure and the size of the animals. Excretion of Cd was not observed over a period of 75 d in a clean environment.

We suggest that bioaccumulation of Cd depends largely on the amount (concentration) of Cd leached from the sediment and concentration in the aqueous phase, which in turn depends on the organic carbon content and the cation exchange capacity of the sediment.

ACKNOWLEDGMENTS

We thank C. Sergeant and M. R. Peterson for technical assistance, B. McCullough and J. Hurley for typing, and R. Garnett for editing.

REFERENCES

Akagi, H. M. and D. J. Wildish. 1975. Determination of the sorting characteristics and organic carbon content of the estuarine sediments. Manuscript Report 1370, Fisheries Research Board of Canada, Ottawa, 15 pp.

Boyden, C. R. 1977. Effect of size upon metal content of shellfish. *Journal of the Marine Biological Association of the United Kingdom*, **57**, 675–714.

Bryan, G. W. 1968. Concentrations of zinc and copper in the tissues of decapod crustaceans. *Journal of the Marine Biological Association of the United Kingdom*, **48**, 303–321.

Bryan, G. W. and L. G. Hummerstone. 1973. Adaptation of the polychaete *Nereis diversicolor* to estuarine sediments containing high concentrations of zinc and cadmium. *Journal of the Marine Biological Association of the United Kingdom*, **53**, 839–857.

Bryan, G. W. and H. Uysal. 1978. Heavy metals in the burrowing bivalve *Scrobicularia plana* from the Tamar estuary in relation to environmental levels. *Journal of the Marine Biological Association of the United Kingdom*, **58**, 89–108.

Canada Gazette. 1975. Ocean Dumping Control Act. (19 June 1975). Senate and House of Commons of Canada. Canada Gazette, Part 1, **109** No. 9. Ottawa. See also: Ocean Dumping Control Regulations (2 October 1975). Canada Gazette, Part II, **109**, No. 20, pp. 2786–2803.

Dethlefsen, V. 1977/1978. Uptake, retention and loss of cadmium by brown shrimp (*Crangon crangon*). *Merresforsch*, **26**, 137–152.

Goldberg, E. D., V. T. Bowen, J. W. Farrington, G. Harvey, J. H. Martin, P. L.

Parker, R. W. Risebrough, W. Robertson, E. Schneider, and E. Gamble. 1978. Mussel watch. *Environmental Conservation*, **5**, 101–126.

Hesse, P. R. 1971. A textbook of soil chemical analysis. Chemical Publishing Co., New York, 520 pp.

Holmes, C. W., E. A. Slade, and C. J. McLerran. 1974. Migration and redistribution of zinc and cadmium in marine estuarine system. *Environmental Science and Technology*, **8**, 255–258.

Jenne, E. A. and S. N. Luoma. 1977. Forms of trace elements in soils, sediments and associated waters. *In*: Biological Implications of Metals in the Environment, R. E. Wildung and H. Drucker (Eds.), CONF-750929, NTIS, Springfield, Virginia, pp. 110–143.

Lu, J. C. S. and K. Y. Chen. 1977. Migration of trace metals in interfaces of seawater and polluted surficial sediments. *Environmental Science and Technology*, **11**, 174–182.

Neff, J. W., R. S. Foster, and J. F. Slowey. 1978. Availability of sediment absorbed heavy metals to benthos with particular emphasis on deposit feeding infauna. Dredged Material Research Program. Technical Report D-78-42 (August 1978). U.S. Army Engineer Waterways Experiment Station, Vicksburg, Mississippi, 286 pp.

Ratkowski, D. W., S. J. Thrower, J. J. Eustace, and J. Olley. 1974. A numerical study of the concentration of some heavy metals in Tasmanian waters. *Journal of the Fisheries Research Board of Canada*, **31**, 1165–1171.

Ray, S. and D. W. McLeese. 1980. Bioavailability of chlorinated hydrocarbons and heavy metals in sediments in marine invertebrates. *International Council for the Exploration of the Sea*, C.M.1980/E:20, 13 pp.

Ray, S., D. W. McLeese, and C. D. Metcalfe. 1979. Heavy metals in sediments and in invertebrates from three coastal areas in New Brunswick, Canada. A natural bioassay. *International Council for the Exploration of the Sea*, C.M.1979/E:29, 11 pp.

Ray, S., D. W. McLeese, and D. Pezzack. 1980. Accumulation of Cd by *Nereis virens*. *Archives of Environmental Contamination and Toxicology*, **9**, 1–8.

Wolfe, D. A. and T. R. Rice. 1972. Cycling of elements in estuaries. *Fisheries Bulletin*, **70**, 959–972.

10

CHANGES IN THE LEVELS OF PCBs IN *MYTILUS EDULIS* ASSOCIATED WITH DREDGED-MATERIAL DISPOSAL

Richard Arimoto and S. Y. Feng

Marine Sciences Institute
University of Connecticut
Groton, Connecticut

Dr. Arimoto's present address: Center for Atmospheric Chemistry Studies, Graduate School of Oceanography, University of Rhode Island, Kingston, Rhode Island.

ABSTRACT

Experimental populations of mussels (*Mytilus edulis*) were deployed on or near the New London, Connecticut, Dumpsite and used as indicators of polychlorinated biphenyl (PCB) concentrations during and after the disposal of dredged material. During the dumping operations, the mean PCB concentrations of the dumpsite populations ranged from 520 to 800 ng g^{-1} dry weight whereas those of reference populations from outside the disposal area ranged from 700 to 720 ng g^{-1}. After dumping ceased, the mean PCB concentrations of the dumpsite mussels decreased (range = 510-590 ng g^{-1}) as did those of the reference animals (range = 480-510 ng g^{-1}). The difference between the mean PCB concentrations for the two sampling periods was significant at $p = .07$, but two lines of evidence indicated that dumping has, at most, a minor influence on PCB uptake. First, the mean PCB concentrations of the dumpsite populations were not higher than those of the reference populations either during or after dumping. Second, regression analyses showed that even though the PCB concentrations of the dumpsite animals were related to the volume of material dumped, the levels also were related to the rate of discharge from a nearby river. Furthermore, the multiple regression functions could account for no more than 40% of the observed variance in PCB concentrations, and most of the variance apparently was caused by factors that were not included in the regression functions.

10.1. INTRODUCTION

Polychlorinated biphenyls (PCBs: $C_{12}Cl_nH_{10-n}$, $n = 1$ to 10) are ubiquitous environmental contaminants that were first identified in wildlife samples in 1966 (Jensen, 1966). These industrially useful synthetic compounds were first manufactured in the United States in 1929, and the highest rates of production occurred between 1950 and 1970. PCBs are virtually insoluble in water. Primarily through terrestrial runoff and industrial discharges, PCBs have accumulated in the bottom sediments of channels and harbors. The resuspension of fine sediments and concomitant release of interstitial water during maintenance dredging and subsequent dumping of the dredged material may disperse PCBs in the environment (Nisbet and Sarofim, 1972). We are concerned with the transport and fate of these contaminants and their potential effects on living marine resources.

Efforts to monitor the biological impacts of dumping most often have been directed toward the examination of benthic community structure (Saila et al., 1972) or the analysis of indicator organisms for chemical or physiological changes (Anderlini et al., 1975; DeCoursey and Vernberg, 1975; Engler, 1979). Spatial and temporal variability in community structure has rendered the interpretation of descriptive surveys difficult. But in general, benthic communities have been found to recover from burial in 1–3 y (Oliver et al., 1977).

We monitored some effects of dumping operations in eastern Long Island Sound by deploying experimental populations of the blue mussel *Mytilus edulis* L. in the vicinity of the New London, Connecticut, Dumpsite and regularly measuring the concentrations of PCBs in the animals' tissues. Mussels were selected as indicator organisms because they are endemic, sessile, active for a major portion of the year, available in sufficient quantity to permit frequent sampling, and of recognized commerical and ecological importance. In addition, *M. edulis* and related species concentrate PCBs several orders of magnitude over ambient seawater levels, and large scale monitoring programs, such as the Mussel Watch (Goldberg et al., 1978), have established a substantial data base on the pollutant levels in these animals.

The primary objective of our research was to determine whether changes in the PCB concentrations of the monitoring organisms were associated with the dumping operations. This chapter describes the temporal and spatial changes that occurred, and it presents results of statistical analyses which were conducted to identify other factors that may have contributed to the variance in PCB concentrations.

10.2. EXPERIMENTAL

10.2.1. Site Locations and Sampling Design

Located in eastern Long Island Sound slightly more than 3.8 km (~2 nautical miles) south of the Thames River, the New London Dumpsite has been used for the disposal of dredged material since 1943. In August 1974, the U.S. Navy began dredging the lower Thames River, and by the completion of dredging, in July 1975, approximately 1.2×10^6 m^3 of material had been dumped in New London. Our monitoring studies included the period between July 1977 and June 1978 when a second phase of dredging occurred; during Phase II dredging, 1.3×10^6 m^3 of material was dumped.

Experimental field populations of *M. edulis*, designated D1, D2, and D3 (Fig. 10.1), were established in April 1977 using mussels collected from a subtidal population at North Dumpling, New York, near Fishers Island. The PCB concentrations of the dumpsite populations were compared with those of natural reference populations at North Dumpling and at Seaside, Connecticut. Samples from all stations were collected by divers approximately every three months, but logistical problems occasionally caused longer sampling intervals. Mortalities of the populations were not recorded, but continued studies at New London have shown that mortalities during 14 months of monitoring were less than 50%.

The hardware used for the monitoring studies was modified several times. Initially, polyethylene mesh bags (2-cm mesh), containing 50 mussels each, were deployed in plastic-coated steel cages (76 $\times$ 46 $\times$ 33 cm, 5-cm mesh) that were elevated from the seafloor by concrete footings. Later, in August and September 1977, the bags of mussels from stations D1 and D2 were transferred to 1-m-tall epoxy-painted steel platforms. Station D3 was lost in late August, but was reestablished in October 1977 with new bags of mussels and a 1-m-high polyvinyl chloride (PVC) platform. Station D3 was, thereafter, continously maintained until the end of monitoring, and because the PVC arrays (Fig. 10.2) proved successful, stations D1 and D2 were changed to this type in May 1978. The mussels for stations D1 and D2 were replenished in November 1978 and June 1978, respectively.

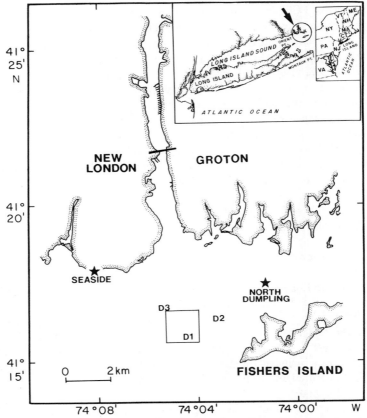

Figure 10.1. Station locations for the New London dumpsite project. Experimental dumpsite populations of *Mytilus edulis* are designated D1, D2, and D3. Stars denote reference populations at Seaside, Connecticut and North Dumpling, New York.

10.2.2. Chemical Analyses

Pooled samples of 24 animals normally were analyzed in our studies, and the coefficient of variation for replicate samples fell within the analytical precision (coefficient of variation = 20%). To prepare the samples for analysis, a 25- to 30-g aliquot of soft tissue homogenate was lyophilized, and 1 g of the freeze-dried tissue was extracted for 3 h with nanograde petroleum ether (Mallinckrodt Inc., St. Louis, Missouri) in soxhlet apparatus. The crude extract was concentrated with Kuderna-Danish apparatus, and interfering substances were removed by chromatography with a Florisil (Fisher Scientific Co., Fair Lawn, New Jersey) packed column (Reynolds, 1969). The extract was eluted with nanograde *n*-hexane (Mallinckrodt Inc.,) and concentrated to 1 ml with Kuderna-Danish apparatus before injection into the gas chromatograph.

The samples were analyzed with a Hewlett Packard 7620A gas chromatograph

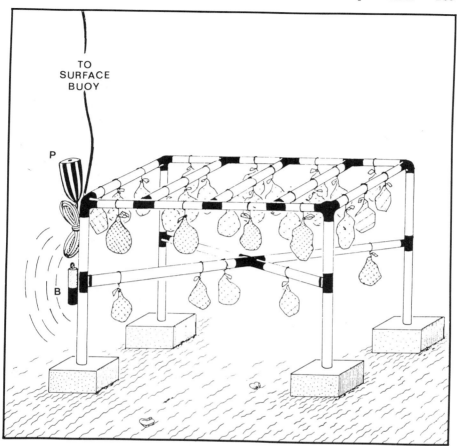

Figure 10.2. Drawing of a monitoring array with attached bags of mussels. Each array was equipped with sonic beacon (B), a surface float, and a subsurface float (P). The subsurface float was released if the surface float was pulled free.

(Hewlett Packard Co., Paramas, New Jersey) equipped with a ^{63}Ni electron capture detector and a 2 m $\times$ 4 mm (i.d.) glass column packed with 3% OV-1 (methyl silicone gum) on a silane treated diatomite support of 100/120 mesh Gas Chrom Q (Applied Science Labs, State College, Pennsylvania). The analyses were done isothermally (injection port = 225°C, oven = 190°C, detector = 300°C) and required about 45 min for the final compounds to elute. The carrier gas was a mixture of 95% argon and 5% methane. The signal from the chromatograph was digitized with a Varian CDS 111C chromatography data system (Varian Corp., Palo Alto, California)

10.2.3. Treatment of Data

We developed a statistical procedure to discriminate PCBs from interfering substances because preliminary analyses of sample chromatograms indicated that not all of the sample peaks were PCBs. For this procedure, tolerance limits for peak retention times were calculated to include 99.9% of the PCB peaks at the 95% confidence level (Dixon and Massey, 1969). The tolerance limits were computed from five injections of a composite standard [equal parts of Aroclors 1242, 1254, and 1260 (Monsanto Co., St. Louis, Missouri)] dissolved in hexane. Because the tolerance limits linearly increased with retention time (correlation coefficient, $r = 0.987$), a least squares regression equation was used to compute the tolerance limits for the peaks in each composite standard used for the daily calibration of the instrumentation.

In an attempt to identify the compounds responsible for the spurious peaks, a sample with a particularly large contamination peak, with a retention time of approximately 30 min, was submitted to Dr. George Frame of the U.S. Coast Guard Research and Development Center (Groton, Connecticut) for mass spectrometric analysis.

The concentrations of PCBs in the mussel tissues were determined by the method of Webb and McCall (1973). For quantitative analysis, the sample chromatograms were divided into three separate areas based on the retention times of the peaks relative to DDE [1,1-dichloro-2,2-*bis*(*p*-chlorophenyl)ethylene]. The instrument response factors that were calculated for three PCB standards (Aroclors 1242, 1254, and 1260) were then applied to the appropriate sample peaks. Through the use of this procedure, it was possible to estimate the amounts of the three Aroclors in the samples. We used the nonparametric *Kruskal–Wallis test* to determine whether the mean levels of the three Aroclors in the ensemble of all samples differed significantly.

Statistical analyses were performed using an IBM S-370 computer and the BMDP Biomedical Computer P-series programs of Dixon and Brown (1979) for two-way analysis of variance (*two-way ANOVA*) program BMDP7D and for stepwise multiple regression, program BMDP2R. For the *two-way ANOVA*s, the samples were classified by station and sampling period, that is during or after dumping. The data for the predumping period were not included in the analyses because samples were unavailable for experimental populations D2 and D3. We used the *two-way ANOVA*s to test the null hypotheses that the mean PCB and Aroclor concentrations in the mussels from the five monitoring populations were not different either during or after dumping.

Stepwise multiple regression was used to uncover relationships between PCB concentrations and environmental parameters that would be appropriate focal points for future research. We used this statistical technique to determine whether the variance in the PCB concentrations of the mussels was related to any or all of three predictor variables: (1) the volume of dredged material dumped; (2) the rate of Thames River discharge; and (3) the amount of precipitation. Two separate regressions were performed on the data, one for the dumpsite populations and the other for reference populations. The step-up method was chosen for the analyses. Predictor variables were sequentially entered into regression functions based on their absolute or partial correlations with the dependent variable. If the contribution of any variable was made insignificant by the subsequent addition of other variables, it was removed from the function.

We assumed that the mussels could not immediately respond to the changes in the environment that were measured by the three predictor variables. Therefore, in the regression analyses, we used the data collected during the month before the mussel populations were sampled. The one month offset also produced the highest correlations. Data for the volume of material dumped each month were obtained from the U.S. Army Corps of Engineers, Waltham, Massachusetts. The U.S. Geological Survey, Hartford, Connecticut, provided the information on the rate of Thames River discharge. The Groton Water Works, Groton, Connecticut supplied the precipitation data. All values were converted to metric equivalents.

10.3. RESULTS

The mass spectrometric analysis of a contaminated sample revealed the presence of phthalate esters (plasticizers), silicones, and several unidentified compounds. Phthalate esters previously have been detected in marine organisms (Giam et al., 1978); the mussels we analyzed may have accumulated these esters from the environment. However, the plasticizers and unidentifed compounds also may have been contaminants introduced during sample preparation. Unidentified compounds have been detected in gas chromatograms of shellfish samples analyzed by the Mussel Watch (Goldberg et al., 1978).

The mean concentrations of the three Aroclors in the ensemble of all samples differed significantly. The χ^2 value of 99.99 (degrees of freedom, $d.f. = 2$) deter-

Table 10.1. Total Polychlorinated Biphenyl (PCB) and Aroclor Concentrations in *Mytilus edulis* (± 1 Standard Deviation)

Station	$(n)^a$	Aroclor 1242	Aroclor 1254	Aroclor 1260	Total PCB[b]
Dumpsite 1					
During[c]	(5)	360 ± 130	410 ± 180	30 ± 30	800 ± 320
After	(3)	220 ± 190	360 ± 170	10 ± 10	590 ± 270
Dumpsite 2					
During	(8)	230 ± 90	430 ± 90	40 ± 20	690 ± 170
After	(2)	200 ± 120	300 ± 80	20 ± 10	510 ± 40
Dumpsite 3					
During	(6)	210 ± 220	290 ± 100	10 ± 10	520 ± 310
After	(3)	300 ± 140	260 ± 90	40 ± 40	590 ± 260
Seaside					
During	(5)	280 ± 150	400 ± 140	30 ± 10	720 ± 260
After	(3)	180 ± 100	320 ± 140	10 ± 10	510 ± 230
North Dumpling					
During	(5)	250 ± 60	410 ± 100	30 ± 10	700 ± 140
After	(4)	140 ± 50	320 ± 160	30 ± 20	480 ± 220

a_n = number of samples analyzed.
[b]Computed as the sum of the Aroclors.
[c]During dredging: July 1977 to June 1978; after dredging: July 1978 to April 1979.

mined by the *Kruskal-Wallis test* indicated that the probablility for chance occurrence was $p < .0001$. Although the analyses of PCB standards indicated that the quantification procedure consistently underestimated the relative concentration of Aroclor 1260 by about 13%, the levels of Aroclor 1260 clearly were lower than either 1242 or 1254 (Table 10.1).

Total PCB and Aroclor 1254 levels were higher during the dumping operations than after the completion of dredging, but the differences were not clearly significant, with $p = 0.07$ (Table 10.2). Of the five monitoring populations, only dumpsite 3 did not have higher levels during dumping. Even though the differences were not significant, the pattern of higher levels during dumping also was evident for Aroclors 1242 and 1260. PCB concentrations of both dumpsite and reference animals varied temporally even during periods when no dredging occurred (Fig. 10.3).

The *two-way ANOVAs* (Table 10.2) also showed that the PCB concentrations of the five monitoring populations did not differ significantly either during or after dumping. The data, therefore, demonstrate that the disposal of the dredged material did not cause a localized elevation in the PCB concentrations of the experimental dumpsite populations. The interaction between sampling periods and stations was not significant.

Table 10.2. Analyses of Variance in the Aroclor and Total Polychlorinated Biphenyl (PCB) Concentrations in Five Populations of *Mytilus edulis* Sampled During and After Dumping.

Source of Variation	DF^b	F-Value	Probability
Aroclor 1242			
Site S	4	0.58	0.68, ns[a]
Sampling period SP	1	1.87	0.18, ns
Interaction $S \times SP$	4	0.91	0.47, ns
Error	34		
Aroclor 1254			
Site S	4	0.91	0.47, ns
Sampling Period SP	1	3.51	0.07
Interaction $S \times SP$	4	0.14	0.97, ns
Error	34		
Aroclor 1260			
Site S	4	0.18	0.95, ns
Sampling period SP	1	1.90	0.18, ns
Interaction $S \times SP$	4	2.14	0.10, ns
Error	34		
Total PCB			
Site S	4	0.37	0.83, ns
Sampling period SP	1	3.59	0.07
Interaction $S \times SP$	4	0.54	0.71, ns
Error	34		

[a]ns = not significant.
[b]DF is the number of degrees of freedom.

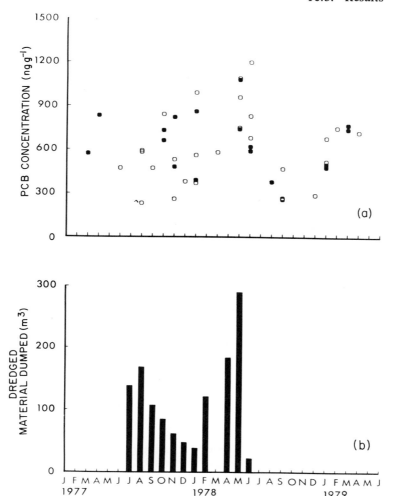

Figure 10.3. (*a*) Temporal changes in the total polychlorinated biphenyl (PCB) concentrations (dry wt) with *Mytilus edulis* from dumpsite (filled circles) and reference (open circles) populations. (*b*) Total monthly volume of dredged material dumped at the New London Disposal Site, Connecticut.

Stepwise multiple regression (Table 10.3) showed that both river discharge and the volume of material dumped were related to the concentrations of Aroclors 1242, 1254, and total PCBs in the dumpsite populations. In contrast, for the reference populations, only river discharge was entered into the regression functions. Rainfall apparently did not directly influence the PCB concentrations of either the dumpsite or reference populations because the variable was never entered into a regression function. The concentrations of Aroclor 1260 in the monitoring populations were not related to any of the independent variables.

Table 10.3. Stepwise Regressions of River Discharge and Dredged-Material Volume on Polychlorinated Biphenyl (PCB) and Aroclor Concentrations in *Mytilus edulis*

Dependent Variable	Variable Entered	F-to-enter	Multiple R^2	Increase in R^2	Intercept
Dumpsite Populations					
Aroclor 1242					
Step 1	River discharge	4.41	0.145	0.145	158
Step 2	Dredged-material volume	6.10	0.313	0.168	84
Aroclor 1254					
Step 1	Dredged-material volume	6.22	0.193	0.193	297
Step 2	River discharge	4.80	0.323	0.130	215
Aroclor 1260					
	No variables entered	—	—	—	—
Total PCB					
Step 1	Dredged-material volume	6.92	0.210	0.210	512
Step 2	River discharge	9.05	0.420	0.210	308
Reference Populations					
Aroclor 1242					
Step 1	River discharge	8.31	0.328	0.328	119
Aroclor 1254					
Step 1	River discharge	4.13	0.196	0.196	270
Aroclor 1260					
	No variables entered	—	—	—	—
Total PCB					
Step 1	River discharge	7.76	0.313	0.313	405

10.4. DISCUSSION

The potential for pollutant uptake during dredged-material dumping operations clearly is greatest for animals living within the disposal area. Consequently, our efforts to monitor the impacts of dredged-material disposal have focused on comparing the PCB concentrations of experimental dumpsite populations with those of reference animals from outside the disposal area. Total PCB concentrations of the dumpsite and reference populations did not differ significantly either during or after dumping; the data indicate that dumping did not cause a localized increase in pollutant concentrations.

Temporal changes in the PCB concentrations of mussels from the dumpsite were related to the volume of material dumped, but the relationship was not evident for the reference populations. Regression analyses showed that the changes in the PCB concentrations of the dumpsite and reference populations were related to the rate of discharge from a nearby river. The multiple regression functions could account for only 20–40% of the observed variance in concentrations. Hence, most of the variance must be attributed to factors not included in the analyses. The regression analyses thus indicated that dumping was a minor influence on the PCB concentrations of the monitoring animals, even for those living on or near the dumpsite.

Mussels have been used to monitor changes in the concentrations of PCBs and other potentially harmful substances during dredged-material dumping operations in the San Francisco Bay (Anderlini et al., 1975) and in Puget Sound (Engler, 1979). Dumping increased the availability of DDE (a decomposition product of DDT) to mussels at the San Francisco Bay Site, but the levels of PCBs were not affected. During the three-week monitoring period in Puget Sound, mussels accumulated PCBs to levels above background, but the increases were not significant. Direct comparisons among the monitoring programs in the San Francisco Bay and Puget Sound, and our studies in Long Island Sound are not appropriate because the characteristics and volumes of dredged material were different. Nevertheless, these studies have lead to the same conclusion: the effects of dumping on PCB uptake were minor.

The PCB concentrations in bottom sediments from Long Island Sound, as well as in mussels, apparently are governed by factors other than the dumping of dredged material. Sediment samples from three dumpsites in Long Island Sound were contaminated with PCBs, but the concentrations were not significantly higher than those in samples from control areas (Chytalo, 1979). Sediments from the New London Dumpsite had a mean PCB concentration of 0.14 $\mu g\ g^{-1}$ dry weight, but the variability between samples was high, with a coefficient of variation of more than 50%. These sediments were one of the possible sources of PCBs for the dumpsite populations of mussels, and despite their apparent heterogeneity, the PCB concentrations of the dumpsite sediments evidently were lower than those of the mussels.

The PCB concentrations of the dumpsite and reference mussel populations were related to Thames River discharge. These results suggest that fluvial materials were a source of PCBs for the mussels. Even though regression analyses cannot be used to affirm cause-and-effect relationships for field studies such as ours, they are useful for identifying relationships that warrant further study. Moreover, rivers have been implicated as major sources of PCBs for other estuarine ecosystems. Drainage from the Susquehanna River has been identified as the most important source of chlorinated hydrocarbons for the upper Chesapeake Bay (Palmer et al., 1976), and freshwater runoff has been characterized as one of the predominant sources of PCBs for Puget Sound (Pavlou and Dexter, 1979). Changes in the PCB concentrations of the amphipod *Gammarus pulex* also have been attributed to variations in freshwater runoff (Södergren et al., 1972).

Mussels and other aquatic organisms may accumulate PCBs and other pollutants from contaminated food or through direct uptake from the water. Data supporting each of these theories have been presented, and it is now clear that the relative contributions of uptake from food and by partitioning vary among species (Addison, 1976). No conclusive evidence of equilibrium partitioning has been obtained for mussels or oysters *Crassostrea virginica* (Marchand et al., 1976; Vreeland, 1974). However, both of these species display marked seasonal cycles in body lipid concentrations, and the metabolism and mobilization of fats may prevent the PCB concentrations in water and tissue from reaching equilibrium.

Mussels and most other bivalve molluscs obtain their food by filtering particles out of suspension. Thus, contaminated suspended material is a potentially important source of PCBs for these animals. The organochlorine pesticide dieldrin can be transferred through the food chain, from phytoplankton to clams (Petrocelli et al., 1975); organochlorines are highly concentrated in the digestive tissues of mussels and other filter-feeding molluscs (Roberts, 1975; Ernst et al., 1976; Courtney and Denton, 1976). If mussels assimilate organochlorine pollutants from contaminated particles, as these studies indicate, then changes in the suspended material field may ultimately affect the PCB concentrations of monitoring animals.

Short-term (<0.5 h) increases in PCB concentrations have been demonstrated for water samples from dredged-material plumes in the San Francisco Bay and Puget Sound (Anderlini et al., 1975; Wright, 1978). Moreover, the PCBs apparently were associated with suspended material because the pollutant concentrations returned to ambient levels when the suspended-material concentrations decreased. Therefore, the mussels deployed at the New London Dumpsite may have assimilated some PCBs from the plumes of suspended material induced by the dumping operations. In addition, streamflow strongly influences the suspended-material field in eastern Long Island Sound (Bohlen, 1975), and consequently, discharge from rivers also may have affected the types of materials ingested by the mussels.

Many of the biological and geochemical processes responsible for the flux of PCBs through acquatic environments have been identified (Nisbet and Sarofim, 1972). But information on the relative importances of the processes for specific regions is very limited. Our analyses uncovered relationships between river discharge, dredged-material volume, and the PCB concentrations of the monitoring organisms *a posteriori*; the chlorobiphenyl compositions of the fluvial material and dredged material were not determined. The characterization of the chlorobiphenyls in these materials and from other inputs, including atmospheric deposition and sewage treatment plant effluents, would appear to have high priority for future research.

10.5. CONCLUSION

Our studies indicated that the dumping of dredged material has only a minor influence on the PCB concentrations of mussel populations deployed on or near a disposal area in eastern Long Island Sound. Statistical analyses showed that river discharge may have contributed to the variance in PCB concentrations. But the inputs from rivers and other sources must be quantified before data from field monitoring programs such as ours can be thoroughly evaluated. Laboratory and field studies on the environmental and physiological factors contributing to the variance in PCB concentrations of mussels also remain to be done.

ACKNOWLEDGMENTS

We gratefully acknowledge the assistance of the staff of the Marine Sciences Institute, University of Connecticut, especially Joseph Lanier who helped with many phases of sample analyses and data interpretation. Robert DeGoursey coordinated the field operations and Elizabeth Haddad, John Watson, and Richard Grillo helped process the samples. Drs. Uwe Koehn and Robert Whitlatch, and graduate students James Weinberg and Victoria Starczak all contributed to the statistical analyses. Dr. Arthur Libbey, Hartford State Technical College, helped develop the methods of chemical analysis. The dedication and expertise of laboratory assistants Susan Ho, Michael Davis, and Kathleen Shea proved invaluable. The project was supported by a grant from U.S. Navy (contract No. 00140-77-6536) to S. Y. Feng.

REFERENCES

Addison, R. F.   1976.   Organochlorine compounds in aquatic organisms: their distribution, transport and physiological significance. *In*: Effects of Pollutants on Aquatic Organisms, A. P. M. Lockwood (Ed.). Cambridge University Press, London, pp. 127–143.

Anderlini, V. C., J. W. Chapman, A. S. Newton, R. W. Risebrough, B. E. Cole, B. W. deLappe, D. C. Girvin, A. T. Hodgson, S. J. McCormick, L. Nelbach, R. K. Okazaki, M. H. Panietz, and T. T. Schmidt. 1975. Pollutant Availability Study, Dredge Disposal Study, San Francisco Bay and Estuary, Appendix I: Pollutant Availability. U.S. Army Engineer District, San Francisco, 88 pp. + appendix.

Bohlen, W. F.   1975.   An investigation of suspended material concentrations in eastern Long Island Sound. *Journal of Geophysical Research*, **80**, 5089–5100.

Chytalo, K. N. 1979. PCBs in Dredged Materials and Benthic Organisms in Long Island Sound. Master's Thesis. State University of New York, Stony Brook, New York, 109 pp.

Courtney, W. A. M. and G. W. Denton. 1976. Persistence of polychlorinated biphenyls in the hard-clam (*Mercenaria mercenaria*) and the effect upon the distribution of these pollutants in the estuarine evironment. *Environmental Pollution*, **10**, 55–64.

DeCoursey, P. J. and W. B. Vernberg. 1975. The effect of dredging in a polluted estuary on the physiology of larval zooplankton. *Water Research*, **9**, 149–154.

Dixon, W. J. and M. B. Brown. 1979. BMDP-79 Biomedical Computer Programs P-Series. University of California Press, Berkeley, 880 pp.

Dixon, W. J. and F. J. Massey, Jr. 1969. Introduction to Statistical Analysis, 3rd edition. McGraw Hill, New York, 638 pp.

Engler, R. M. 1979. Bioaccumulation of toxic substances from contaminated sediments by fish and benthic organisms. *In*: Management of Bottom Sediments Containing Toxic Substances, Proceedings of the fourth U.S.–Japan Experts' Meeting. October 1978, Tokyo, Japan, pp. 325–354.

Ernst, W., H. Goerke, G. Eder, and R. G. Shaefer. 1976. Residues of chlorinated hydrocarbons in marine organisms in relation to size and ecological parameters. I. PCB, DDT, DDE and DDD in fish and molluscs from the English Channel. *Bulletin of Environmental Contamination and Toxicology*, 15, 55–65.

Giam, C. S., H. S. Chan, G. S. Neff, and E. L. Atlas. 1978. Phthalate ester plasticizers: a new class of marine pollutant. *Science*, 199, 419–421.

Goldberg, E. D., V. T. Bowen, J. W. Farrington, G. Harvey, J. H. Martin, P. L. Parker, R. W. Risebrough, W. Robertson, E. Schneider, and E. Gamble. 1978. The mussel watch. *Environmental Conservation*, 5, 101–125.

Jensen, S. 1966. Report of a new chemical hazard. *New Scientist*, 32, 612.

Marchand, M., D. Vas, and E. K. Duursma. 1976. Levels of PCBs and DDTs in mussels from the N. W. Mediterranean. *Marine Pollution Bulletin*, 7, 65–69.

Nisbet, I. C. T. and A. F. Sarofim. 1972. Rates and routes of transport of PCBs in the environment. *Environmental Health Perspectives*, 1, 21–38.

Oliver, J. S., P. N. Slattery, L. W. Hulberg, and J. W. Nybakken. 1977. Patterns of succession in benthic infaunal communities following dredging and dredged material disposal in Monterey Bay. Technical Report D-77-27. U.S. Army Engineer Waterways Experiment Station, Vicksburg, Mississippi, 186 pp.

Palmer, H. D., K. T. S. Tzou, and A. Swain. 1976. Transport of chlorinated hydrocarbons in sediments of the upper Chesapeake Bay. Final Report to the Office of Water Research and Technology, Washington, D.C., 155 pp.

Pavlou, S. P. and R. N. Dexter. 1979. Distribution of polychlorinated biphenyls (PCB) in estuarine ecosystems. Testing the concept of equilibrium partitioning in the marine environment. *Environmental Science and Technology*, 13, 65–71.

Petrocelli, S. R., J. W. Anderson, and A. R. Hanks. 1975. Controlled food chain transfer of Dieldrin residues from phytoplankters to clams. *Marine Biology*, 31, 215–218.

Reynolds, L. M. 1969. Polychlorobiphenyls (PCB's) and their interference with pesticide residue analysis. *Bulletin of Environmental Contamination and Toxicology*, 4, 128–143.

Roberts, D. 1975. Differential uptake of Endosulfan by the tissues of *Mytilus edulis*. *Bulletin of Environmental Contamination and Toxicology*, 13, 170–176.

Saila, S. B., S. D. Pratt, and T. T. Polgar. 1972. Dredged Spoil Disposal in Rhode Island Sound. University of Rhode Island Marine Technology Report No. 2. University of Rhode Island, Kingston, 48 pp.

Södergren, A., B. J. Svensson, and S. Ulfstrand. 1972. DDT and PCB in South Swedish streams. *Environmental Pollution*, 3, 25–36.

Vreeland, V. 1974. Uptake of chlorobiphenyls by oysters. *Environmental Pollution*, 6, 135–140.

Webb, R. G. and A. C. McCall. 1973. Quantitative PCB standards for electron capture gas chromatography. *Journal of Chromatographic Science*, 11, 366–373.

Wright, T. D. 1978. Aquatic Dredged Material Disposal Impacts. Technical Report DS-78-1, August 1978. U.S. Army Engineer Waterways Experiment Station, Vicksburg, Mississippi, 57 pp.

PART IV: ALTERNATIVE PROCEDURES FOR DREDGED MATERIAL DISPOSAL

11

SUBMARINE BORROW PITS AS CONTAINMENT SITES FOR DREDGED SEDIMENT

Henry J. Bokuniewicz

Marine Sciences Research Center
State University of New York
Stony Brook, New York

ABSTRACT

Sand-mining operations in New York Harbor have left several large pits on the harbor floor. Two of these were examined. The larger pit has a volume of about 25×10^6 m^3. The pits are typically 7–10 m deeper than the ambient seafloor and have side slopes of between 10 and 25°. Although the harbor floor is sandy, more than 3×10^6 m^3 of mud has accumulated naturally in these pits. In the larger pit the layer of mud is up to 1 m thick. The average rate of accumulation is estimated to be between 0.05 and 0.10 m y^{-1}.

The technology is available to deposit dredged sediment into the pits. Hopper dredged disposal operations may be used to forecast the short-term behavior of the dredged sediment during the emplacement process. The side slopes of the pits in New York Harbor should be sufficient to prevent the spread of dredged sediment outside of the pit until the pit is about half filled. The dredged-material deposit will have low side slopes ($<3°$). The most effective form for the deposit would be a truncated cone or pyramid in order to maintain a shallow trough around the inside edge of the pit. While the thickness of the mud deposit is small compared to the depth of the pit, the naturally high sedimentation rate will enhance containment, alternatively the surface might be covered, or capped, with sand.

11.1. INTRODUCTION

The combination of submarine sand mining and the disposal of dredged sediment into mined pits is an interesting possibility that should be critically examined. Coupling of these activities has the potential for solving two problems at once—the need to obtain sand and gravel for construction aggregate and fill, and the need to contain contaminated, dredged sediment. Both of these problems are particularly acute in the greater New York Metropolitan Area.

Although sand deposits are common here, those that may be mined on land are severely limited. There are several reasons for this—urban sprawl, increased land value, and restrictive zoning, to name a few (Courtney et al., 1979). As a result, the sources of sand and gravel on land are becoming more restricted and more distant. The cost of hauling aggregate becomes prohibitive when the extraction sites are farther than about 100 km from the demand sites (Courtney et al., 1979). In an area within 170 km of New York City the demand for sand and gravel in the 1980s has been predicted to about 10×10^6 m^3 y^{-1} (Courtney et al., 1979). It appears that offshore sand resources will need to be further developed in the future to avert shortages (Cruickshank and Hess, 1975).

The volume of sediment dredged annually in the port of New York is comparable to the volume of sand and gravel required. In the 1970s, $6\text{–}8 \times 10^6$ m^3 y^{-1} have been dredged (MITRE Corp., 1977) to maintain navigation channels in the harbor. Because this is maintenance work, it is reasonable to assume that sediment will be removed at about the same rate for at least the next decade. Most of this sediment will probably be judged to be acceptable for disposal in the ocean; this has been the case in the past. Ten to twenty percent of this volume, however, may be unacceptable for normal ocean disposal because of its contamination by harbor pollutants (Mayer, 1982). Strategies for containing this contaminated sediment must be developed. The designation of alternative disposal sites will become more urgent as onshore and offshore disposal sites become more costly and more scarce.

The use of submarine pits as disposal sites is an attractive alternative for several reasons. In many areas, mined pits have been shown to trap fine-grained sediments (Broughton, 1977) and there is evidence that this is the case for some of the pits in the floor of New York Harbor. Because the most troublesome contaminants are usually associated with the fine fraction of dredged sediments, it seems that conditions in some mined pits would favor the containment of contaminated dredged sediment. The isolation of the dredged sediment from the marine environment might be enhanced by covering, or capping, the deposit with a layer of clean sand. In some areas, too, the presence of the pits could have a potentially adverse effect on the marine environment. If deep holes are trapping fine-grained sediment with a high organic content, anoxic conditions may result, or the presence of deep holes may modify the ambient waves and tides to aggravate shore erosion or shoaling. In these cases, the possible ill effects due to the presence of the pits may be minimized by filling, especially if the deposit is capped with sand so that the seafloor is returned to its premined condition. If dredged sediment could be used to fill these pits, the number of sites that could be safely and economically mined might be increased. The mined pits are also usually close to the dredging sites and would, therefore, be economical disposal areas.

The filling of borrow pits with fine-grained sediment would, of course, remove these areas as future sources of construction aggregate, fill, or beach nourishment material. If the filling of pits is warranted, it may be useful to reconsider the designation of both mining and disposal sites to make the most efficient use of our resources. This option only becomes available, however, if it can be shown that such operations are both feasible and environmentally safe.

The idea that mined pits could be used as containment sites for contaminated sediment is not new. It was suggested at least a decade ago (Carpenter, 1973). There is a good discussion of this disposal alternative in a report to the Dredged Material Research Program by Johanson et al. (1976).

The technology is available to carry out a disposal operation over a borrow pit (Johanson et al., 1976) and areas that are natural traps for fine-grained sediment would be favorable containment areas (Bokuniewicz and Gordon, 1979). A capping operation wherein a mound of dredged mud was covered with sand using conventional techniques has been successfully done (Morton, 1980; see also Chapter 5). Several questions remain to be addressed, however, before the burial of dredged mud in borrow pits can be considered a viable disposal alternative. Some of these are:

1. How much dredged sediment will escape from the pit during the disposal operation?
2. What will be the form of the deposit of dredged sediment?
3. Will the dredged sediment remain in the pit until it can be capped?
4. How thick must the sand cap be in order to isolate the dredged mud?
5. Once the sand layer is in place, will it be mechanically stable?

In this chapter I will attempt to address these questions. While none of the answers will be completely satisfactory, they will point out the areas where work is needed and they will develop a working hypothesis to be expanded and tested by future research. I will rely primarily on the results of the U.S. Army Corps of Engineers' Dredged Material Research Program and on my own speculations about how the disposal processes will be affected by conditions in the borrow pits.

11.2. BORROW PITS IN NEW YORK HARBOR

The floor of the Lower Bay in New York Harbor is composed primarily of sand and gravel (Jones et al., 1979). Tidal currents here are typically less than 0.5 m s^{-1}. Between 1950 and 1976, sand has been removed from both the West Bank and the East Bank of Ambrose Channel (Fig. 11.1). No mining has been done since 1976. The seafloor lies at a depth of about 4.5 m and the floors of the borrow pits are usually at a depth of about 14 m.

Conditions in the pits on the East Bank are different from those on the West Bank. The pits on the East Bank have been mined so that they are connected to the main channel while, on the West Bank, a strip of the bay floor forms a ridge which separates the borrow pits there from the channel. The floors of the pits on the East Bank are sandy; apparently tidal currents are able to sweep into the pits through their connection with the channel and to prevent the deposition of mud. The floors of the pits on the West Bank, on the other hand, are muddy. Conditions here favor the deposition of fine-grained sediment and, as a result, we confine our attention to the pits on the West Bank.

There are three pits on the West Bank (Fig. 11.1). The southernmost hole had been mined to a depth of 30 m and has been partially filled with sand. It covers an area of about 0.6×10^6 m^2 and it has a volume of about 7×10^6 m^3. The middle pit is the largest. It covers an area of 3.1×10^6 m^2 and its volume is estimated to be about 25×10^6 m^3. The northernmost pit has been studied most extensively. Figure 11.2 shows the depth of the floor of this pit below the ambient bay floor. The feature covers an area of about 0.5×10^6 m^2 and has a volume of about 3×10^6 m^3.

Figure 11.3 shows two bathymetric transects across the northern and middle pits in the West Bank. The side walls of the pits are steep, typically between 10° and 25°, but below the angle of repose for sand (32°). The pit floors are irregular as a result of the mining. Hills or ridges on the floor of the northern pit are typically about 20 m across and rise 1 m above the surrounding pit floor. Some parts of the bathymetric records are characterized by a flat, diffuse reflection. These areas were identified as mud by bottom sampling. Core samples showed a layer of mud overlying sand on the pit floor. In the northern pit, this mud layer was about 0.5 m thick when it was sampled in 1978–1979. In the middle pit, it was about 0.9 m thick (B. Brinkhuis, Marine Sciences Research Center, State University of New York, Stony Brook, New York, personal communication). These thicknesses of mud have accumulated since 1968 when mining operations in the pits were completed, which means that the average sedimentation rate has been very rapid. Mud has accumulated at rates of 0.05 m y^{-1} in the northern pit and about 0.09 m y^{-1} in the larger pit.

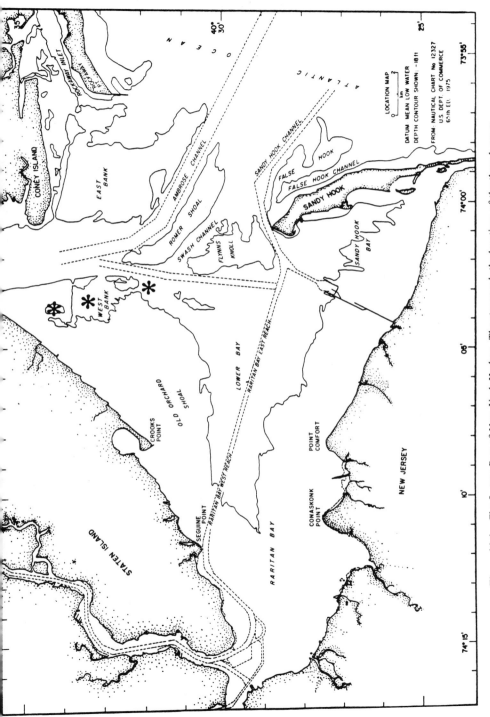

Figure 11.1. The Lower Bay of New York Harbor. The stars mark the locations of the three borrow pits discussed in this report. The depth contour is 5.5 m.

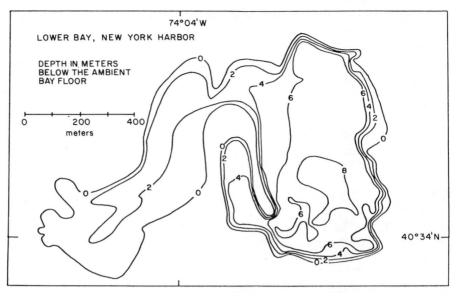

Figure 11.2. Contours of the depth of the northernmost pit on the West Bank of the Lower Bay below the ambient bay floor.

The distribution of mud on the pit floors has been mapped by using the bathymetric records. The mud layer appears to cover almost the entire floor of the pits with the exception of the tops of some of the more pronounced bottom irregularities. The mud layer generally begins at a depth of about 6 m or about 2 m below the undisturbed bay floor. The northern pit would, therefore, contain about 0.2×10^6 m^3 of mud and the middle pit about 2.7×10^6 m^3. If the southern pit can be assumed to have been accumulating mud naturally and at a comparable rate, then fine-grained sediment is being trapped by these features at a rate of 0.3×10^6 m^3 y^{-1}.

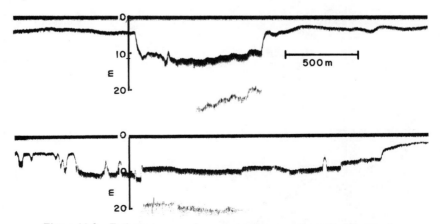

Figure 11.3. Fathometer records across two borrow pits on the West Bank.

11.3. THE DISPOSAL OPERATION

11.3.1. How Much Dredged Sediment Will Escape from the Pits During the Disposal Operation?

After a typical disposal operation from a scow or hopper dredge only between 1 and 5% of the released sediment remains in suspension in the water column. This diffuse cloud of material drifts with the currents and settles slowly. A few percent of the dredged sediment should be expected to escape from the disposal area.

Almost all of the material that is released is deposited on the seafloor in three steps. These were first described by Gordon (1974). Upon release, the dredged sediment descends rapidly through the water column as a well-developed jet of high density which may contain solid blocks. This jet had been observed to fall at speeds in excess of 1 m s^{-1}. Ambient water is entrained during the descent phase so that the total volume of the descending jet may be increased 50- to a 100-fold before it reaches the seafloor in depths of about 20 m. After passing through the water column, the material impacts the bottom. Large blocks of sediment stay in the impact area but some of the released material spreads radially outward from the impact point as a toroidal density surge only a few meters thick. The bottom surge slows and thins as it travels outward. Over a flat bottom it has been observed to run a few hundred meters, at most, from the impact point. Initially, the surge moves swiftly and carries sediment particles away from the impact point until the surge velocity is reduced sufficiently to permit deposition.

These three steps—descent of the jet, impact on the bottom, and the spread of the bottom surge—have been observed to occur under a wide range of hydrographical conditions, dredged-material characteristics, and dredging and disposal equipment (Bokuniewicz et al., 1978; Custar and Wakeman, 1977). The limiting conditions under which these steps will occur have not been determined but they have been documented in water depths of up to 67 m and ambient currents of up to 2 m s^{-1}. In the mined pits, however, the relief is much greater than it was in any of the areas where direct observations of the disposal processes had been made in the past.

During a normal point-dumping operation with good navigational control, most of the dredged sediment can be deposited on the pit floor, but will the bottom surge that is generated be able to escape from the pit? Little is known about the dynamics of the spreading bottom surge but we can get some idea of its ability to climb the pit walls from energy considerations. The energy of a bottom surge in a lake has been estimated from measurements of its velocity, its thickness, and the concentration of suspended sediment within it (Bokuniewicz et al., 1978). The energy density was found to be 150 joules m^{-3} immediately after the impact phase was completed. At this time the concentration of solids was 6 kg m^{-3}. Although these data were collected over a flat lake floor, we may use them to predict the minimum amount of work needed to move a unit volume of the surge up a slope and compare that value to the total amount of energy available in a unit volume. The work done in raising our unit volume a distance h is $(\rho - \rho_0) gh$ where ρ is the bulk density, ρ_0 is the density of water and g is the acceleration due to gravity. If we ignore all other forms of energy losses, such as frictional losses, we find that raising a unit volume a height of 4.26 m would require all of its 150 joules of energy. It appears that, no matter what the side slopes are, once the pit becomes shallower than 4.26 m there may be the danger of the surge escaping onto the surrounding seafloor. The borrow pits in the Lower Bay could be about half filled with dredged mud before this condition is met.

11.3.2. What Will Be the Form of the Deposit of Dredged Sediment?

The most efficient form would be that of a truncated cone or pyramid. Its top surface should be relatively flat and below the elevation of the ambient bay floor. At its edges the surface of the deposit will slope downward toward the pit walls so that a shallow trough will be formed inside of the edge of the pit to hinder the escape of the bottom surges during the filling.

The slope of the surface will depend on the type of equipment used and the nature of the dredged sediment. If all of the dredged sediment is deposited from a bottom surge, as will probably be the case if a hopper dredge is used, the slope will be less than 0.05 (3°C). This value has been calculated from energy considerations (Bokuniewicz and Gordon, 1980) which were based on the same data used earlier (Bokuniewicz et al., 1978). Such low slopes were found on the flanks of a deposit of dredged sediment in Long Island Sound (Bokuniewicz and Gordon, 1980) and a dredged-sediment deposit in Chesapeake Bay was found to have a maximum surface slope of 0.01 and an average slope of 0.002 (Biggs, 1970). In both of these cases, it appeared that the sediment had been deposited from a slurry.

If, on the other hand, the sediment is cohesive and removed with a clamshell dredge, there may be large blocks of material in the descending jet. Some will be broken on impact and add particles to the surge, but some will remain intact and accumulate in a pile on the pit floor under the discharge point (Bokuniewicz and Gordon, 1980). In principle, the angle of repose on this pile could reach the angle of repose for coarse material, ~32°, but at a disposal site in Long Island Sound such a pile had side slopes of 0.1 (6°). The radius of this pile was 250 m (Bokuniewicz and Gordon, 1980).

11.3.3. Will the Dredged Sediment Remain in the Pit Until It Can Be Capped?

The answer depends on the susceptibility of the material to erosion, the time for which the surface remains uncovered, and the current and wave regime, especially during storms. In borrow pits in the Lower Bay, a deposit that is 4 m thick will lie about 4 m below the ambient bay floor and 8 or 9 m below the water surface. The bathymetric records suggest that over the last decade mud has accumulated in parts of the borrow pit that are only 2 m below the ambient, sandy bay floor and 5.5 m below the water surface. The deposition of mud has been widespread where the pit floor is more than 6 m below the water surface, although in the middle pit there are occasional peaks on the pit floor in water depths of 9 m that are apparently free of mud. This all suggests that the dredged-mud deposit as described will not undergo net erosion over long time periods; however, some loss of material due to resuspension during storms is possible. As a result, it would seem best to cap the deposit as soon as possible and not have it exposed during the period of winter storms.

11.3.4. How Thick Must the Sand Cap Be in Order To Isolate the Dredged Mud?

The cap must be thick enough to prevent resuspension of the underlying mud. In the Lower Bay the natural sand bottom appears to be relatively stable. A study of bathymetric surveys that were conducted over a period in excess of 100 y show minor shifting of the depth contours but no major changes in the water depth with the exception of dredged channels (Fray, 1969). There does not appear to be any net erosion of the harbor floor in this area. In addition, there are no large bedforms on the natural surface of the West Bank which might indicate that large amounts of sand are not moved regularly by the tides. During severe storms, however, a considerable layer may be disturbed without net erosion. There are no data from the bay to suggest how deep into the sediment a storm disturbance might extend. On the submerged shoreface off the exposed coast of Long Island, the depth of disturbance may be as deep as 1 m (Sanders and Komar, 1975) but in the protected bay, it should be much less. A cap with a thickness of at least 0.5 m would seem to be desirable.

The cap should also be sufficiently thick so that burrowing animals will not reach the mud. Pratt and O'Connor (1973) found that in nearby Long Island Sound most benthic species occurred at depths of less than 0.1 m but two species penetrated to depths of 0.3 m. Bivalves in the coastal waters of Long Island may burrow to depths of 0.3 m (R. Malouf, Marine Sciences Research Center, State University of New York, Stony Brook, New York, personal communication). By this criterion, a capping layer should be at least 0.3 m thick.

If the sand cap is also intended to return the seafloor as closely as possible to its original condition, a much thicker cover may be needed. It may only be possible to fill the pit half-way with contaminated material, using normal overboard disposal techniques. Several meters of cap material would then be needed to restore the mined area to its original bathymetry. This does not need to be all sand, however. A two-layer cap may be considered. The contaminated sediment might first be covered with uncontaminated mud. Because the pit would now be nearly filled, more of the dredged sediment would escape from the site during the operation, but presumably some dispersion of uncontaminated, fine-grained sediment could be tolerated. A thinner sand cap could then be placed over the top. Several meters of cap material would then be needed to restore the mined area to its original bathymetry.

11.3.5. Once the Sand Layer Is in Place Will It Be Mechanically Stable?

The capping operation will result in a layer of dense sand overlying a layer of less dense mud. Such a configuration is inherently unstable, although we know that under some conditions it can persist for very long periods of time because sand-over-mud layers are preserved in the geologic record.

After deposition, what will happen to these layers? The mud will consolidate with the expulsion of pore water and the sand layer may deform. The consolidation of dredged sediments may be predicted from standard laboratory tests. The consolidation is proportional to the thickness of the mud layer and the submerged weight of the overlying sand. A 2-m thick layer of estuarine mud that might have been dredged with a clamshell bucket should be expected to consolidate 5–10% (0.1–0.2 m) under a sand layer 1 m thick; a volume of pore water equal to 5–10% of the volume of mud will be expelled from the deposit. Under certain conditions, however, the sand may sink into the mud. This mode of deformation results in what is known as "ball-and-pillow" structure. The conditions under which this deformation will occur are not well known, but some guidelines can be established from measurements of the densities and shear strengths of the sediments.

Two conditions must be met for convective instability to arise in a layered sediment (Artyushkov, 1963). The first is that the upper layer (the cap) must be heavier than the lower. The second condition is that the shear stresses along the interface between the layers must be greater than the shear strength of the layered deposit. If the interface is irregular and the height of the irregularities is Δh then the magnitude of the shear along the interface is $\Delta \rho g \, \Delta h$ where $\Delta \rho$ is the density difference between the layers. For motion to start, $\Delta \rho g \, \Delta h$ must be larger than some critical value. Artyushkov (1963) defined the critical value to be the maximum of the values of the shear strength for both layers; Pettijohn et al. (1972) suggested that the critical value should be the shear strength between the two layers.

A sample calculation might be instructive. We have made some preliminary measurements of geotechnical parameters on sediments from the pits in the Lower Bay. In many places within the pits a core will penetrate through the mud layer and into sand underneath so that both layers and the interface can be retrieved. The bulk density of the mud is about 1.2 g cm^{-3} and the sand has a bulk density of about 1.8 g cm^{-3}. The muddy sand near the sand–mud transition has a shear strength of about 10^3 Newton m^{-2}. With these values, instability should occur if the irregularities in the interface are larger than 0.2 m. It seems unlikely, therefore, that a stable deposit can be made of such material by using conventional techniques. The layered deposit would have a finite lifetime although it could be extremely long.

Mud that is removed with a clamshell bucket dredge, however, is likely to form a deposit that has a bulk density and shear strength that is significantly higher than those values used in the preceding example. If the mud has a density of 1.5 g cm^{-3} and a strength of 10^4 Newton m^{-2}, the deposit can support irregularities over a meter high. With this material, it is likely that a stable deposit can be formed using the usual disposal techniques.

11.4. CONCLUSIONS

The submarine burial of dredged mud in mined pits is technically feasible. The pit should be a natural trap for fine-grained sediment. It must have a radius of at least 200 m and it must be at least several meters deep. The minimum volume of material for a filling operation, therefore, would be about 0.5×10^6 m^3. If a sand cap is to be used, the mud must have a sufficient density and strength to support the cap. This probably means that the dredging would have to be done with a clamshell bucket dredge. Because the thickness of the sand cap is independent of the depth of the pit, a deeper pit would have a disproportionately larger capacity for mud than a shallower pit covering the same area.

The sand cap is expected to isolate effectively and contain the dredged sediment particles. In order to assess the environmental impact of the deposit, however, other problems need to be studied. Some pore water will be lost from the deposit due to consolidation and more may be lost if there are regional pore-water flows. Little work has been done on the flow of water through offshore sediments. If it exists, flow velocities should be seaward and upward and they are likely to be very slow except within a few hundred meters of the shore (Bokuniewicz, 1980). In addition the mud deposit will be relatively impermeable; this would reduce the pore-water flow through the deposit. In the absence of advective fluxes, dissolved chemical species may leave the deposit by diffusion but such fluxes would be very small. Another problem that deserves attention is the effects of gas generation in the deposit. Methane or hydrogen sulfide generated in the deposit may bubble through the cap. Not only could gas be released directly into the overlying water but also the percolation of bubbles through the deposit could promote the exchange of pore water. If gas bubbles are generated in the mud but do not escape, a rise in the pore pressure could reduce the strength of the deposit and lead to instability.

Several problems remain unresolved but at least one point is clear. The type of project we have described should not be thought of as a disposal project but as an engineering project to construct a sediment deposit on the seafloor. The operation must be carefully planned and closely controlled. Such an operation requires much more planning than has traditionally been devoted to overboard disposals.

ACKNOWLEDGMENTS

This work was supported by the New York Sea Grant Institute through a contract with the New York Office of General Services and by the U.S. Department of Commerce, Maritime Administration. I would also like to thank the National Park Service and Assistant Superintendent J. E. Moyers for giving us permission to use islands in the Lower Bay during our surveys. Contribution No. 288 of the Marine Sciences Research Center of the State University of New York.

REFERENCES

Artyushkov, Y. V. 1963. Possibility of convective instability in sedimentary rocks and the general laws of its development. *Doklady Akademiia Nauk SSSR*, **153**, 26–28.

Biggs, R. B. 1970. Project A, Geology and Hydrography. *In*: Gross Physical and Biological Effects of Overboard Spoil Disposal in the Upper Chesapeake Bay.

Natural Resources Institute Special Report 3, Chesapeake Biological Laboratory, University of Maryland, pp. 7–15.

Bokuniewicz, H. J. 1980. Groundwater seepage into Great South Bay, New York. *Estuarine and Coastal Marine Science*, 10, 437–444.

Bokuniewicz, H. J. and R. B. Gordon. 1979. Containment of particulate wastes at open-water disposal sites. *In*: Ocean Dumping and Marine Pollution, H. D. Palmer and M. G. Gross (Eds.). Dowden Hutchinson and Ross, Inc., Stroudsburg, Pennsylvania, pp. 109–130.

Bokuniewicz, H. J. and R. B. Gordon. 1980. Deposition of dredged sediment at open-water sites. *Estuarine and Coastal Marine Science*, 10, 289–303.

Bokuniewicz, H. J., J. A. Gebert, R. B. Gordon, J. L. Higgins, P. Kaminsky, C. C. Pilbeam, M. W. Reed, and C. B. Tuttle. 1978. Field study of the mechanics of the placement of dredged material at open-water disposal sites. Technical Report D-78-F. Vol. I, U.S. Army Corps of Engineer Waterways Experiment Station, Environmental Effects Laboratory, Vicksburg, Mississippi, 94 pp. and appendices.

Broughton, J. D. 1977. Investigation of subaqueous borrow pits as potential sites for dredged-material disposal. Technical Report D-77-5. U.S. Army Corps of Engineer Waterways Experiment Station, Environmental Effects Laboratory, Vicksburg, Mississippi, 39 pp.

Carpenter, J. E. 1973. Determining ultimate capacity of the coastal zone for wastewater and wastewater residuals. *In*: Ultimate Disposal of Wastewaters and Their Residuals, F. E. McJunkin and P. A. Visilind (Eds.). Water Resources Research Institute, North Carolina State University, Raleigh, North Carolina, 216–224.

Courtney, K., J. Dehais, and W. A. Wallace. 1979. The demand for construction minerals in the greater New York metropolitan area. New York Sea Grant Report Series 79-10, Albany, 35 pp.

Cruickshank, M. J. and H. D. Hess. 1975. Marine sand and gravel mining. *Oceanus*, 19, 32–44.

Custar, C. and T. Wakeman. 1977. Dredge disposal study. San Francisco Bay and Estuary. Main Report. U.S. Army Corps of Engineers. San Francisco, California, 83 pp.

Fray, C. T. 1969. Final Report, Raritan Estuary sedimentation study. Prepared for the Federal Water Pollution Control Administration, Department of the Interior. Alpine Geophysical Associates, Inc., Norwood, New Jersey, 164 pp. and appendix, A1–A56 pp.

Gordon, R. B. 1974. Dispersion of dredged spoil dumped in near-shore waters. *Estuarine and Coastal Marine Science*, 2, 349–358.

Johanson, E. E., S. P. Bowen, and G. Henry. 1976. State-of-the-art survey and evaluation of open-water dredged material placement methodology. Contract Report D-76-3. U.S. Army Corps of Engineers' Waterways Experiment Station, Environmental Effects Laboratory, Vicksburg, Mississippi, 145 pp. and appendices.

Jones, C. R., C. T. Fray, and J. R. Schubel. 1979. Textural properties of surficial sediments of Lower Bay of New York Harbor. Marine Sciences Research Center Special Report 21, New York Sea Grant Institute Reference 79-4, 113 pp.

Mayer, G. (Ed.). 1982. Ecological Stress and the New York Bight: Science and Management. Estuarine Research Federation, Columbia, South Carolina. 715 pp.

MITRE Corp. 1977. The proceedings of the New York Dredged Material Disposal Alternatives Workshop, sponsored by the U.S. Army Corps of Engineers, New York District, coordinated by the MITRE Corporation-METREX Division, New York, New York (October 11–13), 107 pp. and appendices.

Morton, R. W. 1980. "Capping" procedures as an alternative technique to isolate contaminated dredged material in the marine environment. DAMOS Cont. II, Science Applications, Inc., Newport, Rhode Island, 27 pp.

Pettijohn, F. J., P. E. Potter, and R. Siever. 1972. Sand and Sandstone. Springer-Verlag, New York, 618 pp.

Pratt, S. D. and T. P. O'Connor. 1973. Burial of dredge spoil in Long Island Sound. Marine Experiment Station, University of Rhode Island, 29 pp.

Sanders, J. E. and N. Komar. 1975. Evidence of shoreface retreat and in-place "drowning" during Holocene submergence of barriers, shelf off Fire Island, New York. *Geological Society of America, Bulletin*, **86**, 65–76.

12

SOME ASPECTS OF DEEP OCEAN DISPOSAL OF DREDGED MATERIAL

Willis E. Pequegnat

TerEco Corporation
College Station, Texas

ABSTRACT

The continuing need for maintenance dredging of existing marine waterways and extant plans for future deepening of major ports and harbors indicate that the U.S. Army Corps of Engineers must solve the problem of disposing of increasing amounts of salt-laden dredged material.   At the same time public sentiment is growing against placing this material, whether contaminated or not, on land or on the continental shelf.   One solution to the problem involves disposing of the material in the deep ocean.   After a discussion of why the deep ocean is a good receiving environment for dredged material, there follows a description of the fate and effects of dredged material dumped into the open ocean.   Finally, the principal arguments generally raised against deep-ocean disposal are countered, and it is concluded that to dispose dredged material in the deep ocean entails minimal environmental risk.

12.1. INTRODUCTION

12.1.1. Basic Rationale

This chapter deals with deep-ocean disposal of dredged material and the potential impacts that such actions may have on the receiving environment. The thrust of the discussion is based upon three basic considerations. First, there is the premise that even in the face of serious environmental constraints the United States and other countries will contine to dredge existing marine waterways to assist in achieving safe passage of vessels of commerce. Present plans under consideration by the U.S. Congress call for the deepening of certain major harbors to receive deep-draft vessels. This will be done not only because the vessels' export cargoes, such as coal and grain, and import cargoes of strategic metals are vital to maintenance of a sound economy but also because accidental spillage of some cargoes in poorly maintained channels could have far more profound effects on marine ecological systems and thus on the welfare of the American people than the effects of dredging. Second, there is the assumption that public pressures will increase against continuing use of some present-day types of disposal techniques and environments. Because they are sensitive to public sentiment, involved personnel of the U.S. Army Corps of Engineers will eventually discontinue use of these environments for placement of dredged material. Third, it is believed by the author that the deep-sea disposal of dredged material will be utilized increasingly as a viable alternative to previous sites. It is stressed, however, that no matter what sites are used, good management of the dredging-disposal process is essential to the continued welfare of the marine environment.

12.1.2. Objectives

The principal objectives of this chapter are to estimate the need for ocean disposal and to evaluate the capacity of the deepwater marine ecosystems to receive dredged material with environmental impunity. The functioning of marine systems in the deep ocean is examined in sufficient detail to permit delineation of generalized and specific responses to and impacts of the introduction of dredged material. A discussion is provided of those physical and other oceanographic properties and processes that will act on and control the spatial distribution and chemical fate of dredged material following release.

12.1.3. Philosophical Position

As man is required to study more penetratingly his relationship to the global environment by one or another major environmental problem, he will learn not to rely soley on costly technology to minimize the effects of his waste products on ecosystems. Instead, he must recognize that certain natural ecosystems have the capacity to serve as effective processors of his wastes at little monetary or environmental cost after disposal. The ideal goal is to utilize what may be called final receiving environments rather than transient disposal sites that can mean shifting the problems associated with the waste from one ecosystem to another. In terms of dredged material removed from marine environments, it seems possible that the deep ocean may be such a terminal environment.

At present, there are two major arguments that are often raised against deep ocean disposal, namely, an increase of project costs due to longer hauling distances, and a presumed lack of knowledge of the deep sea. It is true that in some places the costs of deepwater disposal will be high. For example, barging is considered the most likely means of transport of dredged material for deepwater disposal. At present, disposal costs for mechanical dredging and barge transport of dredged material are three to five times more expensive than hydraulically dredged volumes, even though most delivery is to relatively close-in shallow-water sites. Thus, instead of $1.50 m^{-3} for hydraulic dredging, one must calculate anywhere from $3.93 to $6.55 m^{-3} for producing and barging the material to the dumpsite. It should be pointed out, however, that in some instances estimates as high as $13.75 m^{-3} for upland disposal have been submitted to port authorities (Baltimore Port Authority, personal communication). Such a figure is not as unreasonable as one might think. Unless the land site is to remain a useless, unsightly, and soggy quagmire beneath a hardened crust, it must be manipulated by heavy machinery, the leachate controlled, perhaps nutrients added, and then, planted to appropriate vegetation. These are cost factors that are seldom included when comparative estimates of disposal costs are made between upland and ocean sites.

As for the second objection, we can always express and possibly demonstrate a need for more scientific knowledge about the functioning of the marine environment. But if the matter is considered in perspective, this argument is beside the point in the present context because very little of the deep ocean will ever be affected by dredged material. According to U.S. Environmental Protection Agency (1976) figures, the volumes of dredged material discharged in the ocean annually are on the order of 68-76 $\times$ 10^6 m^3, which is about 20-22% of the 342 $\times$ 10^6 m^3 projected annual dredging (Fig. 12.1). Moreover, only a few percent of the 68-76 $\times$ 10^6 m^3 are presently going into deepwater sites. Thus, if for purposes of this study we take the upper limit of the deep sea to coincide with the 1000-m isobath, then about 60% of the globe is covered by deep ocean. Certainly only a few square kilometers of the millions involved will ever be affected by man's input of even several million m^3 dredged material. Shortly we shall discuss a natural source of sediment that enters the deep ocean in vast quantities each year without appearing to strain its assimilative capacity.

12.2. CONSIDERATIONS

12.2.1. General

At the present time most of the dredged material going into the open ocean is dumped on the continental shelf. Although there is very little evidence that this

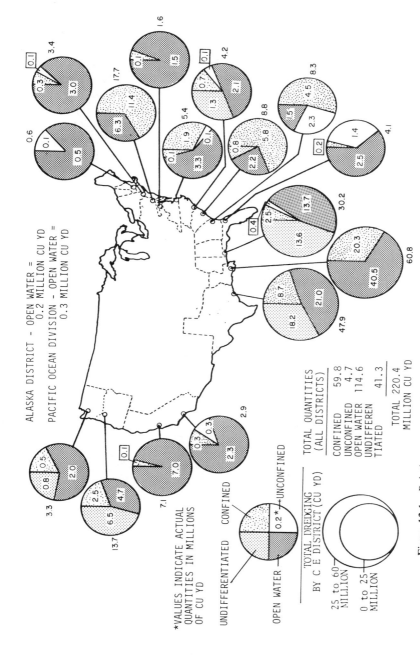

ALASKA DISTRICT - OPEN WATER = 0.2 MILLION CU YD
PACIFIC OCEAN DIVISION - OPEN WATER = 0.3 MILLION CU YD

*VALUES INDICATE ACTUAL QUANTITIES IN MILLIONS OF CU YD

UNDIFFERENTIATED   CONFINED

OPEN WATER   UNCONFINED

TOTAL QUANTITIES (ALL DISTRICTS)	
CONFINED	59.8
UNCONFINED	4.7
OPEN WATER	114.6
UNDIFFERENTIATED	41.3
TOTAL	220.4 MILLION CU YD

TOTAL DREDGING BY C E DISTRICT (CU YD)

25 to 60 MILLION

0 to 25 MILLION

Figure 12.1. Relative amounts of material dredged from shipping channels in the United States and the principal method of disposal (1 yd^3 = 0.765 m^3).

233

causes significant harm to the ecosystem, there are several reasons why it may be curtailed in the future. Compared with the vast areas and water volumes of the deep ocean, the combined worldwide area of the continental shelf constitutes less than 8% of the ocean floor. Also, only 0.1% of the ocean's waters lie over these shelves. Yet it is on this narrow, shallow ledge that we harvest about 90% of our seafood, exploit huge volumes of gas, oil, and other minerals, dispose of large quantities of industrial and municipal wastes, and manage heavy shipping traffic. The deep ocean on the other hand has served man in very few ways, but because of its great capacity for receiving sediments and a small capacity for food production, it could become a terminal receiving environment for some kinds of polluted sediments.

12.2.2. Assimilative Capacity of the Deep Ocean

The term *assimilative capacity* has connotations for engineering and physiology as well, perhaps, as for other fields. Here it is used as a measure of the ability of the deep ocean to receive dredged material without losing its capacity to sustain the life processes in kind and amount characteristic of the receiving region. The amount of terrigenous sediment normally reaching the ocean by natural means has an important bearing on this topic.

The bulk of the fine-grained inorganic matter entering the marine environment is carried there by rivers (Drake, 1976). Holeman (1968) estimates that annually this input amounts to about 18×10^9 tons of suspended solids. Drake (1976) estimates that some 8×10^9 tons of this riverine sediment are eventually deposited in the deep sea adjacent to major river mouths. An equivalent amount is deposited in deep basins by transport through the atmosphere. At least 40% of the riverine load is carried by 11 rivers (Lisitzin, 1972), led by the Yellow River of China and the Ganges of India. In the United States the Mississippi River transports between 150 and 200×10^6 m^3 of sediment to its mouth each year and much of it is deposited within a radius of 20 km. As to the small effects of this sediment on benthic life, it is germane to note that St. Amant (1971) estimated that Louisiana waters yield about 20% of the total U.S. catch of finfish and shellfish. Much of this is fished from waters west of the Delta, which is downstream along the main current in the region and in a major area of sedimentation. Pequegnat et al. (1976) report that the upper continental slope in this northern part of the Gulf of Mexico is also very productive of epibenthic life.

12.2.3. Food-Producing Capacities of the Land, Continental Shelf, and Deep Ocean

It is generally accepted that the land is now and always will be the major source of human foodstuffs and potable water. The marine 71% of the earth's surface produces no more than 1-2% of the world's food supply, albeit this may represent 8-10% of the worldwide utilization of protein. About a decade ago Boyd et al. (1972), in referring to the deep ocean, stated, "from the standpoint of commercial fisheries, these areas are of virtually no value, either now or in the future." The immediate prospect of obtaining greater quantities of food from marine sources seems to lie mainly in the possibility of wider, controlled exploitation of natural stocks. As McHugh (1976) points out, some species are overfished while others are not, but the overall view seems to be that there can be some increase in annual tonnage, but not from the deep sea. It is predicted by Tait and DeSanto (1972) that the deep ocean will never contribute more than 1% of the total world fish catch, and that will be of pelagic origin. This view is shared also by Moiseev (1971), who has concluded that the abyssal depths show no potential at all for the development of a commercial fishery.

Next to the land, then, the estuarine–shelf complex is the best food producer. About 90% of the worldwide total catch of bottom fish comes from the shelf. On the other hand, the catch of the ocean pelagic fishery, which is composed primarily of tunas and sharks, amounts to less than 5% of the shelf–slope tonnage. The foregoing seems to support the opinion that neither the land nor the estuary should be the recipient of various wastes, especially those that are highly toxic, including contaminated or polluted dredged materials. This feeling appears to be shared by vocal elements of the general public.

12.2.4. Rising Pressures Against Land and Estuary Disposal

As coastal populations continue to grow by relocations, and the rate of growth in the southern United States is now estimated to be between 3 and 5% y^{-1}, the need for living space and the utilization of coastal regions for industry and recreation will press harder against food-producing acreage. About 70 million people now live within the 80-km-wide coastal zone of the United States. Thus, roughly 33% of the population lives in only 8% of the total land area. This expansion has usurped coastal land in Texas which in the recent past was planted to rice, truck crops, and forage grasses.

The estuaries, especially those of the southeastern Atlantic and Gulf of Mexico coasts, are also important as food-producing and recreational areas. McHugh (1976) has estimated that something over three-quarters of the weight of finfishes and shellfishes landed in the United States by domestic fishermen are dependent on an estuary and usually the continental shelf as well. To dispose dredged material in estuaries will only serve to hasten the rate of natural sedimentation that will eventually fill them unless dredging is undertaken on a regular basis. It is often suggested that enhancement of the estuarine environment can be accomplished by creating artificial marshes in shallow portions of estuaries or embayments. It must be realized, however, that only certain types of organic and nutrient-rich dredged materials lend themselves to this development (Meccia, 1975). Moreover, this is a self-limiting process simply because a given estuary can only accommodate a finite number of marshes and grass beds without severe degradation of the ecosystem.

Anyone who has attended a public hearing concerning the selection of a method of disposal or the location of a site on land or in the estuarine shelf complex hears some of the preceding points in the form of arguments that are based on a mixture of fact and opinion and are delivered with varying degrees of emotion. Proponents of marsh formation in embayments cite the increases in biological productivity as a plus factor; opponents, on the other hand, are quick to argue that rather than a marsh a malodorous quagmire spawning mosquitoes will be created. Plans to dump dredged material in shallow water on the inner continental shelf, although attractive to some for economic reasons, are met by arguments from fishermen that usurpation of fishing space, turbidity, and toxic-metal contamination of the water will reduce their catch. Because there is an element of truth in all of these allegations, it is difficult if not impossible to obtain a consensus agreement on the selection of a dumpsite.

At this point, it seems worthwhile to determine whether deep-ocean disposal of dredged material is an environmentally sound alternative to some presently unsatisfactory disposal operations. Although there are multiple effects that dredged material can and will exert upon any region or ecological system, it is anticipated that these impacts will be less severe in the deep ocean than elsewhere in the marine environment. Certainly chemical changes resulting from the disposal of dredged material in deep water and the effects that these changes have on benthic biota is the single most important category of impacts at issue. The following analysis first examines the effects (impacts) of the ocean on the dredged material as it falls through the water column and comes to rest on the bottom after disposal from a barge or a hopper dredge. Then I shall attempt to determine what effects the material will have on benthic life as it impacts the seabed and undergoes diagenesis.

12.3. EFFECTS ON DREDGED MATERIAL OF DISPOSAL IN THE OCEAN

12.3.1. Where the Deep Ocean Begins

Here the term *deep ocean* is interpreted to mean that part of the open sea at and beyond the outer edge of the continental shelf (Fig. 12.2). This edge, which is ordinarily marked by a noticeable change of slope, is referred to as the "shelf break." The depth of the break varies considerably around the shelves of the United States. Some breaks occur at depths little more than 10-m deep, but generally they occur in anywhere from 60 to 200 m of water (Emery and Uchupi, 1972). It is at breaks of this latter depth or considerably more, depending on other topographic features, that it is proposed some dredged-material disposal sites should be located.

There have been very few truly deep-ocean disposals of dredged material that have been studied from the standpoint of impacts on the biota (Towill Corp., 1972). Nevertheless, there is an impressive amount of indirect evidence that the impacts in the deep ocean will not have serious effects on the fauna. This view was subscribed to by a majority of marine scientists that TerEco Corporation convened at two advisory panel meetings in the fall of 1976. The same sentiment was voiced by K. O. Emery of Woods Hole Oceanographic Institution in 1971 (Andreliunas and Hard, 1972) when he indicated that there is much more ocean

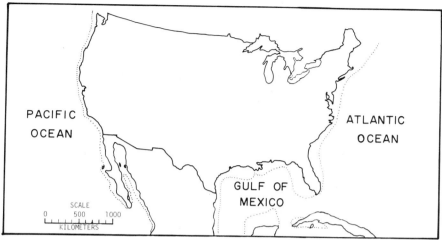

Figure 12.2. Relative widths of the continental shelves of the United States. Comparison with Fig. 12.1 shows most dredging of shipping channels occurs where shelves are widest.

floor to waste than dry land and advised that the deep ocean should be used for waste disposal, provided it is done under knowledgeable management to minimize ecological problems. Several natural occurrences in the form of turbidity flows provide some information on the effects of rapid sediment introduction to the ocean floor. Such flows are now known to be a common feature of certain continental slopes. For example, Griggs et al. (1969) found that the Cascadia Channel (~2600 m deep) off the coast of Oregon and Washington had been the receiving environment of numerous postglacial-age turbidity currents. Even so, the benthic animal populations were four times as abundant as those of the adjacent Cascadia Abyssal Plain that has not been affected by such currents. These authors postulated that the turbidity flows created a superior environment of coarser and organically enriched sediments. Also, those marine scientists who favor deep-ocean disposal believe that there will be an amelioration of some possible impacts on the bottom during a long transit in the water column. To evaluate this, it is necessary to study briefly what happens to a slug of dredged material after it is released from a barge or hopper dredge.

12.3.2. Changes in the Form and Behavior of Dredged Material During Descent Through the Water Column

12.3.2a. Physical Changes and Fates in the Water Column

Several intrinsic factors will determine the spatial disposition and ultimate physical fate of dredged material pursuant to disposal (Fig. 12.3). The percent moisture content (PCM) of the dredged material is an important characteristic that is defined as

$$\frac{W_w}{W_s} \times 100$$

where W_w is weight of water and W_s is dry weight of the solids. PCM varies with (1) the nature of the material being dredged, (2) the type of dredge being used, (3) the vertical position of the material within the bins of a hopper dredge, and (4) the time between dredging and disposal.

Other things being equal, the PCM of dredged material, which will be low in a barge filled by clamshell dredge and high in a hopper dredge, will determine (1) the amount of dredged material that will reach the bottom in a short time, (2) the area on the bottom it covers, (3) the direct and immediate impact on the pelagic and benthic fauna, and (4) the effects of the environment on the disposed material.

For clay or silt, or mixtures thereof, disposal characteristics of the dredged material are separable into two distinct classes, solid and liquid, that behave differently upon disposal (Table 12.1). The initial PCM of the disposed material will

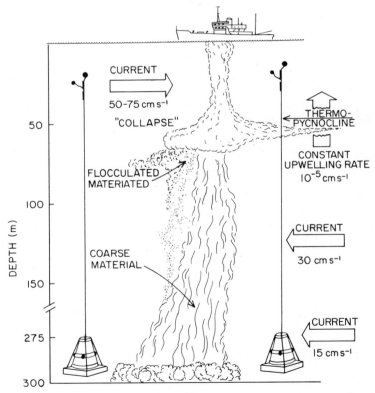

Figure 12.3. A schematic view of a hopper dredge discharging about 1500 m³ of dredged material in deep water. Note the thermo- and pycnoclines and current structure. Shown also are two devices for conducting in situ bioassays of the impacts of dredged material.

Table 12.1.   Characteristics of Solid and Liquid Fractions of Dredged Material (from JBF Scientific Corp., 1975)

Solid Mode	Liquid Mode
1. Low PCM.	1. High PCM.
2. Observed in barge filled by clamshell dredge.	2. Observed in material of upper few feet of hopper dredge, depending on transit time.
3. Usually found in bottom half of hopper dredge.	3. Characteristic of pipeline dredge material.
4. Falls as solid blocks.	4. Falls as a liquid cloud.
5. Rapid descent, no deceleration before impact.	5. Slower descent phase.
6. Little cloud growth.	6. Cloud expands due to entrainment.
7. Trails a small turbidity plume.	7. Deceleration of descent rate is significant.
8. Little spread of material on bottom after impact, but this depends on cohesiveness of material disposal.	8. Horizontal momentum on bottom considerable, producing laterally spreading cloud.
9. Pycnocline has effect only on small trailing turbidity plume.	9. Pycnocline has effect on falling cloud, possibly producing first collapse.
10. Generally some mounding on bottom, even in deeper water.	10. Little or no mounding on bottom, especially in deeper water.

partly determine the influence of currents on its transport. The transit time of low-PCM material for depths of 1000 m or so will be sufficiently small (several minutes to tens of minutes) that the influence of currents in transporting the material laterally will be minimal. On the other hand, for the initially moderate- to high-PCM material that can produce an entraining cloud, which collapses either at the thermocline or at middepth, the fine silts and clays whose settling rate is less than 0.001 cm s^{-1} can clearly be carried large distances (thousand of kilometers) by typical subsurface currents (approaching speeds of 10 cm s^{-1}) before settling to the bottom. In fact, clay particles of the order of 1 μm in diameter might be suspended in the thermocline indefinitely. The reason for this is that throughout most of the ocean where a well-developed permanent thermocline exists, it is generally associated with a slight upwelling rate of about 1 cm d^{-1}. This is sufficient to keep the fine clay particles suspended. One can speculate as to the implications of this with respect to a possible buildup of turbidity of the upper layers due to continual deepwater disposal (as may occur in mining of manganese nodules). On the other hand, dredged material would be swept by the ocean currents over vast areas of the oceans from periodic dumps at a finite number of potential sites. Thus it is improbable that any significant localized buildup of turbidity would occur much above that associated with naturally occurring organic detritus.

12.3.2b. Chemical Changes of Dredged Material During Descent

Any disposal of dredged material at sea is certain to result in some interaction between the dredged material and seawater, regardless of how rapidly the material sinks to the bottom. Obviously the interaction will depend in its detail on the chemical and physical nature of the dredged material. Most dredging operations will be conducted to remove material that has been rapidly deposited in harbors, bays, estuaries, and other nearshore environments. The chemical and physical characteristics of such material are considerably different from those of sediments lying in deeper and more open oceanic environments. Thus, one can see that natural processes work to chemically and physically alter and fractionate material during its transport to and deposition in deeper water. The same factors that affect material during natural transport will also affect dredged material during and after disposal. The most important of these controlling factors are changes in redox potential, pH, and salinity.

In almost all open ocean environments it is the level of dissolved oxygen that determines the redox potential. Even when free from all products of human activities, nearshore sediments of the type likely to be dredged have a large oxygen demand. This is because their rapid rate of sedimentation results in trapping organic matter and other reduced substances that did not oxidize before being cut off from the overlying water by burial. The reintroduction of oxygen into a falling mass of dredged material enriched with organic and inorganic substances can bring about rather drastic chemical and physical changes in the material. For example, a black, smelly mud, rich in reduced forms of nitrogen, sulfur, iron, manganese, and other trace components may be changed both physically and chemically to what would superficially appear to be a normal open-shelf marine sediment.

Removing dredged material from very near shore and depositing it in deeper, open ocean water will almost always result in exposing the material to a higher pH. The importance of pH to dredged-material disposal is that adsorption-desorption reactions involving trace metals are controlled by specific pH-dependent surface reactions whereby metal ions are exchanged for surface-bound hydrogen ions. Metals will be adsorbed with increasing pH and desorbed with decreasing pH. For example, Burks and Engler (1978) found that significant release of zinc, mercury, and cadmium to the water-soluble phase occurs at pH 5 under oxidizing conditions (see also Chapter 1). It is doubtful, however, that such releases would occur in deep-water disposals because anaerobic sediments should remain near neutral pH and the oxidization processes that occur in the water column do not produce an acidic condition (Gambrell et al., 1977). Removing estuarine and nearshore material to the open ocean would generally tend to increase the pH of the aqueous phase of dredged material and thus favor adsorption over desorption reactions. Salinity, however, may have an opposite effect and it must be considered next.

It is not always possible to predict the effect of salinity changes on adsorption-desorption reactions between trace metals and sediment. Commonly, however, increases in ionic strength of an aqueous medium result in desorption. Murray and Murray (1973), however, show the effect of salinity on desorption of zinc to be small, as compared with pH effects. Trefry and Presley (1976) also found that manganese was the only one of a suite of metals to undergo extensive desorption as Mississippi River suspended matter mixed with seawater outside the river mouth. It appears that only minor changes in the chemistry of dredged material can be expected in response to salinity changes.

12.3.3. After Bottom Contact

12.3.3a. Physical Changes on the Bottom

That part of the dredged material that penetrates the pycnocline will impact on the bottom and may produce a mound and a bottom cloud (Fig. 12.3). Formation of the bottom cloud may be inferred from observations made in 17 m of water (Gordon, 1974) and 20 m of water (Bokuniewicz et al., 1975). When bottom contact is made, a density surge of highly turbid water occurs. Its exact nature will depend on the sedimentary composition of the material that reaches the bottom as well as the bottom material. The velocity of the vertical falling density cloud will decrease due to entrainment and head drag and to the changes occurring at the pycnoclinal collapse. At the moment of bottom contact horizontal spreading of the bottom turbid cloud begins and lasts for varying but generally short periods. While the cloud is spreading, it is also thinning; hence its effects on the bottom fauna are rapidly lessening on all radii from the point of bottom contact.

In water no more than 50 m deep, a high percentage of disposed material falls within a radius of 200 m or less from the impact point. Bokuniewicz et al. (1975) found that 80% or so of the material disposed from a stationary barge reached the bottom within a radius of 30 m around the dropsite and 90% within a radius of 120 m, and that only 1% was dispersed over greater distances in the bottom cloud. In deep water both the pycnocline and currents can be expected to have considerable effects, especially on the fine material. Thus, the amount of fine material available to create the bottom density surge would be reduced. Furthermore, because the water column transit would be greater, the dilution of fines in the water column would be sufficiently great as to cause little or no irreversible effects upon pelagic life.

12.3.3b. Chemical Changes of Dredged Material After Bottom Contact

After dredged material reaches the seabed the elements and compounds in it will be subject to conditions that greatly differ from those in the overlying water column (see Chapter 6) and thereby be released and made available to the benthic community.

Organic material in the dredged material not destroyed during passage through the water column is subject to bacterial and fungal decomposition in the seabed. If oxygen is available in a sediment's interstitial water, organic degradation is promoted by heterotrophic bacteria. However, if oxygen has been depleted in the sediment column, which occurs in the case of frequent disposals of material with high organic content, organic degradation is mediated by anaerobic bacteria that use such electron acceptors as nitrite, nitrate, or sulfate. If sizeable amounts of dredged material are rapidly deposited in oxygenated water there will be a limited oxygen supply except in the top centimeters of sediment where biological mixing occurs, and anoxic conditions will develop at depth. In the anoxic region, some chemical species may be released to the interstitial water whereas others may be rendered immobile. When the entire sediment column is anoxic, there will be a diffusive flux of solubilized species to the overlying seawater. When anoxic sediment is covered by oxic sediment, mobilized species may dissolve at depth, diffuse upward, reoxidize in the surface sediment, and thus greatly concentrate a given species over natural levels in a surface layer. The extent of these processes will depend on mixing in the water column. Likewise, species rendered more soluble by oxidizing conditions may be released from sediment where there is a thin oxic zone.

Of the primary dissolved species in interstitial water of surface sediments, it is the nutrient elements (nitrogen, phosphorus, and silicon) that are subject to the greatest concentration changes. Except for silicon, these changes are controlled by the decomposition of organic matter and thus are greatest in sediments that have abundant organic matter and are consequently anoxic. Production of ammonia and phosphate in anoxic sediments may be considerable and allow concentration gradients between the interstitial water and the overlying seawater to be set up. Large gradients, as for example of phosphate, can support a diffusive flux from sediments on the order of 3 μmole cm^{-2} y^{-1} (Berner, 1974). Anaerobic conditions can likewise support sizeable ammonia and even sulfide gradients within and from the sediment column.

Iron and manganese are the metals most often cited as being susceptible to dissolution under anoxic conditions. Dredged material accumulating on the bottom probably creates one or both of two anoxic conditions: (1) where the sediment column is anoxic throughout, resulting in maximum metal remobilization at the sediment–water interface or in the top millimeters of sediment; and (2) where mildly reducing conditions allow a well-defined oxic zone to develop, wherein remobilized metals may be trapped and greatly concentrated over natural levels. Manheim (1976) notes that in addition to iron and manganese, cerium and perhaps lead, cobalt, and nickel are also solubilized in the reduced state and have a net diffusive flux from anoxic sediments.

12.4. BIOLOGICAL IMPACTS OF DREDGED-MATERIAL DISPOSAL IN THE DEEP OCEAN

12.4.1. General

Engler (1981) reviewed much of the work undertaken by the U.S. Army Corps of Engineers Dredged Material Research Program on the impacts of dredged material on the marine environment and some of its biological components. He concluded that with few exceptions impacts of dredged material are mainly associated with physical effects, and that biochemical interactions are infrequent and bioaccumulation of metals and hydrocarbons are usually negligible. His data suggest that water column ecological impact during disposal appears to be minimal to nonexistent, and the effect is predominantly aesthetic in nature. As a result, the minor impacts in the water column will be considered very briefly here, reserving more detailed analyses for benthic problems.

12.4.2. Impacts on Pelagic Biota

Results of laboratory investigations of the impacts of dredged material on water quality that could harm pelagic organisms have shown that ammonium, manganese, iron, and orthophosphate were released from anaerobic sediments during simulated disposal (Burks and Engler, 1978). Turbidity studies by Peddicord (1980) conducted with adult marine organisms have shown lethal concentrations of suspended dredged material to be an order of magnitude or more higher than maximal water column concentrations observed in the field during dredging operations (Wright, 1978). Moreover, it was found, that the sediments scavenged or cleaned the water column of numerous toxic heavy metals and nutrients when the fine-grained components were dispersed in the water column. No release of chlorinated hydrocarbons from a broad selection of marine sediments occurred during the simulated open-water disposal of dredged material. Release of toxic metals was not shown to occur under conditions simulating an open-ocean disposal (Gambrell et al., 1977). Turbidity studies conducted by Peddicord and his colleagues (Peddicord et al., 1975, 1978, 1980) showed that mortality occurred in 21 d or less when concentrations of suspended dredged material exceeded 2–20 g liter^{-1}. Field observations have shown turbidity or suspended particulate levels to be less than 1 g liter^{-1}. These observations suggest that, with the possible exception of some hermatypic corals, the physical effect of turbidity from dredged-material discharge in open water would be of minimal biological impact.

12.4.3. Benthic Impacts

12.4.3a. Biological Uptake of Toxic Metals and Hydrocarbons

There are several documented instances of biological accumulation of heavy metals from water, but there is no such clear evidence for the biological accumulation of metals from sediments. Toxic-metal uptake studies conducted with various marine species in the laboratory and in the field demonstrate minimal impacts from marine and estuarine sediments. For most metals studied by Neff et al. (1978), uptake by organisms was either marginal or not evident. Of 168 animal–sediment–salinity combinations tested by Neff et al. only 37 showed significant accumulation due to sediment exposure. But in most of these cases the significant uptake was attributable to iron, a metal that is relatively nontoxic to biological systems. The polychaete *Neanthes arenaceodentata* exhibited uptake of lead thought to be ecologically significant, but the possibility of depuration under natural conditions could reduce the importance of this observation.

Results of some studies reveal that elevated concentrations of heavy metals in benthic invertebrates are not necessarily indicative of high levels of metals in either water or ambient sediment. Uptake results depend on the species of organisms, the particular metal and its form, types of exposures, and such edaphic factors as temperature and salinity. For example, both Neff et al. (1978) and Anderlini et al. (1976) found that trends in their data indicated that uptake of metals increases at lower salinities. Peddicord and McFarland (1978), working with several species of heavy metals, pesticides, and PCBs, and Disalvo et al. (1977), working with oil and grease that contained PCBs and chlorinated hydrocarbons, found uptake of some contaminants, but none were accumulated to levels exceeding those levels generally considered acceptable in the edible portions for human consumption. There was no mortality of such test organisms as crabs (*Hemigrapsus* and *Cancer*), mussels (*Mytilus*), snails (*Acanthina*), and a caridean shrimp. Attempts have been made to trace pathways of uptake of DDT and related analogs from sediment into tissues of deposit-feeding marine infauna. Laboratory studies indicate that these compounds are much more readily sorbed than desorbed from sediment particles. It appears that release of these water-insoluble pesticides will not occur to an appreciable extent during disposal. In fact, Anderlini et al. (1976) monitored a disposal operation in San Francisco Bay and found that the levels in *Mytilus edulis* of all PCBs and chlorinated hydrocarbons except p,p'-DDE were unchanged. The uptake of the latter compound was judged to be of minor importance.

12.4.3b. A Field Study of Benthic Impacts

Elliott Bay and the Duwamish Waterway, which are part of Puget Sound, form a typical estuary with a surface layer of low-salinity water over a deeper layer of more saline water. Tatem and Johnson (1977) studied the impacts resulting from the open-water disposal of 114,000 m^3 of material dredged from the waterway in 1974. This material was fine silt, rich in organics, and oil-black. Because of its cohesiveness, it left the disposal barge in clumps that fell rapidly to the bottom. Bottom contact resulted in an outward, concentric surge of material that was evident along a radius of some 200 m. There was some low mounding, but the mounds gradually subsided over a period of about 9 months. Using PCBs as a tag, it was shown that the material did not move beyond the site boundaries.

Postdisposal investigations revealed no significant changes in the chemistry of the water column more than an hour after dumping. The sediments in the disposal site had essentially the same composition and concentrations of contaminants as found at the dredging site. Organisms captured during and after the disposal operations had not accumulated metals or PCBs. PCBs increased only slightly in caged mussels held for three weeks at the disposal site. The principal biological changes observed were ecological, involving reductions in numbers of species, individuals, and biomass of benthic invertebrates. Species diversity and density returned to predisposal levels within a year, but biomass values remained depressed. Interestingly, shrimp were attracted to the disposal site so that larger catches were made some months after disposal than before.

Although the foregoing observations appear to warrant the conclusion that the disposal of even contaminated dredged material in the shallow ocean has little lasting impact upon the macrobiota, one must examine the possibility that this conclusion may not be valid for the deep ocean.

12.5.   AN ASSESSMENT OF OPPOSITION TO DEEP-OCEAN DISPOSAL

12.5.1.   Potential Problems of Minor Importance

The disposal of dredged material into any part of the ocean produces impacts some of which are harmful and others of which may be beneficial. An example of the latter may be the structuring of the bottom in such manner as to be attractive to mobile epifauna. Harmful impacts may be of either major or minor environmental importance. It is convenient to discuss first those that produce relatively minor impacts before examining those that the opponents of deep-ocean disposal of dredged material repeatedly bring forth.

12.5.1a.   Turbidity Increases

It is anticipated that deep-ocean disposal will not produce significant turbidity in the upper water column, although it may add minor amounts of suspended sediment to the nepheloid layer. The nepheloid is a layer of turbid bottom water, varying in thickness from a few hundred meters to more than a kilometer, that occurs over wide areas of the ocean. For example, Baker et al. (1979) discussed the nepheloid layer at the DOMES site in the Tropical Central North Pacific Ocean. Based on data provided by Ewing et al. (1971), it is estimated that up to 300×10^6 metric tons of material occur in the Argentine Basin alone. It is unlikely that the United States would ever dump more than 100×10^6 tons y^{-1} of dredged material into the deep ocean, and only a small part of that would contribute to the nepheloid layer. Thus, it is unlikely that deep-ocean disposal will create significant turbidity.

12.5.1b.   Dissolved Oxygen Depletion

All nearshore sediments, whether clean or contaminated, will contain substances susceptible to oxidation by the dissolved oxygen in normal seawater. Considering the small ratio between the disposal volume and the receiving water column, it is unlikely that the disposal of dredged material into deep ocean water would result in significant oxygen demand. Natural sediment transport and deposition processes result in much larger and more persistent additions of oxygen-demanding substances to natural waters than those resulting from dredging. Nevertheless, serious oxygen depletion is caused by these natural sedimentation processes in only rare times or rare environments.

12.5.1c. Nutrient Cycling

Nutrients in measurable amounts are likely to be released to, or in the case of phosphate sometimes taken up from (due to adsorption on iron oxide particles), the disposal site water, both during settling of dredged material and from the sedimented mass. Potentially this activity could have significant effects on both pelagic and benthic organisms, but the extent of the biological effects is largely dependent on the rate of dilution of added nutrients and the rate of renewal of water. In the case of typical open ocean areas, and considering the limited exposure of the settling material to the water column during disposal, it seems unlikely that pelagic organisms would be significantly affected. Benthic organisms, such as bacteria and meiofauna, may be affected over a small area if the dredged material is richer in nutrients and organic carbon than the sediments on which it is depositing.

12.5.1d. Other Minor Impacts

Other potential impacts in deep water such as reduction of light penetration, flocculation of phytoplankton, and the driving away of mobile organisms are likely to be extremely localized and consequently of little importance to the pelagic marine environment.

12.5.2. Problems of Potential Importance

Opponents to the dumping of dredged material into the open ocean base their negative position largely upon five arguments that superficially appear much more serious than the above. Some of the considerations that refute these arguments are indicated in previous sections of this chapter. In the following sections the opposing problem will be stated first and then followed by an answer.

12.5.2a. Potential for Significant Uptake of Toxic Metals

As was pointed out earlier the literature provides some documented cases of experimental accumulation of heavy metals from water, but clear evidence for significant uptake from sediments is lacking. The major sediment properties that will influence the release of contaminants from dredged material are the amount and type of clay, organic matter content, amount and type of cations and anions associated with the sediment, the amount of potentially reactive iron and manganese, salinity, Eh, and pH. The importance of pH was stressed previously because it controls adsorption-desorption reactions involving trace metals and other substances on sediment particles. Noting that increasing pH favors adsorption and because sediment dredged from nearshore or estuarine sites and deposited in open ocean water will be exposed to a higher pH, trace metals will be immobilized in the water column and on the seabed. This will reduce the availability of metals and other substances to organisms.

12.5.2b. Deep-Sea Organisms Will Be Exposed to Synthetic Organic Substances and to Petroleum Hydrocarbons

This argument might be true for remote areas of the Central Pacific Ocean, but not for the continental slopes and the seabed along major shipping lanes. It is well known that many synthetic organic compounds such as DDT and PCBs are already present in the sediments of these latter parts of the deep ocean where dredged material might well be disposed. The same is true for petroleum hydrocarbons (Pequegnat and Jeffrey, 1979). Thus, deep-sea species have already been exposed to these substances, for long periods of time in the case of natural seeps of petroleum. But this is largely beside the point for, as was pointed out earlier, investigators have found only minimal uptake from sediments of these contaminants, and then only to levels less than those considered acceptable for human consumption.

12.5.2c. The Deep Ocean Is Not Only a Stable Environment but It Also Comprises a Fragile Ecosystem

There is certainly more evidence that the environment of the deep ocean is generally stable, at least as compared with the continental shelf, than there is that it supports a fragile ecosystem. But even the concept of stability in a geological sense must be challenged when applied to several parts of the deep ocean. Many parts of the seabed of the deep ocean have been, and continue to be, subjected to massive invasions of sediment from turbidity flows and slumps originating on the continental slope. In fact, the Gulf of Mexico, which represents a subsided oceanic area (Antoine, 1972), is filled with some 10 km of sediment, most of which is of Tertiary and later origin (Ewing et al., 1962). These findings do not support the generalization of stability in the deep ocean over geologically significant time scales.

As for fragility of the ecosystem, it is difficult to regard an ecosystem to be fragile when it contains organisms hardy enough to withstand the rigors of the deep ocean. Moreover, if the concept of fragility implies that recovery from perturbations will be slow, this too may be erroneous in light of some field experimentation. Turner (1973) found that so-called opportunistic epifaunal species capable of colonizing new substrata exist at depths of at least about 1800 m. Since recolonization of an area after habitat disturbance is one measure of the vigor of an ecosystem, the fact that Turner found that wood panels were heavily infested with two settlements of pholadid molluscs in a period of 104 d does not support the concept of fragility. Quite likely, opportunistic infaunal species will be found in the deep ocean when proper experiments or, more likely, fortunate observations are made. The concepts of stability and fragility are coupled in the next argument.

12.5.2d. Metabolic Processes and Physiologic Functions Are Much Slower in the Deep Sea Than in Shelf Waters

Some few opponents of deep-ocean disposal of dredged material have assured the author that recovery from anthropogenic impacts would be prolonged in part because of their assumption that biologic activities are slow in deep water primarily because of reduced water temperatures.

Again, this argument is not unequivocal. As early as 1936, Fox (1936) found that, when cold- and warm-water echinoderm eggs are kept at the same intermediate temperatures, cleavage is faster in the cold-water eggs. Scholander et al. (1953) found that although at their habitat temperature 0°C Arctic animals have a 3-10 times lower metabolic rate than have tropical forms at a habitat temperature of 30°C, when the tropical metabolic curves are extrapolated to 0° they are lowered by 30-40 times. This exhibits a remarkable adaptation of metabolic function to low temperature. Recently Dr. William A. Newman of Scripps Institution of Oceanography called my attention to the fact that two species of barnacle [*Bathylasma coralliforme* (Hoek) and *Arctoscalpellum*] transplanted experimentally under the Ross Sea Ice grew at rates characteristic of shallow shelf water in spite of an ambient water temperature of -1.86°C (Dayton et al., in press).

Finally the concept of slowness as a characteristic of the deep ocean is not acceptable to anyone who has been fortunate enough to see invertebrates and vertebrates darting about bait cans in the films made by the late John Isaacs, and by Dr. Robert Carney (on pelagic holothurians) and the author (on the giant isopod *Bathynomus giganteus* and many fishes).

12.5.2e. We Do Not Know Enough About the Deep Ocean and Disposal Will Jeopardize Future Studies

Research during the last 20 y has advanced our knowledge about and comprehension of deep-sea ecosystems. Documentation of the existence of an unexpectedly diverse assemblage of species in the deep ocean by Sanders et al. (1965) led to speculation as to the mechanisms causing and maintaining the high diversity. Two prominent theories emerged. Both depend to different degrees on the proposition that environmental stability of the deep sea enabled numerous species to coexist through specializations that diminished interspecific competition (Slobodkin and Sanders, 1969) which if unchecked would eliminate species. Later Dayton and Hessler (1972) argued that the high diversity could have resulted from widespread predation. Predation may prevent prey species from reaching sufficiently high densities to require a high degree of niche diversification. Because very little direct evidence supports either mechanism, both must be considered highly speculative. Hence a case can be made that additional research in deep-sea biology is certainly needed.

Nevertheless, it is the author's contention that the disposal of dredged material will have little effect on future research efforts. After all, over half the globe (57%) is covered by water 2000 m or deeper. Balancing this against the probability that all of the dredged material that man is ever likely to need to dispose in the deep ocean could be accommodated in a few hundred square kilometers, the argument that dredged-material disposal will interfere with future research is indeed tenuous.

12.6. CONCLUSIONS

1. Many port authorities of the United States face an urgent need to find suitable disposal sites for increasing amounts of dredged material.

2. Conventional sites on land, in the estuary, and parts of the continental shelf are increasingly unacceptable to the general public for disposal of large quantities of dredged material.

3. The deep ocean regularly assimilates immense quantities of sediment brought to it by rivers and aeolian processes.

4. Recent research indicates that dredged-material particles sequester various contaminants so that their release for accumulation in organisms is minimized.

5. Therefore, the deep ocean is concluded to be a final receiving environment into which dredged material may be disposed with minimal environmental risk.

REFERENCES

Anderlini, V. C., J. W. Chapman, A. S. Newton, and R. W. Risebrough. 1976. Pollutant Availability Study, Dredge Disposal Study, San Francisco Bay and Estuary, Appendix I: Pollutant Availability. U.S. Army Corps of Engineers District, San Francisco, California, 130 pp.

Andreliunas, V. L. and C. G. Hard. 1972. Dredging disposal: Real or imaginary dilemma? *Water Spectrum*, 4, 16–21.

Antoine, J. W. 1972. Structure of the Gulf of Mexico. *In*: Contributions on the Geological and Geophysical Oceanography of the Gulf of Mexico, R. Rezak and V. J. Henry (Eds.). Gulf Publishing Co., Houston, Texas, 303 pp.

Baker, E. T., R. A. Feeley, and K. Takahashi. 1979. Chemical composition, size distribution, and particle morphology of suspended particulate matter at DOMES Sites A, B, and C: Relationships with local sediment composition. *In*: Marine Geology and Oceanography of the Pacific Manganese Nodule Province, J. L. Bischoff and D. Z. Piper (Eds.). Plenum Press, New York. 842 pp.

Berner, R. A. 1974. Kinetic models for the early diagenesis of nitrogen, sulfur, phosphorus, and silicon in anoxic marine sediments. *In*: The Sea, Vol. 5, E. D. Goldberg (Ed.). John Wiley & Sons, Inc., New York, pp. 427–450.

Bokuniewicz, H., J. A. Gerbert, R. B. Gordon, P. Kiminsky, C. C. Pilbeam, and M. W. Reed. 1975. Environmental Consequences of Dredge Spoil Disposal in Long Island Sound, Phase II. Geophysical Studies Nov. 1973–Nov. 1974. Unpublished Report SR-8. Yale University, New Haven, Connecticut. Submitted to New England Division of the U.S. Army Corps of Engineers, Boston, Massachusetts, 34 pp.

Boyd, M. B., R. T. Saucier, J. W. Keeley, R. L. Montgomery, R. D. Brown, D. B. Mathis, and C. J. Guice. 1972. Disposal of Dredge Spoil Problem Identification and Assessment and Research Program Development. Technical Report H-72-8. U.S. Army Engineer Waterways Experiment Station, Vicksburg, Mississippi, 121 pp.

Burks, S. L. and R. M. Engler. 1978. Water-Quality Impacts of Aquatic Dredged Disposal (Laboratory Investigations). Synthesis Report DS-78-4. U.S. Army Engineer Waterways Experiment Station, Vicksburg, Mississippi, 35 pp + appendix.

Dayton, P. K. and R. R. Hessler. 1972. Role of biological disturbance in maintaining diversity in the deep sea. *Deep-Sea Research*, **19**, 199–208.

Dayton, P. K., W. A. Newman, and J. Oliver (in press). The vertical zonation of the deep-sea Antarctic acorn barnacle, *Bathylasma coralliforme* (Hoek); experimental transplants from the shelf into shallow water. *Journal of Biogeography*.

Disalvo, L. H., H. E. Guard, N. D. Hirsh, and J. Nq. 1977. Assessment and Significance of Sediment Associated Oil and Grease in Aquatic Environments. Technical Report D-77-26. U.S. Army Engineer Waterways Experiment Station, Vicksburg, Mississippi, 120 pp.

Drake, D. E. 1976. Suspended sediment-transport and mud deposition on continental shelves. *In*: Marine Sediment Transport and Environmental Management, D. J. Stanley and D. J. P. Swift (Eds.). John Wiley & Sons, Inc., New York, pp. 127–158.

Emery, K. O. and E. Uchupi. 1972. Western North Atlantic Ocean: Topography, rocks, structure, water, life, and sediments. American Association of Petroleum Geologist Memoir 17, Tulsa, Oklahoma, 532 pp.

Engler, R. M. 1981. Impacts Associated with the Discharge of Dredged Material: Management Approach. Unpublished Manuscript. Paper presented to the Ad Hoc Scientific Group of the London Dumping Convention.

Ewing, J. I., J. L. Worzel, and M. Ewing. 1962. Sediments and oceanic structural history of the Gulf of Mexico. *Journal of Geophysical Research*, **67**, 2509–2527.

Ewing, M., S. L. Eittreim, J. L. Ewing, and X. Pichon. 1971. Sediment transport and distribution in the Argentine Basin. 3. Nepheloid layer and processes of sedimentation, *In*: Physics and Chemistry of the Earth. No. 8, L. H. Ahrens, F. Press, S. K. Runcorn, and H. C. Vrey (Eds.). Pergamon Press, New York, pp. 49–77.

Fox, H. M., 1936. Rates of cleavage of sea urchin eggs in different latitudes. *Nature*, **178**, 389–396.

Gambrell, R. P., R. A. Khalid, M. G. Verloo, and W. H. Patrick, Jr. 1977. Transformations of Heavy Metals and Plant Nutrients in Dredged Sediments as affected by Oxidation Reduction Potential and pH, Vol. II: Materials and Methods/Results and Discussion. Contract Report D-77-4, U.S. Army Engineer Waterways Experiment Station, Vicksburg, Mississippi, 112 pp.

Gordon, R. B. 1974. Dispersion of dredged spoil dumped in nearshore waters. *Estuarine Coastal Marine Science*, **2**, 349–358.

Griggs, G. B., A. G. Carey, and L. D. Kulm. 1969. Deep-sea sedimentation and sediment-fauna interaction in Cascadia Channel and on Cascadia Abyssal Plain. *Deep-Sea Research*, **16**, 157–170.

Holeman, J. H. 1968. The sediment yield of major rivers of the world. *Water Resources Research*, **4**, 737–747.

JBF Scientific Corp. 1975. Dredging Technology Study, San Francisco Bay and

Estuary. A Report to the Corps of Engineers, San Francisco District, Contract DACW 07-75-C-0045. JBF Scientific Corp., San Francisco, California, 240 pp.

Lisitzin, A. P. 1972. Sedimentation in the world ocean. Society of Economic Paleontologists and Minerologists, Special Publication 17, 218 pp.

McHugh, J. L. 1976. Living resources of the United States continental shelf. AIBS Symposium (TerEco Corp.) Ecology and Management of the Continental Shelf, New Orleans, Louisiana, unpublished proceedings.

Manheim, F. T. 1976. Interstitial waters of marine sediments. *In*: Chemical Oceanography, Vol. 6, J. P. Riley and R. Chester (Eds.). Academic Press, New York, pp. 115–186.

Meccia, R. M. 1975. Dredged material disposal effects and alternatives. *In*: Proceedings of the Seventh Dredging Seminar. Sea Grant Report TAMU-SG-76-105. Texas A & M University, College Station, Texas, pp. 29–42.

Moiseev, P. A. 1971. The Living Resources of the World Ocean. Israel Program for Scientific Translations, Jerusalem. National Science Foundation, Washington D.C., 334 pp.

Murray, C. N. and L. Murray. 1973. Adsorption-desorption equilibria of some radionuclides in sediment–freshwater, and sediment–seawater systems. *In*: Radioactive Contamination of the Marine Environment. International Atomic Energy Agency, Vienna, pp. 105–124.

Neff, J. W., R. S. Foster, and J. F. Slowey. 1978. Availability of Sediment-Adsorbed Heavy Metals to Benthos with Particular Emphasis on Deposit-Feeding Infauna. Technical Report D-78-42. U.S. Army Engineer Waterways Experiment Station, Vicksburg, Mississippi, 120 pp.

Peddicord, R. K., V. A. McFarland, D. P. Belfiori, and T. E. Byrd. 1975. Effects of Suspended Solids on San Francisco Bay Organisms Dredge Disposal Study, San Francisco Bay and Estuary, Appendix G: Physical Impact Study. U.S. Army Engineers District, San Francisco, California, 158 pp. + appendices.

Peddicord, R. K. and V. A. McFarland. 1978. Effects of Suspended Dredged Material on Aquatic Animals. Technical Report D-78-29. U.S. Army Engineer Waterways Experiment Station, Vicksburg, Mississippi, 102 pp.

Peddicord, R. K. 1980. Direct Effects of Suspended Sediments on Aquatic Organisms. *In*: Contaminants and Sediments, A. Baker (Ed.). Ann Arbor Science Pub. Inc., Ann Arbor, Michigan, pp. 500–536.

Pequegnat, W. E., R. M. Darnell, B. M. James, E. A. Kennedy, L. H. Pequegnat, and J. T. Turner. 1976. Ecological Aspects of the Upper Continental Slope of the Gulf of Mexico. Technical Report (Contract No. 08550-CT4-12). U.S. Department of the Interior, Bureau of Land Management, Washington, D.C., 305 pp.

Pequegnat, W. E. and L. M. Jeffrey. 1979. Petroleum in Deep Benthic Ecosystems of the Gulf of Mexico and Caribbean Sea. *In*: Contributions in Marine Science, Vol. 22, D. E. Wohlschlag (Ed.). Port Aransas Marine Laboratory, University of Texas Marine Science Institute, Port Aransas, Texas, pp. 63–75.

Sanders, H. L., R. R. Hessler, and G. R. Hampson. 1965. An introduction to the study of deep-sea benthic faunal assemblages along the Gay Head-Bermuda transect. *Deep-Sea Research*, **12**, 845–867.

Scholander, P. F., F. Hogg, V. Walters, and L. Irving. 1953. Climatic adaptation in Arctic and tropical poikilothermo. *Physiological Zoology*, 26, 67–92.

Slobodkin, L. B. and H. L. Sanders. 1969. On the contribution of environmental predictability to species diversity. Brookhaven Biological Symposium, 22, 82–93.

St. Amant, L. S. 1971. Impacts of oil on the Gulf Coast. Transactions of Wildlife Management Institute, Washington, D.C., 15 pp.

Tait, R. V. and R. S. DeSanto. 1972. Elements of Marine Ecology. Springer-Verlag, New York, 327 pp.

Tatem, H. E., and J. H. Johnson. 1977. Aquatic Disposal Field Investigations Duwamish Waterway Disposal Site, Puget Sound, Washington; Evaluative Summary. Technical Report D-77-24. U.S. Army Engineer Waterways Experiment Station, Vicksburg, Mississippi, 25 pp.

Towill Corporation. 1972. Environmental Assessment of Maintenance Dredging Operations. Rep. to U.S. Army Corps of Engineers, Pacific Ocean Division, Honolulu, Hawaii, 41 pp. + appendices.

Trefry, J. H. and B. J. Presley. 1976. Heavy metal transport from the Mississippi River to the Gulf of Mexico. *In*: Marine Pollutant Transfer, H. L. Windom and R. A. Duce (Eds.). Lexington Books, D. L. Heath and Co., Lexington, Massachusetts, pp. 39–76.

Turner, R. D. 1973. Wood-boring bivalves, opportunistic species in the deep-sea. *Science*, 180, 1377–1379.

U.S. Environmental Protection Agency. 1976. Ocean Disposal in the U.S.–1976. 4th Annual Report of the Environmental Protection Agency, U.S. Environmental Protection Agency, Washington, D.C., 76 pp.

Wright, T. D. 1978. Aquatic Dredged Material Disposal Impacts. Technical Report DS-78-1. U.S. Army Engineer Waterways Experiment Station, Vicksburg, Mississippi, 57 pp.

13

FLUIDIZATION APPLIED TO SEDIMENT TRANSPORT (FAST) AS AN ALTERNATIVE TO MAINTENANCE DREDGING OF NAVIGATION CHANNELS IN TIDAL INLETS

James M. Parks

Center for Marine and Environmental Studies
Lehigh University
Bethlehem, Pennsylvania

Richard N. Weisman and Anthony G. Collins

Department of Civil Engineering
Lehigh University
Bethlehem, Pennsylvania

Dr. Collins' present address: Department of Civil and Environmental Engineering, Clarkson College of Technology, Potsdam, New York.

ABSTRACT

Sedimentation in tidal inlets is strongly influenced by a bottom current regime that varies with the tidal cycle in both direction and velocity. This variation induces unstable shoaling and meandering of navigation channels. The concept of keeping a channel open by fluidizing the bottom sediments was suggested in New Zealand in 1969, but the idea was not pursued there. Preliminary testing of this concept in the United States indicated fundamental difficulties in achieving longitudinally continuous fluidization.

Laboratory flume studies show that fully continuous fluidization along the length of the distribution pipe can be achieved when flowrates on the order of 4 liters s^{-1} m^{-1} of pipe length are used. In a two-dimensional physical model of a vertical transverse section across a fluidization system, the optimum configuration of fluidizing orifices was determined to be horizontally opposed pairs, and the practical orifice size was found to be 3.16-mm diameter for sand commonly found in inlets. The studies were then extended to the third dimension in a flume with a 3-m fluidization distribution pipe buried in sand. An orifice spacing on 5-cm centers appears to be nearly optimum. Uneven burial depth along the length of the fluidization pipe does not appear to be a problem. A series of experiments were performed to determine quantitatively the relationships between the width of the fluidized zone and the flowrate through the fluidizing pipe for different configurations of the flume system. Fluidized sand was removed from the channel by pumping of the sand–water slurry, by gravity flow down a gentle slope, and by erosion by bottom currents of sufficient velocity. Currents of about 80 cm s^{-1} velocity eroded fluidized sand without affecting nearby unfluidized sediment. When fluidized sand was removed, the sides of the channel slumped and were fluidized and were removed, increasing the channel width by 50%.

Limited-scale field tests were performed in a natural environment in the margins of Corsons Inlet, southern New Jersey. Although some unanticipated operational problems were encountered, the results of the laboratory studies were substantiated.

13.1. INTRODUCTION

For much of the U.S. coastline from Massachusetts to Texas, tidal inlets between barrier islands are the principal means of access to the open ocean for recreational and commercial fishing boats from the harbors and marinas on the protected landward side of the islands. Maintaining navigable channels through these inlets is a problem: strong ebb and flow tidal currents move considerable amount of sediment back and forth, forming shifting shoals in and near the inlets. Conventional methods for maintaining these navigable channels—frequent dredging or permanent jetties— are expensive and often ineffective, or have undesirable side-effects on nearby beaches. An economically and environmentally acceptable alternative to present methods of dredging and disposal, even if applicable to only a portion of the tidal inlets, could have an appreciable national impact.

13.1.1. Previous Work

Hagyard et al. (1969) first suggested a surprisingly simple solution to the problem of keeping a channel open through a sand bar closing an estuary harbor. They proposed burying a perforated pipe in the sand bar and pumping water through it at sufficient pressure and flowrate to fluidize the sand above the pipe; the sand would then flow as a liquid down a slight slope (1:400) to the seaward side of the bar. They estimated the power requirements to pump the fluidization water to be quite small-61 joule s^{-1} (96 hp) for 12 submerged pumps along a 2100-m pipe (disregarding friction losses)—because it is gravity that moves the sand and the fluidizing water merely provides lubrication. Some laboratory experimentation was done, but for various reasons including the death of the principal investigator, the concept of fluidization was not pursued further in New Zealand (I. A. Gilmour, personal communication).

Wilson and Mudie (1970a) experimented at Scripps Beach, La Jolla, California, with fluidization on an unsaturated beach face, where the sand surface was not covered by water. They used a distribution pipe of 19-mm inside diameter polyvinyl chloride (PVC), with 2.4-mm holes spaced 5 cm apart, fed from a standard 16-mm inside diameter garden hose. In a series of experiments, they used fluidization pipe lengths from 1 to 3 m, with the orifices pointed either up or down, burial depths to 0.5 m, and water flowrates from 0.15 to 0.94 liters s^{-1} m^{-1}. Under these conditions, they found that the fluidization was linearly inhomogeneous and unstable (Wilson and Mudie, 1970b); that is, along the length of the buried pipe there were several turbulent "fluid holes" separated by water-saturated, but not fluid, "dams" that obstructed the longitudinal downslope flow of sand. The deeper the fluidizing pipe was buried (up to 0.5 m), the more distinct and widely spaced the fluid holes became, and they concluded that this vertical channeling effect was a serious impediment to the implementation of the fluidization concept. Most of their experiments involved digging a ditch, burying the pipe (with disturbed sand), and then turning on the water. They found that if the pipe was buried and allowed to sit overnight, the sand would achieve a natural dense compaction from the tidal cycle that washed over it, preventing fluidization at pressures and flowrates available (Wilson and Mudie, 1970a).

In part because of the vertical channeling problem, further research in the United States on sand transport by fluidization has been directed toward "duct-flow fluidization," in which jets of water from downward pointed orifices angled 45° forward "suspend and simultaneously transport sand as bed load within an artificial duct formed in the sand beneath the fluidizing pipe" (Bailard and Inman, 1975). The duct-flow fluidization process was first described by Harris et al. (1976). They explained that the forward momentum exchange between the 45° angle of water jets and the sand–water mixture beneath the fluidizing pipe effectively overcomes the flow instabilities inherent in the previous fluidization techniques. Duct-flow fluidization has been proposed for relatively short distances in conjunction with a crater-sink sand transfer system (Inman and Harris, 1971) as part of a coastal sand management system (Brush, 1972). As sand is removed from beneath the pipe, it is replaced by sand from the overburden immediately above the pipe, forming a crater or channel in the sand surface.

The simple fluidization concept of Hagyard et al. (1969) still appeared attractive, and preliminary nonquantitative experiments performed at Lehigh University in 1976 and 1977 did not encounter the difficulties described by Wilson and Mudie (1970a). Our initial experiments were done in a flume under a cover of water, and longitudinally homogeneous and continuous fluidization was achieved without fail under a variety of conditions. This success encouraged us to undertake a more rigorous quantitative investigation, the results of which are reported in this chapter.

13.1.2. Objective

The objective of this study was to investigate the feasibility of using sand fluidization to maintain a navigable channel in a tidal inlet. The navigation channel would first be dredged by conventional means, with a floor that slopes gently seaward. Two or more fluidization distribution pipes would then be laid parallel to the axis of the channel. Periodically, as sediment accumulated in the channel, the fluidization system would be activated to assist in moving this sediment seaward during ebb tide current. Sediment would not be allowed to accumulate to more than a few tens of centimeters in thickness before fluidizing it and allowing gravity (and perhaps ebb flow bottom currents) to move the sediment down the slope of the channel to deeper water beyond the seaward limits of the ebb delta but not beyond the influence of longshore currents.

Fluidization is visualized as a means of keeping a navigable channel free of shoaling accumulations of sediment, and is thus an alternative to frequent maintenance

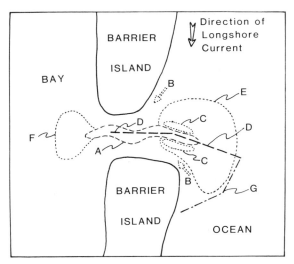

Figure 13.1. Map view of idealized tidal inlet, with fluidization pipe (*D*) along axis of main ebb channel (*A*) and through ebb delta swash platform (*E*). Other abbreviations: *B*, marginal flood channels; *C*, channel margin linear bars; *F*, flood delta; and *G*, sand discharge pipe.

dredging. In preventing shoals from developing in the channel, fluidization will further act to stabilize the position of the channel, that is, to hold the axis of the channel in alignment with the fluidization distribution pipes and thus prevent the natural tendency of the ebb channel to shift laterally with time, or to meander within the confines of the inlet (Fig. 13.1). The relatively straight navigable channel, maintained deeper than the rest of the inlet, will funnel and guide a major portion of the ebb tidal flow through the deeper channel, thus enhancing the scouring action of the strong ebb tide bottom currents. The action of the processes—gravity flow of fluidized sediment down a slight slope, and scouring action of confined ebb tide bottom currents—will reinforce each other to maintain the navigation channel in position, cross-section and longitudinal profiles, in a condition similar to the original dredged navigation channel. It may also be desirable to bend the seaward end of the channel in the downstream longshore current direction (Fig. 13.1), to enhance the ability of the longshore current and wave action to move sand from the seaward terminus of the fluidized channel back shoreward to the beaches of the downstream barrier island. In this way sand removed from the inlet to maintain the navigation channel will be effectively bypassed around the inlet and not be lost to the barrier island beach system. If necessary, the fluidized sand could be pumped in its fluid state to a location closer to shore in shallower water where normal wave action would be able to move it onto the beach (Fig. 13.1).

A further objective of this study is to define and characterize, through laboratory-scale studies, the relationships and parameters needed for the engineering design of a prototype fluidization system for a real tidal inlet. The laboratory studies were not intended to model a tidal inlet. The experiments were meant to reveal relationships between the flow discharging from the fluidization pipe and the resulting fluidized sediments.   Particular attention was devoted to determine quantitatively the relationships between the following:

1. Distribution pipe size (internal diameter),
2. Sand burial depth of distribution pipe,
3. Fluidization hole size,
4. Longitudinal hole spacing,
5. Configuration or orientation of holes,
6. Flowrate through the system.

Other factors, such as the interactions between parallel distribution of pipes and the effects of ebb flow currents on nonfluidized sand between the pipes, remain to be studied.

13.2. EXPERIMENTAL SETUP AND PROCEDURES

13.2.1. Apparatus

13.2.1a. Two-Dimensional Model

Two types of experimental setups were used in this study. The first type, referred to as the two-dimensional model (Fig. 13.2), was designed (Kelley, 1977) to investigate the cross-sectional size and shape of the fluidized zone as related to fluidization hole size, the configuration or orientation of the holes, and flowrates of the fluidizing water. The model, constructed of 6.35-mm-thick Plexiglas, has the shape of a thin vertical box, approximately 122 cm wide, 71 cm deep, and 7.6 cm thick. To provide rigidity to the front and rear faces of the model, 2.54-cm steel box supports spanned the width of the model at vertical intervals of approximately 23 cm. A short section of 3.8-cm internal diameter PVC pipe, capped at both ends, simulated a cross-section of a fluidization distribution pipe; this was placed within the Plexiglas box with the capped ends against the two viewing faces of the model. Fluidizing water flowed into the distribution section under pressure through an inflow pipe. Outlet orifices, of different sizes and in different configurations for successive tests, were drilled into the short length of the distributor. Thirteen pressure taps, in a partial grid on the rear face of the model, were connected by plastic tubing to a manometer board to allow simultaneous pressure readings from all taps.

In operation, the section of fluidization distribution pipe was clamped into position, sand was emplaced up to the desired level, saturated with water and carefully packed down, and then the experimental run was conducted by opening the inlet valve in small increments. Flow rates and pressures were recorded for each incremental step, after a short pause to allow equilibrium to be established. Each run was duplicated to provide additional data points and to check the repeatability of the process.

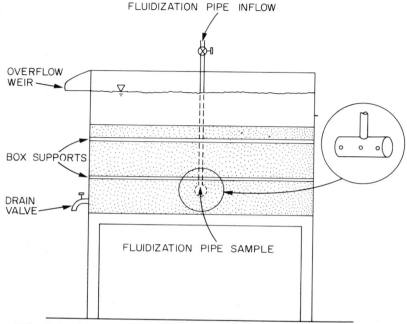

FLUIDIZATION PIPE INFLOW

OVERFLOW
WEIR

BOX SUPPORTS

DRAIN
VALVE

FLUIDIZATION PIPE SAMPLE

Figure 13.2. End view of two-dimensional physical model for orifice orientation and orifice size experiments.

13.2.1b. *Three-Dimensional Model*

To investigate the longitudinal effects, a fluidization distribution pipe approximately 3 m long, capped at the downstream end, was placed in a flume approximately 4.5 m long by 1.5 m wide by 1.2 m deep. Figure 13.3 shows the features of this three-dimensional model. The distribution pipe was galvanized steel of 3.8-cm internal diameter, with orifices the same as in the most successful two-dimensional experiment: 3.16-mm holes at 5.08-cm intervals in the horizontally opposed configuration. Although the flume bottom was horizontal, either or both the pipe and the sand surface could be sloped toward the downstream end of the flume. The distribution pipe was supported off the bottom of the flume by blocks a few centimeters thick.

Later, the length of the distribution pipe was reduced to 1.5 m. This length was sufficient to give the three-dimensional effect while reducing the total flowrate to half what it was with the longer pipe. This allowed the system to reach the higher flowrates per meter of pipe length that were needed to investigate the desired relationships and still remain within the capacity of the laboratory water system.

The flume was provided with overlying flowing water by a 16 joule s^{-1} (35 hp) pump capable of discharging 6000 liter min^{-1} (1600 gallon min^{-1}) through a 20.3-cm diameter pipe into a header tank. The flow was streamlined by passing it through a basket of gravel and allowing it to discharge over the surface of the sand

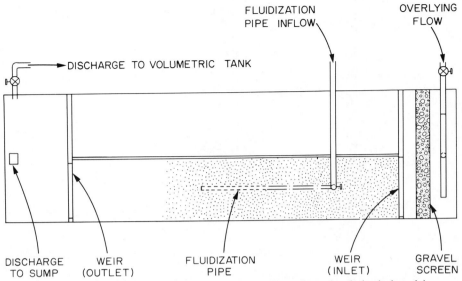

Figure 13.3. Longitudinal vertical section of the three-dimensional physical model.

in the flume. Current velocities were estimated by timing the movement of a float over a measured distance.

13.2.2. Sediments Used in Models

The sediments naturally occurring in and near tidal inlets are mainly sand in a narrow range of sizes. Along the coasts of the United States, the median sand sizes found in inlets range from approximately 0.2 to 0.5-mm (Bruun and Gerritsen, 1959).

Two types of sand were used in these experiments (Fig. 13.4): (1) Kelley sand, which was a clean well-sorted quartz sand with a median diameter of 0.5 mm; and (2) New Jersey beach sand (commercial designation) which was a "dirtier" less well sorted quartz sand that initially had a mean grain size of 0.23 mm. Repeated use of this sand in fluidization experiments produced an obvious change in color and texture, and it was apparent that the finer sizes were being selectively washed out. A size analysis of this sand after several cycles of fluidization showed less fines, with a median diameter of about 0.4 mm (Fig. 13.4).

13.2.3. Procedure

13.2.3a. Two-Dimensional Model

For each run, a short length (7 cm) of 3.8-cm diameter plastic pipe was prepared with holes of the size and configuration to be tested, and was capped at both ends and connected to the vertical inlet pipe. This assembly was then placed in the

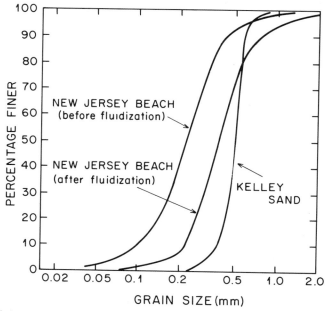

Figure 13.4.   Cumulative grain size distributions of sands used in both physical models.

Plexiglas box and clamped into position. Sand was added to the box to the desired depth, and the box was flooded with water to the overflow level. A thin metal rod was thrust through the sand at several points from the open top of the box to insure removal of air pockets and uniformity of packing. The sand was leveled and depth of coverage checked. The experiment was run by opening the inlet valve in several small increments, with a brief pause between each incremental flowrate increase to allow equilibrium to be established and observations and measurements to be made. At each step, flowrate through the short fluidization pipe was measured by collecting the discharge from the overflow weir in a graduated container over a known length of time. The extent and shape of the fluidized zone could be observed through the Plexiglas sides of the model, and the width of the fluidized zone was measured at the sediment–water interface. Each run was duplicated to provide additional data points and to check the repeatability of the process.

13.2.3b.   Three-Dimensional Model

Initially, the fluidization pipe was installed in the empty flume, and clamped into a fixed position on blocks a few centimeters off the bottom of the flume. Then sand was shovelled into the flume to a thickness of about 16.5 cm above the pipe. The flume was flooded with water and the sand carefully compacted by rodding and tamping. For subsequent runs with the pipe and sand already in place, it was only necessary to check and correct, or adjust if necessary, the position of the pipe, and to redistribute the sand in the flume to a desired condition, and tamp it into as uniform packing as possible. To change the orifice spacing, the pipe was exposed by shovelling the sand aside, and selected holes were closed by wrapping the pipe with tape.

With the pipe and the sand cover in the desired configuration and the flume flooded to the overflow level, the experiment was carried out by opening the inlet valve in small steps to increase the flowrate through the fluidization pipe in several small increments, with a pause of several minutes between each step to allow equilibrium to be attained and observations to be made. The flowrate was measured at each step by diverting the overflow from the flume into a volumetric tank over a known time interval. At low flowrates, only observations of completeness and longitudinal uniformity of fluidization were made. At higher flowrates, after full fluidization was achieved, the width of fluidized channel was measured.

A typical test run would include about eight flowrate increments, each with detailed observations and measurements. Each run lasted approximately an hour. Preparations for a run took from one half hour to several hours, depending on how many changes were made.

In a typical run, several stages of fluidization were observed in the following sequence:

1. Along the length of the fluidization pipe, a series of "pressure circles" or low-relief sand mounds 5–10 cm in diameter developed on the sand surface, at low pressures and flowrates.

2. "Sand boils" or point source eruptions of fluidized sand, 5–10 cm in diameter, began to appear on either side of the buried pipe. These did not all appear at once, or begin every time in the same place, but in every run they eventually appeared along both sides of the entire length of the buried pipe.

3. With increased, but still relatively low flow and pressure, a stage of "partial fluidization" was reached, corresponding perhaps to that described by Wilson and Mudie (1970a) as linearly inhomogeneous and unstable. There would be a small number (2–6) of large (30–50 cm) circular or elongate sand boils or turbulent fluidized areas, separated by dams or zones of clearly unfluidized or less-fluidized sand. These few large boils formed by the merging longitudinal and lateral expansion of a number of the smaller boils in a nonuniform manner. Intensity of color was a clue: the well-fluidized zones were distinctly lighter in color than the intervening poorly fluidized zones, and the turbulent areas showed streaky concentric patterns. If the flowrate was held constant for several minutes, the sand remained in a dynamic state of partial fluidization.

4. With further increases in flowrate, full and complete fluidization was achieved, evidenced by a uniformly lighter color in an unbroken zone of equal width the full length of the buried pipe. On close inspection, individual grains of sand could be seen moving laterally out of this fluidized zone, and then stopping; a fairly well-defined levee of unfluidized sand was thus built up on both sides of the fluidized zone.

5. It was experimentally determined that once the stage of full fluidization was reached, it could be maintained in that condition (without breaking up into individual large sand boils) as the flowrate was decreased as much as 20%. A further

reduction of 20% in the flowrate produced a state of partial fluidization, that is, the uniform full fluidization broke up into a few (2–5) large elongate sand boils with short zones of less fluidized sand (darker in color) between the large sand boils.

13.3. RESULTS

13.3.1. Orifice Configuration

A series of tests were run on the two-dimensional model to determine an optimum size of fluidization orifice, and an optimum configuration for the orifices. As a quantitative measure of the performance of the various combinations tested, we used width of fluidized zone as observed at the upper sediment–water interface, for each measured flowrate through the fluidization distributor pipe. By increasing the flowrate through the system, a relationship between flowrate per unit length of fluidization pipe and fluidized zone width can be established for a given combination of fluidization hole size, spacing, and configuration (Fig. 13.5).

The width of the fluidized zone is an arbitrary measurement, subject to individual interpretation. In practice, the width is measured from peak to peak of the levees formed on each side of the fluidized zone as sand is ejected laterally and is deposited when the sand comes out of fluidized suspension. At low flowrates, these levees are not well defined. In some later three-dimensional model experiments where the fluidized sand was removed down channel, the lateral levees never formed and the width was measured at a different point in the cross-sectional

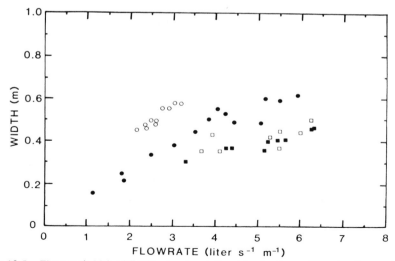

Figure 13.5. Flowrate/width of fluidized zone relationships for four orifice sizes in two-dimensional model (horizontally opposed pairs orifice orientation, 20.3-cm sand burial depth). Symbols for hole size: open circles, 1.59 mm; solid circles, 3.16 mm; open squares, 4.76 mm; solid squares, 6.35 mm.

profile. Consequently, the width measurements should be considered only as an index of performance for comparative purposes.

Previous workers had utilized a single row of orifices, oriented either vertically upward (Hagyard et al., 1969), or directed downward (Mudie and Wilson, 1970a, 1970b). With the criterion of width of fluidized zone, we tested five configurations:

1. Single row of orifices directed downward,
2. Single row of orifices directed upward,
3. Orifices in opposed pairs directed horizontally,
4. Orifices in opposed pairs directed 45° downward from horizontal,
5. A combination of 1 and 3.

Along the short (7 cm) length of the two-dimensional model fluidization distribution pipe, orifices of 2.38-mm diameter (as used by Wilson and Mudie, 1970a) were spaced on 2.54-cm centers. There were a total of three orifices for configurations 1 and 2; six orifices for configurations 3 and 4; and nine orifices for configuration 5.

For each run, as the flowrate was increased incrementally, the flowrate at which fluidization first began was recorded, as well as the maximum flowrate achieved by that configuration of the system. It was assumed that the inflow capacity (laboratory water supply pressure) was identical for the maximum open valve setting: therefore, the maximum flowrate, as measured by the discharge, was limited by the number of orifices and their orientation. A summary of this experimental data is shown in Table 13.1.

It was clearly evident that configuration 3 (horizontally opposed pairs of orifices) produced a significantly wider fluidized zone than any of the other configurations tested. This configuration was used in all subsequent two-dimensional and three-dimensional model tests.

13.3.2. Orifice Size

Four orifice sizes were tested in the two-dimensional model: 0.159 cm, 0.316 cm, 0.476 cm, and 0.635 cm. The smallest size was selected by considering the size of

Table 13.1. Width of Fluidized Zone for Orifice Configurations

Orifice Configuration	Incipient Fluidizing Flow Rate ($cm^3 \ s^{-1}$)	Maximum Flow Rate ($cm^3 \ s^{-1}$)	Width of Fluidized Zone (cm)
1. Downward	87.6	255.7	29
2. Upward	88.7	376.0	28
3. Horizontal pairs	81.7	381.0	71
4. Down 45° pairs	74.2	274.3	51
5. Combination 1 and 3	75.2	455.6	53

the sand grains and the need to provide a jet of water out of the fluidization hole of at least similar size to interact significantly with the grains. From a hydraulic point of view, a smaller hole size will require a greater internal fluidization pipe pressure to force adequate flowrates through the fluidization holes. For holes smaller than 0.159-cm diameter, the pressure required would be impractical. Hydraulic considerations also set a limit to the larger size, as initiation of fluidization is dependent on achieving a certain minimum pressure in the sand. The total flowrate required to achieve the necessary pressure using holes larger than 0.635-cm diameter would also be impractical.

At a given flowrate, the smallest diameter holes produce the largest width of fluidized zone (Fig. 13.5). This effect is probably related to the velocity of the water jet from the orifice, with larger orifices producing lower velocity jets. The width difference for the two larger hole sizes tested appears to be negligible.

13.3.3. Sediment Characteristics

Sediment characteristics (mean grain size and degree of sorting) of different sands have a measurable influence on the flowrate/width relationship as shown in Fig. 13.6. For a given flowrate and orifice size, the width of fluidized zone produced was about 20% larger for the New Jersey beach sand than for the Kelley sand. This effect was small compared with that produced by other parameters.

13.3.4. Depth of Burial

For a given hole size (3.16 mm), the effect of doubling the depth of sand burial (from 20.3 cm to 40.6 cm) was insignificant (Fig. 13.7). Above a flowrate of about

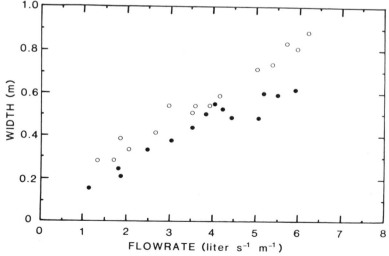

Figure 13.6. Flowrate/width relationships for the two sands in two-dimensional model (horizontally opposed pairs orifice orientation, 3.16-mm hole size, 20.3-cm sand burial depth). Symbols: open circles, New Jersey beach sand; solid circles, Kelley (1977) sand.

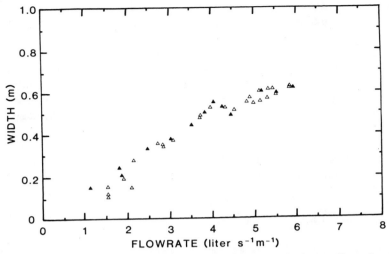

Figure 13.7. Flowrate/width relationships for two burial depths in two-dimensional model (horizontally opposed pairs orifice orientation, 3.16-mm hole size). Symbols for burial depth: open triangles, 40.6 cm; solid triangles, 20.3 cm.

4 liters s^{-1} m^{-1}, the rate of increase in width of fluidized zone with increasing flow-rate appears to level off, and relatively larger flowrate increments are required to produce small increases in fluidized zone widths.

13.3.5. Comparison of Physical Models

The preceding tests were made in the two-dimensional model. The remainder of the test program was performed in the three-dimensional model. Figure 13.8 shows a comparison of the flowrate/width relationship as determined in the two models for identical conditions of sand burial depth (20.3 cm), orifice size (3.16 mm), sand type (New Jersey beach sand), and orifice configuration (horizontally opposed pairs). At a given flowrate, a wider fluidized zone is produced in the three-dimensional model. This difference is probably accounted for by the relatively unconstrained nature of the three-dimensional model. In the two-dimensional model, the fluidizing flow was probably strongly influenced by wall effects.

In addition, the slope of the flowrate/width relationship is steeper for tests run in the three-dimensional model; that is, the same increase in flowrate in the two models will produce a larger increase in fluidized zone width in the three-dimensional model.

13.3.6. Orifice Spacing

Three orifice spacings were tested, 2.54 cm, 5.08 cm, and 10.16 cm (Fig. 13.9). The flowrate necessary to initiate fluidization does not appear to be significantly influenced by the spacing of the orifices. For a given flowrate, the intermediate

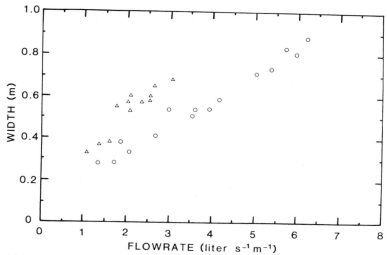

Figure 13.8. Comparison of flowrate/width relationships for two-dimensional and three-dimensional models (horizontally opposed pairs orifice orientation, 3.16-mm hole size, 20.3-cm sand burial depth). Symbols: open circles, two-dimensional model; open triangles, three-dimensional model.

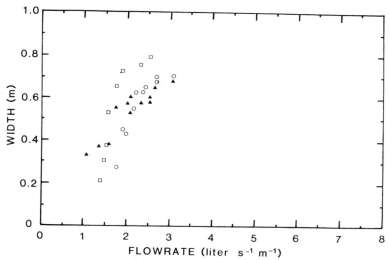

Figure 13.9. Flowrate/width relationships for three orifice spacings in three-dimensional model (horizontally opposed pairs orifice orientation, 3.16-mm hole size, 20.3-cm sand burial depth). Symbols: solid triangles, 2.54-cm spacing; open squares, 5.08-cm spacing; open circles, 10.16-cm spacing.

267

spacing (5.08 cm) appears to produce a significantly larger width of fluidized zone than either the closest spacing (2.54 cm) or the widest spacing (10.16 cm).

13.3.7.   Uneven Sand Burial

Under natural conditions in a tidal inlet, sand deposited by tidal currents and wave action would not be expected to cover the fluidization distributor pipe evenly: at some points along the buried pipe the sand might well accumulate to thicknesses of as much as 20 cm, for example, while at other points there may be virtually no deposition and accumulation of sand. Laboratory flume experiments using an even thickness of sand covering the fluidization distributor pipe obviously is unrealistic. Several experiments were conducted to test the ability of the three-dimensional model fluidization system to achieve longitudinally continuous full fluidization under less than ideal conditions of even sand coverage.

With the pipe fixed in a horizontal position, sand was spread to an even thickness of approximately 12.7 cm over the length of the pipe, and an additional 12.7 cm was built up over the central one-third of the pipe length in the form of a low hummock of 25.4 cm thickness. Fluidization flow was initiated in the distributor pipe, and the flowrate was increased in small increments as previously done. As expected, fluidization began to develop first in the upstream area of thin sand coverage, then appeared in the downstream area of thin sand covereage, and finally as the flowrate approached 3-4 liters s^{-1} m^{-1}, the central area of thicker sand coverage became fluidized.

In subsequent runs, the area of thicker sand coverage was placed over the upstream third of the pipe, over the downstream third of the pipe, and over both ends of the pipe with the central third under thin sand cover. In all cases, fluidization began in the thin coverage areas, and in all cases, fluidization progressed to the usual final state of longitudinally continuous full fluidization at the higher flowrates.

13.3.8.   Removal of Sand from Fluidized Zone

Fluidizing the sand in a linearly continuous zone above the buried distributor pipe is only the first step in achieving a channel; the fluidized sand must be physically removed to produce the channel. Three ways of accomplishing removal of sand were tested.

1. While the sand was kept in a fluidized state, a small submersible centrifugal pump was used to pump the fluidized sand through a short length of a 1.25-cm internal diameter plastic hose to another portion of the flume. All of the fluidized sand could be pumped away from one position; that is, the fluidized sand flowed to the pump intake location at one end of the distributor pipe from the entire length of the distributor pipe. As the level of the fluidized sand was lowered, the walls of the channel slumped down and that material was fluidized and pumped away, creating a channel significantly wider than the measured width of the fluidized zone. The sides of this channel stabilized at the low angle of repose of saturated sand.

2. The fluidized sand could also move down a gentle slope by gravity flow. In all previous tests in the three-dimensional model, the distributor pipe had been placed in a horizontal position. For this experiment the pipe was sloped from the inlet end down to the closed end at a 5% gradient, with a uniform thickness of sand coverage (20.3 cm) whose upper surface also sloped at a 5% gradient. A fluidization flowrate of 3 liters s^{-1} m^{-1} in the buried distributor pipe initially produced the usual fluidized zone with a width of 70 cm. The flow in the fluidization pipe was maintained for 30 min. The fluidized sand was observed to move downslope by gravity flow until halted by the building of a dam and delta across the downstream end of the channel. This obstruction was built in a manner similar to the side-channel levees; as the fluidized sand overflowed the channel end, it quickly reverted to an unfluidized condition. When this dam was continously removed by hand, the fluidized sand drained unimpeded from the channel, and the sides of the channel slumped down to increase the channel width from 70 to 100 cm.

3. Although the laboratory flume and apparatus for providing overlying flowing water was only marginally suitable for simulating the behavior of a fluidized channel under ebb tide flow conditions, encouraging results were obtained. For this experiment, the fluidization pipe was set horizontally with 3.16-mm holes spaced at 5.04 cm, covered by a uniform 20.3-cm thickness of sand. A fluidized channel was created at a fluidization pipe flowrate of 3.06 liters s^{-1} m^{-1} and the valve was opened to the overlying flow apparatus. With this flow extending across the entire width of the flume, a scour velocity of about 30 cm s^{-1} was attained. Although this flow was sufficient to create ripple marks on the sand surface outside the fluidized channel, there appeared to be little tendency of the overlying flow to entrain the fluidized sand. Baffles were then used to direct the overlying flow over the fluidized channel, and a surface velocity estimated at 80 cm s^{-1} was attained. The scouring capacity of the overlying flow was dramatically increased, sweeping all the fluidized sand out of the channel. The walls of the channel simultaneously slumped and were fluidized and then swept out by the overlying current, creating a wider and deeper channel. A low dam and delta eventually accumulated at the downstream end. When the baffles were moved downstream to direct the higher velocity flow over the dam and delta, only a small erosive effect was noted. Apparently a higher velocity is required to erode the unfluidized sand of the dam and delta than is required to transport the fluidized sand.

13.3.9. Preliminary Field Trials

As a first follow-up of these laboratory studies, a few limited-scale field trials were performed in a natural environment in the margins of Corsons Inlet, southern New Jersey. Four 3.1-m lengths of 15.2-cm internal diameter plastic (PVC) pipe were used to provide 12.2 m of fluidization distributor pipe in a single linear configuration, or half that length in a double parallel configuration. Horizontally opposed orifices of 3.16-mm diameter were spaced 5 cm apart. A submersible centrifugal pump capable of delivering 40 liters s^{-1} was used to provide approximately the optimum flowrate (4 liters s^{-1} m^{-1}). Some unanticipated operational problems were encountered. For example occasional clogging of pump intake screens and fluidization orifices by floating algae occurred, as well as the sporadic interference with water jet action by large dead clam shells in the sand. In general, however, the laboratory results and calculations were substantiated.

13.4. DISCUSSION

It is apparent from the results reported here that the problems of linearly inhomogeneous fluidization and the isolation of fluidized holes by nonfluidized dams reported by Wilson and Mudie (1970a, b) are not serious impediments to the implementation of the fluidization concept. Our laboratory three-dimensional experiments invariably achieved a final state of longitudinally continous and full fluidization over a wide variety of conditions. Three differences between our procedures and those of previous workers probably account for the difference in results:

1. We used a configuration of fluidization orifices in horizontally opposed pairs, instead of a single row of orifices directed either upward or downward as used by Wilson and Mudie (1970a).

2. We ran our experiments in water-saturated sand covered by a significant depth of standing or flowing water, instead of on an unsaturated beach face with a sand–air interface as used by Wilson and Mudie (1970a).

3. Perhaps most important, we used flowrates through the buried distributor pipe in a range from 1 to 6 liters s^{-1} m^{-1}, whereas Wilson and Mudie (1970a, b) used flowrates of less than 1 liter s^{-1} m^{-1}. We found that flowrates on the order of 3 to 4 liters s^{-1} m^{-1} were required to attain fully continous fluidization. Wilson and Mudie (1970a, b) were limited in the flowrates they could achieve by the capacity of their pump, by the small diameter (19 mm) of their distributor pipe, and particularly by the small internal diameter (16 mm) of the ordinary garden hose connecting pump to distributor pipe.

13.5. CONCLUSIONS

1. A configuration of fluidization orifices in horizontally opposed pairs produces the widest and most uniform fluidized zone of those arrangements tested.

2. Orifice diameters in the 3–5-mm range are the best compromise between the need for high water jet velocities which favor small holes, the need to minimize clogging which favor holes larger than the maximum sand size to be encountered, and the need to balance pump pressure and volume capabilities and costs.

3. Orifice spacing on 5-cm centers appears to be nearly optimum, as this spacing has a steeper flowrate/width curve (largest width increase per additional flowrate increment) than either closer or wider spacings.

4. For a given set of specifications (i.e., orifice diameter, spacing and configura-

tion, sand type, and burial depth), there is a well-defined relationship between flow-rate per unit length of distributor pipe and the width of the resulting fluidized zone. This relation is steep at first and then flattens out so that finally a large increase in flow results in only a small increase in width.

5. A fluidization flowrate of about 3-4 liters s^{-1} m^{-1} is required to produce longitudinally continuous and full fluidization over a zone 40-60 cm wide, at burial depths of 20-40 cm.

6. When the fluidized sand is removed from the fluidized zone, the sides of the resulting channel slump down and are also fluidized and removed, increasing the channel width by 50%.

7. Fluidized sand can be removed by pumping, by gravity flow down a gentle (5%) slope, or by erosion and transportation by bottom currents of sufficient velocity. In a laboratory flume, currents of about 80 cm s^{-1} velocity appear able to erode fluidized sediment without significant erosion of nearby unfluidized sediment.

8. Limited-scale field tests were performed in a natural environment in the margins of Corsons Inlet, southern New Jersey. Although some unanticipated operational problems were encountered, the laboratory results and calculations were substantiated (Weisman et al., in press).

ACKNOWLEDGMENTS

This project was supported by the U.S. National Oceanic and Atmospheric Administration, Office of Sea Grant under Grant Number NA-79 AAD00063 to the New Jersey Marine Sciences Consortium of which Lehigh University is a member. The U.S. Government is authorized to produce and distribute reprints for governmental purposes notwithstanding any copyright notation that may appear hereon.

An early phase of this work was sponsored by the Pennsylvania Science and Engineering Foundation under Contract Number 390. Additional funds were provided by Lehigh University and the Center for Marine and Environmental Studies.

We thank John T. Kelley, Jr. and Professor Willard Murray, Civil Engineering Department of Lehigh University, for their assistance in the preliminary analysis of the problem. We also thank Ms. Lynne Young and Ms. Patricia Weisse for assistance in the laboratory studies and for the drafting of some of the figures; and Mrs. Jenny Kovak and Ms. Shirley Matlock who typed the various reports and manuscripts.

REFERENCES

Bailard, J. A. and D. L. Inman. 1975. Analytical model of duct-flow fluidization. *In*: Proceedings Second Annual Symposium on Modeling Techniques, American Society Civil Engineers, San Francisco, pp. 1402-1421.

Brush, B. M. 1972. Coastal sand management system. *In*: Proceedings 13th Coastal Engineering Conference, Vol. 2, American Society Civil Engineers, New York, pp. 1503–1513.

Bruun, P. F. and F. Gerritsen. 1959. Natural bypassing of sand at coastal inlets. *Journal of the American Society of Civil Engineers*, **85**, 75–107.

Hagyard, T., I. A. Gilmour, and W. D. Mottram. 1969. A proposal to remove sand bars by fluidization. *New Zealand Journal of Science*, **12**, 851–864.

Harris, R. W., D. L. Inman, J. A. Ballard, and R. L. Oda. 1976. Study and evaluation of remedial sand bypassing procedures. Contract Report H-76-1. U.S. Army Engineer Waterways Experiment Station, Vicksburg, Mississippi, ca 150 pp.

Inman, D. L. and R. W. Harris. 1971. Crater-sink sand transfer system. *In*: Proceedings 12th Coastal Engineering Conference, Vol. 2, American Society Civil Engineers, New York, pp. 919–933.

Kelley, J. T. 1977. Fluidization applied to sediment transport. M. S. Thesis, Lehigh University (Fritz Engineering Laboratory Report 710.1), Bethlehem, Pennsylvania, 100 pp.

Weisman, R. N., J. M. Parks, and A. G. Collins. (In Press). Maintaining tidal inlet channels by fluidization. *Journal of Waterways, American Society of Civil Engineers*, accepted for publication.

Wilson, C. R. and J. D. Mudie. 1970a. Some experiments on fluidization as a means of sand transport. Unpublished manuscript. Scripps Institution of Oceanography, University of California, San Diego, 39 pp.

Wilson, C. R. and J. D. Mudie. 1970b. Comments on the paper, "Removal of sand bars by fluidization" by T. Hagyard, I. Gilmour, and W. Mottram. Unpublished manuscript. Scripps Institution of Oceanography, University of California, San Diego, 6 pp.

PART V: FUTURE DIRECTIONS OF DREDGED-MATERIAL DISPOSAL IN THE OCEAN

14

HAVE THE QUESTIONS CONCERNING DREDGED-MATERIAL DISPOSAL BEEN ANSWERED?

Dana R. Kester

Graduate School of Oceanography
University of Rhode Island
Kingston, Rhode Island

Bostwick H. Ketchum

Senior Scientist, Emeritus
Woods Hole Oceanographic Institution
Woods Hole, Massachusetts

Iver W. Duedall

Department of Oceanography and Ocean Engineering
Florida Institute of Technology
Melbourne, Florida

P. Kilho Park

Ocean Dumping Program
National Oceanic and Atmospheric Administration
Rockville, Maryland

ABSTRACT

There are four major issues which should be addressed when considering dredged-material disposal in the marine environment. (1) Will the environment be degraded? (2) How can we distinguish contaminated and uncontaminated sediment? (3) Will the marine food chain be modified? (4) What is the best way to dispose of dredged material? The short-term effects of dredged-material disposal are readily recognized, but the possible long-term effects are more difficult to determine. Four approaches have been used to identify contaminated sediment. They are (a) the Jensen criteria, (b) the elutriate test, (c) the liquid-phase, suspended-phase, and solid-phase bioassays, and (d) the State of Connecticut chemical classification. Specific biological effects of contaminated sediment can be recognized, but it is difficult to generalize or predict these effects with existing knowledge. Uncontaminated dredged material should be used as a resource wherever possible. Contaminated dredged material should be disposed in a containment environment below the level of fresh ground water.

14.1. INTRODUCTION

The chapters in this volume provide incremental advances in our knowledge of dredged-material disposal in the ocean based on scientific investigations. One may view research in two ways: it can be an evolving and unending acquisition of knowledge; or it can be designed to resolve specific questions. In the first view, research in a particular area is never finished, whereas in the second view, if the research is successful there is a sense of completion. Both of these views apply to the disposal of dredged material. As understanding of processes in the marine environment improves, our ability to assess problems associated with ocean disposal of dredged material will be enhanced. Nevertheless there are numerous instances where dredging is required and where disposal decisions cannot be deferred indefinitely. Thus one must be prepared to make these decisions based on the best information currently available. In this concluding chapter we would like to focus attention on a few major questions concerning dredged-material disposal.

14.2. WHAT ARE THE MAJOR QUESTIONS?

It has often been stated that in scientific studies the proper formulation of a question is probably the most important factor in being able to answer it. The following list of questions will provide the framework for this discussion:

1. Will dredged material disposal cause a degradation of the environment?
2. How can a contaminated sediment be identified?
3. Will contaminants in dredged material enter or modify the food chain?
4. What are the best ways to dispose of dredged material?

For each of these questions we will provide our views on the extent to which they have been answered, and we will try to identify the areas where further study will be helpful.

14.3. ENVIRONMENTAL DEGRADATION RESULTING FROM DREDGED-MATERIAL DISPOSAL

The disposal of dredged material in the ocean may cause either an actual or a supposed deterioration in the environment and its resources. It is difficult to identify a specific case in which the disposal of dredged material has produced an environmental crisis. The New York Bight is often taken as an example of a portion of the coastal ocean which has been impacted by marine waste disposal practices. The apex of the New York Bight receives wastes from several sources including air pollutants, dredged material, sewage sludge, chemical wastes, and wastes discharged in harbor and estuarine waters and transported by the Hudson River plume (Stanford et al., 1981). Consequently it has been difficult to distinguish the role of a specific waste in the degradation of this region. One may conclude that in the absence of any clearly demonstrable crisis in the marine environment related to dredged material, the present practices are adequate. On the other hand one would like to have some assurance based on understanding the behavior of dredged-material wastes that a crisis will not surprise us in the future.

Many scientists who study the marine environment recognize that there are possible impacts resulting from dredged-material disposal, and these are reflected in the research on this problem in recent years. Some people with an interest in maintaining and improving the quality of our nearshore marine environment believe that a problem exists with the disposal of contaminated dredged material. Fishermen have observed changes in their resource which they infer are related to dredged-material disposal (Seavey and Pratt, 1979). In many instances public opinion and political action is more likely to be driven by a belief that an environmental problem exists than by a scientific demonstration that it either does or does not exist. Thus, it is important that the information gained through research be applied to considerations of environmental degradation resulting from dredged-material disposal.

It is useful to distinguish between short-term degradation during dredged-material disposal and long-term degradation due to contaminants in the sediment. The immediate effects of dredged-material disposal are easily observed: water column turbidity, burial of benthic organisms, and changes in grain size and texture of sediment. Increased water column turbidity after discharging dredged material is a transient effect which dissipates rapidly by dispersion and gravitational settling. Burial of organisms is a relatively short-term effect, because if the benthic organisms at the site are not able to burrow through the newly deposited material, the mound will be colonized quite readily by other organisms. The dredged mound may represent a new type of habitat for benthic organisms due to physical changes in sediment type, and consequently there can be a long-term change. This type of change in the marine environment when it occurs on a limited basis, does not represent a degradation. It can, however, result in social and economic costs. For example, a dredging project at Providence, Rhode Island, resulted in the deposition of 7.5×10^6 m^3 of sediment at a site off the mouth of Narragansett Bay. The change in topography and sediment type decreased, or rendered impossible, the clam and finfishing at this site. However, the new habitat was evidently favorable to lobsters, because this fishery increased at the site (Seavey and Pratt, 1979). A change in the environment due to dredged-material disposal can displace one resource by another, but this by itself would not constitute degradation; there could be an actual increase in the overall resource value.

This dredged-material disposal operation in Rhode Island provides an example of another problem that can arise. The waters off the mouth of Narragansett Bay have supported a trap fisheries over several decades. During the period of dredged-material disposal there was a decline in the landings of cod, mackerel, squid, and scup. Fisherman attributed this decline to the dredged material. However, Sissenwine and Saila (1974) found that the decline in scup, which was a major portion of the fishery, occurred along the entire eastern U.S. coast from Cape Hatteras to Cape Cod. They also showed considerable historic variability in the other species over the period 1959 to 1971. Even though the decline in this fishery cannot be attributed to the dredged-material disposal, the belief that an effect existed has been sufficiently strong that no further disposal has been possible at this site since 1971. We cannot separate the assessment of environmental degradation from the consideration of natural variability.

Long-term environmental degradation resulting from dredged-material disposal is an issue primarily with contaminated sediment. Less progress has been made answering this question than the one concerning short-term and physical effects. Long-term degradation may manifest itself in the form of sublethal effects occurring within the biological community that inhabits disposal sites which receive continuous and large inputs of dredged material. Biomagnification of a particular component in a contaminated dredged material and genetic disorder are two examples of sublethal effects which could go unnoticed for years. One way to assess long-term effects is to examine the physiology and chemical composition of organisms that have colonized large and well-established dumpsites. These organisms have successfully overcome the short-term degradation effects of turbidity and burial. And in essence, they represent integrators of years of continual dumping activity. Any abnormalities in these organisms must be compared carefully with the natural variability within the same organisms taken from control or reference sites. For example, natural variability in heavy-metal content of organisms can be large and will depend on several factors such as sediment characteristics, season, fat accumulation, and activity of the organism (Förstner and Wittman, 1981).   Moreover, attributing an effect observed at a dumpsite to a specific cause can be very difficult when there are more than one anthropogenic sources for the contaminant. In the New York Bight apex, for example, dredged-material disposal has been taking place for almost 100 years (Chapter 6) and, the Bight apex also receives large quantities of waste from other sources (see Chapter 1, Fig. 1.4).

Investigations in controlled experimental microcosms provide valuable information on the physical, chemical, and biological behavior of pollutants in marine systems. One of the studies conducted at the Marine Ecosystems Research Laboratory (MERL) of the University of Rhode Island provides a good example. The MERL microcosms consist of cylindrical tanks 2 m in diameter and 5 m deep. They contain a 30-cm layer of sediments and associated benthic organisms. These tanks are filled with seawater from lower Narragansett Bay and they simulate many features of the phytoplankton, zooplankton, and bacterial components of the bay ecosystem. Hunt and Smith (1981) presented the results of a study that relates to the mobility of metals from polluted marine sediments. Sediment was collected from three locations along a pollution gradient: Providence River sediment was highly contaminated, mid-bay sediment was slightly contaminated, and Rhode Island Sound sediment was uncontaminated. Three MERL tanks were set up with each of these three sediments for a total of nine tanks to provide replicability. Several important conclusions may be drawn from the experiment. The concentrations of metals in the three types of sediment indicate the "pollution gradient" associated with this experiment (Table 14.1). According to the U.S. Army Corps of Engineers: "From a geochemical viewpoint, contaminant releases [from dredged material] are usually limited to nutrients with negligible releases of toxic metals and hydrocarbons" (Engler, 1981). However, the MERL study shows removal of some metals from the sediments and in some instances trapping of metals in the microcosms. Metal concentrations in the water column varied during the 17-month experiment, and during much of the experiment the three types of sediment showed similar results (Hunt and Smith, 1981). During the summer period there was a substantial flux of copper and cadmium from the Providence River sediment that was greater than those observed from the other two sediments. This MERL study shows the release of metals from sediment is not a continual process, but it is episodic and perhaps seasonal. The net fluxes of three metals from the microcosm are given in Table 14.1. The mid-Narragansett Bay and Rhode Island Sound sediment microcosms accumulated lead; the other data indicate a loss of metals from the microcosm due to the flow through discharge of bay water to simulate a 27-d residence time of water in the microcosms. Hunt and Smith (1981) estimated the times required to purge the upper 1 cm of the sediments (Table 14.1). These estimates indicate that if the sources of contaminants to polluted estuarine sediments are eliminated, a period of decades to centuries will be required to restore the sediments to an unpolluted state. The MERL type microcosms provide a useful approach to examine moderate term processes related to wastes in the ocean. They have the advantage that the effects of individual inputs of contaminants can be studied, which is often obscured in field studies where multiple sources of pollutants exist.

Table 14.1. Summary of MERL Study of Metal Mobilization from Three Sediments of Varying Degree of Contamination from Narragansett Bay (Data from Hunt and Smith, 1981)

Parameter	Providence River	Mid-Bay	Rhode Island Sound
Composition of Surface Sediment			
Chromium ($\mu g\,g^{-1}$)	180	80	10
Nickel ($\mu g\,g^{-1}$)	36	12	5
Lead ($\mu g\,g^{-1}$)	148	49	15
Zinc ($\mu g\,g^{-1}$)	205	90	40
Cadmium ($\mu g\,g^{-1}$)	1.3	0.2	0.1
Copper ($\mu g\,g^{-1}$)	230	30	10
Net Flux of Metals from Microcosm[a]			
Lead ($\mu mole\,m^{-2}\,day^{-1}$)	−0.058	+0.056	+0.042
Cadmium ($\mu mole\,m^{-2}\,day^{-1}$)	−0.11	−0.06	−0.05
Copper ($\mu mole\,m^{-2}\,day^{-1}$)	−2.3	−0.33	−0.16
Minimum Time to Deplete the Upper 1 cm[b]			
Lead (years)	320	−	−
Cadmium (years)	5	0.9	0.4
Copper (years)	44	46	23

[a]A negative net flux indicates that the metal was lost from the sediment and the water column via the flow-through discharge. A positive net flux indicates that metal was retained within the microcosm.
[b]These values indicate the time scales required to deplete the reservoir of each metal in the upper 1 cm at the average removal rates observed during the experiment.

14.4. IDENTIFICATION OF CONTAMINATED SEDIMENT

Many of the problems associated with dredged material disposal could be managed most effectively if we had a means to distinguish natural and contaminated sediment. Several attempts have been made to establish such criteria. We have identified four approaches to the classification of contaminated sediment:

1. The Jensen criteria set by the U.S. Environmental Protection Agency (EPA) in 1971 (Table 14.2): A sediment will be considered contaminated if one or more of its properties exceeds a permissible limit (Engler, 1980).

2. The elutriate test adopted by the EPA in 1973: A sediment will be considered contaminated if the elutriate procedure of resuspending 1 part of sediment in 4 parts of water (both by volume) increases the concentration of a pollutant in the aqueous phase by more than 50%.

3. The bioassay test adopted by the EPA in 1977: Liquid-phase, suspended-solids, and solid-phase bioassay measurements will be used to determine the presence of significant amounts of pollutants in a sediment. The bioassays will test for lethality of each phase and for bioaccumulation relative to a reference sediment.

4. The State of Connecticut designated three classes of sediment (Table 14.3) such that: Class I are considered to be nondegrading to water quality and nontoxic to marine organisms; Class II are moderately polluted, but are suitable for island or marsh habitat development and for open ocean disposal; Class III are contaminated and potentially hazardous. If bioassays show that Class III sediments are toxic they cannot be ocean-dumped; they must be disposed on land or contained at inshore locations.

The Jensen criteria were based on bulk sediment analysis, and they came under substantial criticism for being arbitrary and not relatable to biological effects. Based on the Jensen criteria some of the naturally occurring sediments in Long Island Sound (and probably elsewhere) would be considered to be polluted and presumably unfit for open water disposal due to their zinc content (Seavey and Pratt, 1979). This approach was replaced by the elutriate test.

Some of the limitations of the elutriate test were described in Chapter 1. In this discussion it is relevant to consider the following point stated by Lee et al. (1975):

Table 14.2. The Jensen Criteria for Contaminated Sediments

Chemical Parameter	Permissible Limit
Chemical oxygen demand	≤ 50 mg g^{-1}
Total Kjeldahl nitrogen	≤ 1 mg g^{-1}
Volatile solids	≤ 60 mg g^{-1}
Oil and grease	≤ 1.5 mg g^{-1}
Mercury	≤ 1 μg g^{-1}
Lead	≤ 50 μg g^{-1}
Zinc	≤ 50 μg g^{-1}

The Elutriate Test is designed to simulate conditions which prevail in the water column during hydraulically dredged sediment disposal in open waters. It is not designed, nor should it be used, to evaluate the significance of chemical contaminants present in dredged sediments at the disposal site once the dredged sediments have been redeposited on the bottom.

Bioassay tests provide the most direct assessment of potential pollutant toxicity of dredged material. Chapters 2 and 3 provide detailed information on the use of bioassays to characterize sediments. Some types of bioassay tests have been formalized into defined procedures, and others are more experimental in nature and are designed to answer specific questions about a contaminant. The 96-h LC_{50} provides an index of acute toxicity. A bioaccumulation measurement over a fixed period of time can assess biological availability, uptake, and retention of a specific chemical in a waste. Behavioral and physiological effects (e.g., feeding rate, metabolic rate, life cycle development) and reproduction efficiency generally require longer term and more sophisticated and costly experimental studies.

More work should be done to develop a general approach for classifying sediment contamination in relation to disposal techniques. This work should address several fundamental biological and chemical processes which are insufficiently understood in the marine environment.

From a chemical perspective we need to better understand the exchange processes between the solid and solution phases in a sediment–seawater system. Adsorption-desorption equilibria have been studied extensively in simple systems (one type of substrate and one adsorbent), but the effects of variable temperature and salinity, of competing adsorbents, and of mixed solid phases are not well known. It is possible that the exchange processes in these complex systems should not be treated as equilibria. A kinetic model in which one considers a series of reactions leading to increases (or decreases) in the strength of the adsorbent–substrate bond,

Table 14.3. The State of Connecticut Classification of Contaminated Sediment (After New England River Basins Commission, 1979)

Parameter	Class I	Class II	Class III
Silt and clay (%)	<60	60–90	>90
Water content (%)	<40	40–60	>60
Volatile solids (%)	<5	5–10	>10
Oil and grease (%)	<0.3	0.3–1.0	>1
Mercury (μg g^{-1})	<0.5	0.5–1.5	>1.5
Lead (μg g^{-1})	<100	100–200	>200
Zinc (μg g^{-1})	<200	200–400	>400
Arsenic (μg g^{-1})	<10	10–20	>20
Cadmium (μg g^{-1})	<5	5–10	>10
Chromium (μg g^{-1})	<100	100–300	>300
Copper (μg g^{-1})	<200	200–400	>400
Nickel (μg g^{-1})	<50	50–100	>100
Vanadium (μg g^{-1})	<75	75–125	>125

may be a more appropriate research approach for the types of processes that occur within sediments. The irreversibility of adsorption–desorption processes indicates that it is not a simple equilibrium reaction. From an empirical approach we find the selective chemical leaching technique (Chapter 1) to be quite attractive and informative. A systematic comparison should be made among the various procedures that have been used, and they should be calibrated with synthetic mixed phases of metals in exchangeable, sulfide, organic, and oxide phases. This technique should be employed in combination with assessments of the biological effects of these phases to establish the correlation between solid-phase speciation and biological impact.

14.5. WILL CONTAMINANTS FROM THE SEDIMENT ENTER OR MODIFY THE FOOD CHAIN?

The biological consequences of contaminated dredged-material disposal are poorly known. There have been numerous bioassay experiments that yield some information, but they show primarily the effect of a certain level of pollutant on an individual organism rather than on a portion of the ecosystem. Peddicord and McFarland (1976) exposed crabs (*Cancer magister*) to suspensions of Oakland Harbor (California) sediment for 25 d. Mortality was related to suspension concentration; and 92% of the mortality occurred during molting. Physical abnormalities (missing or deformed appendages) were observed prior to death in some cases. Alterations of the food chain and of biological marine resources clearly are possible, but bioassays do not identify the causative agents within the sediments.

Bioaccumulation becomes an important issue when considering the transfer of pollutants through the food chain. Laboratory bioassays using a mysid shrimp (*Mysidopsis bahia*), an oyster (*Crassostrea virginica*) and a lugworm (the polychaete, *Arenicola cristata*) demonstrated bioaccumulation of Kepone from James River (Virginia) sediment (Rubinstein et al., 1980). This study also concluded that Houston (Texas) Ship Channel sediment was not harmful based on bioassay responses.

Contaminants may enter benthic organisms from three sources: the aqueous phase, the sediment, and their food. Swartz and Lee (1980) reviewed several aspects of pollutant uptake by organisms. They indicated that in addition to food, the interstitial water fraction of a pollutant is generally the most available form in many instances. However, for the worm, *Nereis diversicolor*, it was estimated that 85% of the PCB body burden was derived from the sediment phase and 15% was from the aqueous phase. The uptake of pollutants by benthic organisms undoubtedly depends on the partitioning and bonding of the pollutant in the solid and aqueous phases and on the feeding habits of the organism. Swartz and Lee reported that biomagnification, the increasing concentration of a substance along increasing trophic levels of a food web, occurs for mercury, DDT and its degradation products, and Aroclor® 1254. Biomagnification does not appear to occur for many other metals including cadmium, chromium, copper, lead, and zinc.

In a review of the benthic fauna of the New York Bight, Pearce et al. (1981) concluded that the species diversity index for the number of species comprising the benthic population was lower for those sediments which contained elevated levels of metals and organic substances. Even though reduced species diversity appears to be related to pollutant loading of the region, specific relationships to dredged-material disposal, sewage sludge disposal, or estuarine pollutants could not be established.

While there is evidence that contaminants can enter and modify the food chain from sediments, our predictive understanding of these processes is very poor. There are no clear case studies from which one can infer that contaminated dredged material has impacted the food chain. To determine the long-term effect of contaminated dredged material an effort should be made to collect a suite of benthic organisms and surface sediments from a variety of existing dredged material mounds and from related reference sites. The sediments should be characterized by a selective leaching procedure and the organisms should be analyzed chemically. The contaminants to be examined should include petroleum hydrocarbons, specific synthetic organic substances such as polychlorinated biphenyl compounds and organo-halogen compounds, and potentially toxic metals (cadmium, copper, mercury, lead, zinc). Such a study must consider that the natural variability of the composition of organisms is large. If no relationship can be found between the contaminant body burdens of the dredged-mound organisms relative to reference-site organisms and the presence of contaminants in the sediment, then it is unlikely that a long-term problem exists.

14.6. WHAT ARE THE BEST WAYS TO DISPOSE OF DREDGED MATERIAL?

There have been many considerations of the various alternatives for the disposal of dredged material. Table 14.4 lists the options that have been examined in a number of recent studies. It is useful to distinguish uncontaminated and contaminated sediment in considering the various disposal methods. The uncontaminated sediment should be regarded as a resource to be utilized whenever possible. Specific types of land improvement use of dredged material include filling of wetlands, sanitary landfill cover, and agricultural soil replenishment. These methods may not be appropriate when sediment is transferred from marine to fresh water environments because of ground water contamination by the leaching of salts from the sediment. Dredged material can provide opportunities to develop habitats such as artificial marshes, reefs, and islands. Medium- to coarse-grain-size dredged material can be useful for replenishing sand on beaches and for construction. Open water disposal of uncontaminated dredged material could be viewed as the method of last resort, it there are no constructive uses of the sediment.

Contaminated sediment represents a more difficult problem for disposal. When the degree of contamination is slight and when there is not convincing evidence that ecological harm will result, the open-water disposal method is the most practical. A general consensus exists that when the sediment is contaminated to the point

Table 14.4. Methods Considered in Recent Studies for the Disposal of Uncontaminated and Contaminated Dredged Material

Disposal Method	Study[a]			
	1	2	3	4
Uncontaminated Sediment				
Land improvement	X	X	X	X
Construction material		X		X
Habitat development	X	X	X	X
Beach nourishment		X	X	X
Open-water disposal	X	X	X	X
Contaminated Sediment				
Open-water disposal	X	X	X	X
Capped deposits	X			X
Subaqueous depressions	X	X	X	X
Contained upland disposal	X	X		X
Offshore island containment		X	X	X
Deep-ocean disposal		X		X

[a]Study 1 = Engler (1981); 2 = MITRE Corporation (1979); 3 = Seavey and Pratt (1979); 4 = this volume.

where biological effects are probable some type of containment disposal should be used. There is controversy, however, concerning whether the containment should be on land or in the marine environment. It has been argued that upland containment provides a more controlled management of contaminated sediment than containment in the marine environment (Chapter 2). On the other hand containment on land includes several risks. The first risk concerns the prospect that containment may not be absolute. Contaminants released either gradually from an imperfect impermeable barrier or catastrophically from failure of the barrier could produce substantial damage. The second risk results from placement of reduced solid phases in an oxidizing or potentially oxidizing environment. Many of the heavy metals (e.g., Hg, Cd, and Cu) form insoluble sulfide phases. Upon exposure to oxygen, the sulfide oxidizes to sulfate which releases many of the bound metals. In addition the transformation from an anion of a weak acid, S^{2-}, to an anion of a strong acid, SO_4^{2-}, can result in a reduction of pH from near neutrality to values as low as pH 2 in the interstitial waters of the sediment. This acidity can further mobilize toxic metals (Engler, 1981). This possible release of metals upon oxidation of sulfide phases is analogous to acidic mine drainage through deposits of pyrite and other sulfide minerals. The third risk associated with on-land containment is that if contaminants are released due to mobilization and breaching of the isolation barrier they may pollute ground waters and thereby have a direct economic or health impact on the community.

It thus appears that the best strategy for disposing of reduced contaminated sediments is to isolate them in a permanently reducing environment below the elevation of fresh ground water. Disposal in capped mound deposits above the prevailing seafloor, disposal in subaqueous depressions, and capping deposits in depressions provide procedures for contaminated sediment. These techniques do not require the costly construction involved in containment islands. In some instances it may be worthwhile to excavate a depression for the disposal site of contaminated sediment that can then be capped with the excavated material or with other clean sediment. This procedure has been proposed for the disposal of 1500 m^3 of Norwalk Harbor (Connecticut) sediment that were contaminated by a chemical spill of napthalene and nitrobenzene. This approach minimizes transport distance for the contaminated material (Morton, 1980). Deep-ocean disposal of dredged material usually will involve greater transport distances than the other methods. Furthermore, it is our opinion that the present understanding of deep-ocean processes is inadequate for a satisfactory assessment of this option (see Chapter 12 for a contrary point of view).

A desirable strategy for disposal of contaminated sediment can be realized by taking advantage of the lateral and vertical pollution gradients which often exist within a dredging project. If the most polluted sediment is dredged first and is deposited deepest in a depression or a mound, it is possible to obtain a capping effect without a major increment in cost. Sequential dredging and disposal of polluted and uncontaminated sediment should be considered whenever possible.

ACKNOWLEDGMENTS

We appreciate the assistance of Marilyn A. Maley and Jo-Anne Degidio in preparing this manuscript. This work was supported by NOAA Grant 04-8-M01-192.

REFERENCES

Engler, R. M. 1980. Prediction of pollution potential through geochemical and biological procedures: Development of regulation guidelines and criteria for the discharge of dredged and fill material. *In*: Contaminants and Sediments, Vol. 1. Fate and Transport, Case Studies, Modeling, Toxicity, R. A. Baker (Ed.). Ann Arbor Science, Michigan, pp. 143–169.

Engler, R. M. 1981. Impacts associated with the discharge of dredged material: Management approaches. *In*: Use of the Ocean for Man's Wastes: Engineering and Scientific Aspects. Marine Board, National Research Council, National Academy Press, Washington, D.C., pp. 129–185.

Förstner, U. and G. T. W. Wittman. 1981. Metal Pollution in the Aquatic Environment. Second Revised Edition. Springer-Verlag, Berlin, 486 pp.

Hunt, C. D. and D. L. Smith. 1981. Remobilization of metals from polluted marine sediments. Presented at "Ocean Pollution 1981," Halifax, Nova Scotia. 27 manuscript pages, plus 12 tables and 6 figures.

Lee, G. F., M. D. Piwoni, J. M. Lopez, G. M. Mariani, J. S. Richardson, D. H. Homer, and F. Saleh. 1975. Research study for the development of dredged material disposal criteria. Dredged Material Research Program Contract Report D-75-4. U.S. Army Engineer Waterways Experiment Station, Vicksburg, Mississippi, 337 pp.

MITRE Corporation. 1979. Disposal of Dredged Material within the New York District: Volume 1. Present Practices and Candidate Alternatives. MITRE Technical Report MTR-7808, Vol. 1. 1820 Dolley Madison Boulevard, McLean, Virginia, 361 pp.

Morton, R. W. 1980. Capping procedures as an alternative technique to isolate contaminant dredged material in the marine environment. Dredged Material Disposal Hearings, 21 May 1980, U.S. House of Representatives, Committee on Merchant Marine and Fisheries. Published by Science Applications, Inc., DAMOS (Disposal Area Monitoring System) Contribution No. 11. 27 pp.

New England River Basins Commission. 1979. Interim Plan for the Disposal of Dredged Material in Long Island Sound. Coastal Programs Division, New England River Basins Commission, 53 State Street, Boston, Massachusetts, 50 pp.

Pearce, J. B., D. J. Rodosh, J. V. Caracciolo, and F. W. Steimle, Jr. 1981. Benthic Fauna. MESA New York Bight Atlas Monograph 14. New York Sea Grant Institute, Albany, New York, 79 pp.

Peddicord, R. and V. McFarland. 1976. Effects of suspended dredged material on the commercial crab, *Cancer magister*. *In*: Dredging and Its Environmental Effects, P. A. Krenkel, J. Harrison, and J. Clement Burdick III (Eds.). American Society of Civil Engineers, New York, pp. 633–644.

Rubinstein, N. I., C. N. D'Asaro, and C. Sommers. 1980. The effects of contaminated sediments on representative estuarine species and developing benthic communities. *In*: Contaminants and Sediments, Vol. 1. Fate and Transport, Case Studies, Modeling, Toxicity, R. A. Baker (Ed.). Ann Arbor Science, Michigan, pp. 445–461.

Seavey, G. L. and S. D. Pratt. 1979. The disposal of dredged material in Rhode Island: An evaluation of past practices and future options. Marine Technical Report 72. Coastal Resources Center, University of Rhode Island, Kingston, Rhode Island, 96 pp.

Sissenwine, M. P. and S. B. Saila. 1974. Rhode Island Sound dredge spoil disposal and trends in the floating trap fishery. *Transactions of the American Fisheries Society*, **103**, 498–506.

Stanford, H. M., J. S. O'Connor, and R. L. Swanson. 1981. The effects of ocean dumping on the New York Bight ecosystem. *In*: Ocean Dumping of Industrial Wastes, B. H. Ketchum, D. R. Kester, P. K. Park (Eds.). Plenum Press, New York, pp. 53–86.

Swartz, R. C. and H. Lee, III. 1980. Biological processes affecting the distribution of pollutants in marine sediments. Part I. Accumulation, trophic transfer, biodegradation and migration. *In*: Contaminants and Sediments, Vol. 2. Analysis, Chemistry, Biology, R. A. Baker (Ed.). Ann Arbor Science, Michigan, pp. 533–553.

NAME INDEX

Numbers in *italics* indicate pages on which full references appear.

Addison, R. F., 209, *211*
Akagi, H. M., 188, *196*
Albaiges, J., 155, *168*
Albrecht, P., 155, 158, *168*
Aller, R. C., 174, *183, 184*
Amer, A., *66*
American Public Health Association, 52, *66*
Anderlini, V. C., 200, 209, 210, *211*, 244, *249*
Anderson, A. R., *68, 149*
Anderson, J. W., *212*
Andreliunas, V. L., 236, *249*
Antoine, J. W., 247, *249*
Artyushkov, Y. V., 224, *225*
Atlas, E. L., *212*
Atlas, R. M., 161, *168*
Atwood, D., 152, *168*
Aurand, D., *66, 67*

Bailard, J. A., 256, *271*
Baker, E. T., 245, *249*
Ballard, J. A., *272*
Belastock, R. A., *68*
Belfiori, D. P., *251*
Bender, M. E., *67, 184*
Berberian, G. A., *169*
Berner, R. A., *184,*242,*249*
Bertine, K., *148*
Biggs, D. C., *68*
Biggs, R. B., 222, *225*
Blackman, R. R., *68*
Blumer, M., 161, *169*
Boehm, P. D., 155, *168*
Bohlen, W. F., 210, *211*
Bokuniewicz, H. J., 217, 221, 222, 225, *226*, 241, *249*
Bowen, S. P., *226*
Bowen, V. T., *196, 212*

Boyd, M. B., 36, *66* 234, *249*
Boyden, C. R., 187, *196*
Brannon, J. M., 15, 16, 17, *25,* 37, *66*
Broughton, J. D., 217, *226*
Brown, D. W., 155, *168*
Brown, M. B., *211*
Brown, R. D., *66, 249*
Bruland, K. W., 23, *25,* 145, 146, 147, *148*
Brush, B. M., 256, *272*
Bruun, P. F., 260, *272*
Bryan, G. W., 186, 189, *196*
Burks, S. L., 240, 243, *250*
Byrd, T. E., *251*

Cabelli, V., *168*
Calder, J. A., *168*
Canada Gazette, 186, *196*
Cantillo, A. Y., *169*
Caracciolo, J. V., *287*
Carey, A. G., *250*
Carmody, D. J., 130, *148*
Carpenter, J. E., 217, *226*
Carver, T. C., *70, 88*
Chan, H. S., *212*
Chapman, J. W., *211, 249*
Chen, K. Y., 18, *25,* 75, *87,* 186, *197*
Chytalo, K. N., 209, *211*
Cochran, J. K., *184*
Cole, B. E., *211*
Cole, F. A., *69*
Collins, A. G., *272*
Conner, W. G., 61, *66*
Courtney, K., 216, *226*
Courtney, W. A. M., *57, 66,* 210, *211*
Cranston, R. E., 23, *25*
Creager, J. S., *27*
Cruickshank, M. J., 216, *266*

289

SUBJECT INDEX